Inter...

FOR YOUNG PEOPLE

NEW CONNECTIONS: NEW PLAYS FOR YOUNG PEOPLE
(*Asleep Under the Dark Earth* by Sian Evans, *The Chrysalids* adapted by David Harrower from the novel by John Wyndham, *Cuba* by Liz Lochhead, *Dog House* by Gina Moxley, *Eclipse* by Simon Armitage, *The Golden Door* by David Ashton, *In the Sweat* by Naomi Wallace and Bruce McLeod, *More Light* by Bryony Lavery, *Shelter* by Simon Bent, *Sparkleshark* by Philip Ridley, *Travel Club* and *Boy Soldier* by Wole Soyinka, *The Ultimate Fudge* by Jane Coles)

NEW CONNECTIONS 99: NEW PLAYS FOR YOUNG PEOPLE
(*After Juliet* by Sharman Macdonald, *Can You Keep a Secret?* by Winsome Pinnock, *The Devil in Drag* by Dario Fo, translated and adapted by Ed Emery, *Don't Eat Little Charlie* by Tankred Dorst with Ursula Ehler translated by Ella Wildridge, *Early Man* by Hannah Vincent, *Friendly Fire* by Peter Gill, *Gizmo* by Alan Ayckbourn, *King of the Castle* by Christina Reid, *The Pilgrimage* by Paul Goetzee, *Taking Breath* by Sarah Daniels)

International Connections

NEW PLAYS
FOR YOUNG PEOPLE

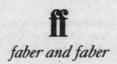

faber and faber

First published in 2002
by Faber and Faber Limited
3 Queen Square London WC1N 3AU
Published in the United States by Faber and Faber Inc.
an affiliate of Farrar, Straus and Giroux LLC, New York

Typeset by Country Setting, Kingsdown, Kent CT14 8ES
Printed in England by Mackays of Chatham plc, Chatham, Kent

Contents

For *The Actor* please apply to Peter Hagan, The Gersh Agency, 130 West 42nd Street, New York, NY 10036

For *The Bear Table*, please apply to Judy Daish Associates, 2 St Charles Place, London, W10 6EG

For *The Exam*, please apply to Marc Berlin, London Management, 2–4 Noel Street, London, W1F 8GB

For *Gold*, please apply to Charmaine Ferenczi, Abrams Artists Agency, 275 Seventh Avenue, 26th Floor, New York, NY 10001 and for the music to Joyce Ketay Agency, 1501 Broadway, Suite 1908, New York, NY 10036

For *Illyria*, *Take Away* and *Lady Chill, Lady Wad, Lady Lurve, Lady God*, please apply to Peters Fraser and Dunlop, Drury House, 34–43 Russell Street, London WC2B 5HA

For *Nuts,* please apply to Luca Scarlini via e-mail on scarlini@dada.it

For *Olive*, please apply to The Rod Hall Agency Ltd, 3 Charlotte Mews, London W1T 4DZ

For *Starstone,* please apply to Rosica Colin Ltd, 1 Clareville Grove Mews, London, SW7 5AH, and for the translator to Alan Brodie Representation Ltd, 211 Piccadilly, London W1J 9HF

For *Team Spirit*, please apply to Guy Rose, Futerman, Rose & Associates, 17 Deanhill Road, London SW14 7DQ

Introduction

International Connections is a new writing programme aimed at teenagers. It is a collaboration between the National Theatre, London, thirteen UK flagship theatres, Teatro Limonaia, Florence, The American Conservatory Theatre, San Francisco, schools and youth theatres across the UK, Ireland, Italy, Finland, Cyprus, Belgium, Canada and the USA and the publishers Faber and Faber.

There are thousands of accomplished, ambitious and diverse young theatre companies, but they are unable to commission world-class writers. We asked those playwrights whose work we most admire to write for the programme but to write their play exactly as they would for a professional company – or exactly as they would their next play. We wanted the best of new writing that takes the youth of the companies involved as a creative opportunity. Writers have responded to this challenge because a particular idea they had would work in this context or because they can write for casts of anything between five and fifty. And everyone likes the idea of a play being premièred around the world.

Over the last year we have been developing a fifth portfolio of ten plays and a brand new musical for young performers. They make up a varied repertoire of challenging and entertaining work. There are tales of mystery, Nordic mythology, miraculous healings, personal courage and unfufilled promises, of quests for love and trust and journeys through horror and self-doubt to hope and resolution. Settings include Germany's thirty-year war, a forest in Finland, the Atlantic Ocean, Italy post the police brutality in Genoa, Texas during the depression and Nazi-occupied

Norway. There are surreal and magical fables and plays with contemporary themes of religious obsession, abandonment, poor parenting and the overwhelming burden of the British exam system.

After the plays were delivered, around 150 companies chose which play they wanted to produce. At a weekend of workshops hosted by Theatre by the Lake, Keswick, the companies, together with established directors and the playwrights, started the rehearsal process. This allowed for questions to be asked and issues to be resolved and for us to insist that the text was not changed or adapted unless, in particular circumstances, the writer agreed. Throughout the process, the directors and young actors continued to keep in touch with their writer and each other via the Connections website.

The plays were then premièred in the companies' own venues at over 150 locations. Then the public festival was launched at Belfast's Lyric Theatre and continued throughout the spring and summer at Keswick Theatre by the Lake, Chichester Festival Theatre, Viirus Theatre, Helsinki, the Albany and Tricycle Theatres, London, Plymouth Theatre Royal, Nottingham Playhouse, Cambridge Arts Theatre, Stephen Joseph Theatre Scarborough, Theatr Clwyd, Mold, Bath Theatre Royal, Eden Court Theatre, Inverness, and Newcastle Theatre Royal. The festival culminated in July 2002 at the National when an example of all eleven pieces was presented in the Lyttelton and Cottesloe theatres.

The plays are now available in this volume for any school, youth theatre or group of young people who want to come together to make theatre. The plays are written to be performed but we know that works from the last four portfolios have found their way into schools as study texts, which is fine, just as long as they're enjoyed.

Plays for the next series are already commissioned and we're also uncovering an alternative history of twentieth-century playwriting for young people aged ten to eighteen.

This was a widespread practice but poorly recorded. We are digging deep into libraries and archives across the world and making startling discoveries, some of which will be included in the next portfolio to be staged in Autumn 2003.

SUZY GRAHAM-ADRIANI

Producer, Youth Theatre Programmes,
National Theatre
May 2002

For up-to-date information on these plays
and the work surrounding the programme
log on to www.internationalconnections.org.uk

THE ACTOR

Horton Foote

Characters

in order of speaking

Horace Robedaux
Susan Kate
Louise
Archie
Vard
Cecil
Marie Jackson
Dorothy
Jim
Elizabeth
Horace Sr

Early Spring, 1932.
  A section of a hall in the Harrison high school.
Horace Robedaux Jr, fifteen, is there. He looks at his
wristwatch, he hums to himself several bars of 'Brother,
Can You Spare a Dime,' looks up and down the hallway
and then begins to sing to himself snatches of 'Brother,
Can You Spare a Dime?'

Horace (*singing*)
  'Once I built a railroad,
  Made it run,
  Made it race against time.
  Once I built a railroad,
  Now it's done,
  Brother, can you spare a dime?'

  Two boys, a year or so older than Horace, come down
  the hall, each with a girl. They are Archie and Vard.
  Susan Kate is with Archie and Louise is with Vard.
  They carry school books.

Susan Kate *and* **Louise** Hello, Horace.
Horace Hi.
Archie Hi, Horace.
Horace Hi.
Vard Rudolph Valentino, what's new?
Horace Not much.

  They walk down the hall. Horace talks to the
  audience as to a close friend.

3

I hate it when somebody calls me Rudolph Valentino. I was walking in front of Rugeley's Drugstore yesterday on the way to the post office when old Blowhard Mayor Douglas came out of the drugstore and called out in a loud voice, 'Heh there, Valentino,' and all the old men sitting in front of the drugstore laughed like it was the funniest thing they had ever heard. I didn't think it was funny at all, but I pretended like I did and I just said, 'Pretty well, thank you, Mr Mayor,' and walked on. When I went to the store to watch it, so my daddy could go for his afternoon coffee, I told him about the Mayor calling out 'Hello, Rudolph Valentino' as I went by and he said I shouldn't be sensitive, that he was just being friendly. Maybe so, but I'm not so sure and I still don't like it.

Another boy, Cecil, walks by.

Cecil Hello, Rudolph Valentino.
Horace Heh.

The boy continues on.

This Rudolph Valentino business all started, you know, when I won the prize for the best actor at the State Drama Festival. They gave me a medal for being the best actor, but my teacher, Miss Prather, accepted it for the school and it's been two weeks since the Festival and she still hasn't given my medal to me. Miss Prather asked me to meet her after school. She says she has something for me. Maybe it's my medal. Anyway, if that's not what she wants I decided today to ask her for it. I hate doing it, but my mother says she is a busy teacher and has just forgotten she has it, and she won't mind at all my reminding her she has it. I hope she won't. Anyway, I'm going to do it. I want the medal, so I can keep it in my room, and it will be there to remind me of what it was like when I got the

medal. Miss Prather said it was very exciting when the
three judges called out her name and asked to speak
with her and she said she couldn't imagine what they
wanted and when she got to them they said, 'Is that
Robedeaux boy, playing the drug addict, afflicted or
is that acting?' and she said, 'It's acting.' 'Very well,'
they said. 'He gets first prize as best actor.' And she
said she waited around a few minutes longer hoping
they were going to say our one-act play won the prize
for the best play, but when they handed her my medal
and said, 'Thank you, you may return to your seat
now,' she knew we hadn't won best play or best
production, only best actor.

Susan Kate comes back in.

Susan Kate Hello, Horace.
Horace Hello.
Susan Kate Waiting for Miss Prather?
Horace Uh huh.
Susan Kate I just saw her in the auditorium.
Horace Thanks.

Susan Kate goes on.

The next day at school in our speech class she told
everybody about my winning best actor, and it was all
over school by then anyway, and she said in her opinion
no one could help being moved at the moment
I confessed to my roommates that I was an addict
and needed drugs, and then she asked me to wait after
class and I did, thinking she would give me my medal,
but she never mentioned the medal but wanted to
know if I was interested in being in the Senior play
which would start rehearsing in a few weeks. I said
I would be and I wanted to tell her I wanted to be an
actor, but I didn't know how to. I don't know why
I couldn't tell her. Of all the people I know around here

she'd likely be the one to understand and encourage me, but I don't know. I just can't bring myself to say out loud: I want to be an actor, not a lawyer or a doctor, an actor.

Cecil walks by.

Cecil You still here, Rudolph Valentino?
Horace What does it look like?

Cecil goes on.

I've known for a long time too that's what I wanted to be. Since I was thirteen. You see, I used to go for walks in the evening with my mother and daddy and we'd always pass on our walks Mr Armstrong's house. I could always tell when we were approaching his house no matter how dark a night it was, because the fences around his house were covered with honeysuckle vines and you could smell the honeysuckle a block away. Anyway, Mr Armstrong, a very old man, would always be sitting in the dark on his gallery and as we passed my daddy would always call out, 'Good evening, Mr Armstrong,' and he would always answer, 'Just fine, thank you. How are you?' even though my daddy had never asked how he was but only wished him a good evening and my Daddy explained to me that he always answered that way because he was deaf and couldn't hear what my Daddy said, and only imagined what he said and then he would always add, 'You know Mr Armstrong was working in the cotton fields in Mississippi when he got a call to come to Texas to preach. And that's what he did. He came here to preach.' I had never heard of anyone getting a call before to preach or anything else, so I asked my parents a lot of questions about getting a call. Could anyone get a call? They weren't sure about that since Mr Armstrong was the only person they ever knew who actually had gotten a call. 'Was that because he was a Baptist, is that why he got a call?' I asked. My mother said no, she had heard about Methodists and Episcopalians getting a call to preach although she hadn't met anyone personally that had except Mr Armstrong.

Louise and Susan Kate approach. They are giggling.

Louise I'm glad you're still here, Horace.
Susan Kate Horace –

They again begin to giggle.

You ask him.
Louise No, you ask him. You said you would ask him.
Susan Kate All right. Horace . . .
Horace Yes.
Susan Kate Are you going to the dance on Friday night?
Horace Yes.
Susan Kate Do you have a date?
Horace Not yet.
Susan Kate Would you do us a favour?
Horace What?
Susan Kate Marie Jackson doesn't have a date and would you please, please be nice and ask her to go?
Louise Please, please.
Horace Did she ask you to ask me?
Susan Kate No. Did she, Louise?
Louise No.
Horace I thought she was going steady with Cecil.
Susan Kate He dropped her.
Louise Susan Kate, you shouldn't say that. She would be so upset if she knew you said that.
Susan Kate Well, he did.
Louise I know but you shouldn't be spreading it all over school.
Susan Kate Will you ask her, Horace? She's very upset.

7

Louise We found her crying in the girls' room.

Horace I asked her for a date once and she turned me down.

Susan Kate Please, Horace.

Louise Please, please, Horace.

Horace Well, you go ask her if she wants me to ask her and then I'll see.

Susan Kate Thanks. We'll be right back.

They leave.

Horace Anyway, a year later when I turned thirteen I got a call, just as sure as Mr Armstrong did. Not to preach but to be an actor. I kept that to myself for a month and then I told Todd Lewis, who was my best friend before he had to move away, about it and he said if I wanted his advice I'd keep it to myself as people would think I was peculiar wanting to be something like that. And for good or bad, I've never told anyone else. I asked my mother one time what she thought Mr Armstrong did when he got his call and she said she couldn't be sure, but she imagined he fell on his knees in the cotton fields and prayed about it and listened to what God wanted him to do and God worked things out for him, so he could come to Texas and preach, and that's what I did, I prayed about it and asked God what I should do and the very next year Miss Prather came here to teach fresh out of college, and she put on plays, and that was encouraging to me and I found out from my daddy where Mr Dude Arthur's tent show would be in the next few weeks. He always had his itinerary because Mr Arthur was a customer and often wrote my daddy to send him clothes while he was on the road with his tent show. He asked me why I wanted his address. I said just to write and tell him how much I liked his tent show and he said that was a good idea as Mr

Arthur and his brother Mickey were always very good customers, even though Mr Arthur was often short of cash and had to have extended credit, since the tent-show business was having hard times because of the movies. Anyway, I learned he was going to be in Tyler, Texas in two weeks and I wrote him there, care of general delivery, which is what my father said I should do, and I reminded him in the letter who I was and that I sometimes waited on him in my father's store when he came to Harrison, and I would appreciate it if he wouldn't mention to anyone, not even my daddy, but the next time he was in Harrison, I would like very much to see him as I wanted to ask him how you go about being an actor. He never answered my letter, so I figured he had never gotten it. So last summer when he came here with his tent show, I went over to the boarding house where he stayed with his wife and brother Mickey, who plays all the juvenile parts in the tent show, and I told Mr Arthur I had written him a letter, and had he gotten it. He was drunk and said he didn't remember any letter, what was it about, and I said I wanted advice as I wanted to be an actor. He said, 'Why in the name of God?' And I said because I wanted to, and I believe I've had a call to be one and he said, 'Well, you're a fool if you think that and get over it.' Mrs Arthur came in then and said, 'Dude, sober up! You have a show tonight,' and I left.

Susan Kate and Louise come back in.

Susan Kate She has a date.
Horace Who with?
Louise Cecil.
Horace I thought he'd dumped her.
Louise We thought so, too, but I guess he changed his mind.

Susan Kate Thank you, anyway. I told her you wanted
   to ask her for a date, but you were too shy.

Horace I didn't say I wanted to ask her for a date.

Susan Kate Don't bite my head off. I thought you
   wanted to ask her for a date.

Horace I certainly did not say that. I said to ask her if
   she wanted me to ask her for a date and then I'd see.

Louise Come on, Susan Kate. Let's don't stand here and
   argue. I have to get home or my mama will kill me.

They leave.

Horace The next day Dude Arthur came to my daddy's
   store and in front of me told my daddy that I had
   come to see him at his boarding house and that I had
   written him a letter about wanting to be an actor, and
   after he left my daddy asked was I out of my mind,
   that being an actor and in a tent show was a terrible
   way to make a living, that Dude Arthur had told him
   he was giving up after this season and he was broke,
   and I said, I guess I shouldn't have, but I did, I said,
   well, Daddy, that's no worse than being a cotton
   farmer or a merchant, they are always broke too. 'But
   at least, young man' – he always calls me young man
   when he's mad at me – 'at least, young man, I have a
   roof over my head and I manage to always put food on
   the table, and I'm not drunk half the time, wandering
   around the country with only a mortgaged tent to my
   name.' Daddy said he hoped now that this would be
   the end of such foolishness, and I decided then and
   there – call or not – I would give it up. But when my
   mother read in the Houston papers that the Ben Greet
   Players would be in Houston for a week with their
   Shakespearean repertoire, she said she thought it
   would be nice for me to go and see them in one of
   their plays. She wrote my grandmother, my daddy's
   mother, who lives in Houston and goes to see plays all

the time, and she wrote back to send me on to Houston
and she would go with me to the play. I went to
Houston but she had a headache and couldn't go to
the play with me after all. She lived on the streetcar
line and she said if I went by myself, she would give
me real clear directions so I couldn't possibly get lost.
So she wrote out for me how to get to the theatre
and back by the streetcar, and I took the streetcar
and I got to the theatre just fine, but when I got off
the streetcar I saw across the street a sign in front of
another theatre that read, 'Florence Reed in *The
Shanghai Gesture.*' I heard my Houston grandmother
say that was a wicked play and one that shouldn't be
allowed in Houston, and so I don't know what devil
got inside me suggesting I go see *The Shanghai Gesture*
instead of the Ben Greet Players, but whatever it was,
I took my money my mother had given me for the Ben
Greet Players and I bought a ticket to see Florence
Reed and I guess it was wicked and immoral like my
grandmother in Houston said, but I thought it was
wonderful and I said to myself, I have to be an actor
now somehow, some way.

Marie Jackson and Cecil come in.

Marie Oh, Horace. I'm so touched you wanted to ask
me to the dance.
Horace Well –
Marie Don't be shy. I would love to go with you. But
Cecil had just asked me when the girls came to tell me
you were too shy to ask me.
Cecil Are you shy, Valentino?
Horace No, I'm not shy.
Marie Why do you call him Valentino?
Cecil Because he won an acting prize. Isn't that right,
Valentino?
Horace Yes.

Marie You did? Oh, that's so sweet.

Cecil Didn't you know that? Miss Prather announced it in study hall.

Marie When? What day?

Cecil What day? I forget. What day was it, Horace?

Horace I forget too.

Marie It must have been the day I was home sick. What kind of part did you play, Horace?

Cecil He played a dope fiend.

Marie How do you know? Did you see it?

Cecil No. I heard about it.

Marie I wish I could have seen it.

They leave.

Horace Anyway, I never told my mother or my Houston grandmother I didn't see the Ben Greet Players and when they asked me what play of Shakespeare I had seen I said *Julius Caesar* because I had read that play in English class my junior year and I had memorised the 'Friends, Romans, countrymen, lend me your ears' speech for the class, and I knew if they asked me questions about the play I could answer them. I didn't realise Adelaide Martin, one of my mother's friends, had gone into Houston that same day to see the Ben Greet Players and when she got back she called my mother to tell her about it and my mother said I had been there too, and had liked it a lot, and Adelaide said she didn't care for it as she thought the Romeo and Juliet looked middle-aged and were too old for their parts. '*Romeo and Juliet*,' Mama said. 'That's not what Horace saw,' she said. 'He saw *Julius Caesar*.' '*Julius Caesar*? Did he go to the matinee or the evening show?' Mother said to the matinee and Adelaide said that's the one she attended and there was no *Julius Caesar*, but *Romeo and Juliet*. When

I got home from school my mother confronted me with this and I had to admit what I had done. She asked me what *The Shanghai Gesture* was about and I said it took place in a Shanghai brothel and that's all she had to know. She said I was deceitful and should be ashamed of myself going to a play like that. I guess I should have been, but I wasn't. All I could think about was how Florence Reed reacted when, as the madame of the brothel, she heard that her daughter, who she hadn't seen in years, turned up as one of the girls in the brothel.

A pause. He sings again.

Horace (*singing*)
'Once I built a railroad,
Made it run,
Made it run against time.
Once I built a railroad,
Now it's done,
Brother, can you spare a dime?'

I love to hear Russ Colombo sing that song. My father hates the song. He says it's too depressing. He says he likes positive songs like 'Happy Days Are Here Again.' He says the country needs to have songs like that so they'll be in an optimistic mood, and not depressed all the time.

Two boys, Archie and Vard, come back by.

Archie Are you still here?
Horace What does it look like?
Vard What are you hanging around here for?
Horace I'm waiting for Miss Prather.
Archie You have a crush on Miss Prather, don't you?
Horace No, I don't have a crush on Miss Prather.
Vard What are you always hanging around her for?

Horace I'm not always hanging around her. I have to see her about something.

Vard About what?

Horace None of your business.

Vard You're in a good mood today?

They start out.

Archie (*calling back*) Have you decided the college you're going to apply to?

Horace No, not yet.

Vard I'm applying to A and M.

They continue on.

Horace Everybody's applying for college that can afford to go. Next time someone asks me about college I think I'll just come right out and say I'm not going to college ever. Not ever. I'm going to be an actor. Yeah. I bet you will. I can't even tell my mother and father. I'm almost scared to, because how my daddy blew up at the store when Dude Arthur told him I wanted to be an actor. I tried last night to tell them. We were sitting together on the porch and there was no moon and it was pitch-dark. I could see lightning bugs everywhere and I thought, I'll tell them now because it's dark and I don't have to look at their faces when I tell them, but dark or not, I couldn't get the words out. My daddy was going on about the Depression and how hard a time he was having and how bad he felt that he couldn't send me to college this year, and I was saying to myself the whole time, I don't want to go to college, so don't worry about it, but dark or not, I just couldn't get the words out. Mama said, 'Are you feeling alright, son? You seem so quiet.' 'Yes, ma'am,' I said, 'I feel fine.' And my daddy started on about college again and he kept saying over and over he's going to work extra hard at the store in the fall when the crops come in, and he knows Roosevelt is going to work a miracle and lick the Depression and we'll all have money again like in 1918 and he'll be able to send me to college next fall. 'Yes, sir,' I said. 'I appreciate your concern.' Then he said, 'Well, I'm going to bed. I have to work tomorrow. You better get to bed too, son. You have school tomorrow.' 'Yes, sir,' I said and Mama said, 'Kiss me goodnight, son,' and I did and went to my room. My daddy and my mother stayed on the porch awhile longer. I undressed and got into bed, but I could hear them talking on the porch and my mother said, 'He's so young, hon. If I had to do it over again, I swear I would never have started him in school at five years old. Fifteen is so young to be graduating from high school.' 'He's not a child, hon,' my Father said. 'He's a young man. He'll be sixteen by the time he graduates.'

Dorothy Prather, twenty-one, comes in. She has some books and papers and a briefcase.

Dorothy Forgive me, Horace, for being late. I got detained by an irate mother who thinks her precious child should of got an A instead of a B. What did you want to see me about?

Horace That's alright.

Dorothy I wanted to give you a copy of the play I'm doing with you Seniors. I want you to read it and tell me how you like it.

Horace Thank you.

She hands him the play.

Dorothy Its called *Not So Long Ago*. It was done in New York several years ago. Eva Le Gallienne played the lead. She is a very gifted actress. She played in *Lilliom* in New York, you know.

Horace Did she?

Dorothy Yes. Anyway, that's all I wanted.

Horace Yes, ma'am.

She starts away.

Miss Prather. I keep meaning to ask you. I never saw the medal I was given for best actor. Do you have it?

She laughs.

Dorothy Oh, Horace, I feel terrible. I didn't tell you because I kept hoping it would turn up. I lost your medal.

Horace Yes, ma'am.

Dorothy I left it at the San Antonio High School after talking to the judges.

Horace I see.

Dorothy It wasn't until I got back here that I realised what I'd done. I called right away and asked if someone had found it, and they said no, but they'd look out for it and if they found it they would get it to me. Obviously they haven't.

Horace Uh huh.

Dorothy You see, when the judges called me up to speak to them about your acting I thought they were calling me to say our play had won first place in the contest and when I realised we hadn't, I was so disappointed I just forgot about your medal. I think I left it on the judges' table or somewhere in the auditorium. Anyway, you won and that's what counts. I'm sorry I lost your medal.

Horace That's alright. Miss Prather . . .

Dorothy (*interrupting*) And Horace, I've been meaning to ask you: did you ever know any addicts?

Horace No, not really. I used to see Miss Sadie Underwood walking past my daddy's store whenever I clerked there on Saturdays and after school. And I heard someone tell my daddy as she walked by that

she was addicted to paregoric. My daddy says you can
get addicted to Coca Colas. He says Strachen Newsome
was addicted to Coca Colas, drank nine or ten a day
until they ate the lining of his stomach and he died
from drinking too many Coca Colas.

Dorothy My heavens. Well. Nice to see you, Horace.
Read the play and tell me what you think.

Horace Yes, ma'am.

She starts away.

Miss Prather?

Dorothy Yes.

Horace I haven't told my mother and daddy about this
yet, so please don't say anything about it to anyone.

A pause.

My daddy can't afford to send me to college next year.

Dorothy I'm sorry, Horace.

Horace That's alright, but he says he hopes to be able to
send me the following year.

Dorothy A year will go quickly, you know.

Horace Yes, ma'am, but I don't want to go to college.

Dorothy Never?

Horace Never.

Dorothy Oh, Horace.

Horace Never.

Dorothy Why, Horace?

Horace Well . . . (*a pause, then almost blurting out*) –
I want to be an actor.

Dorothy Oh, well.

Horace I've heard there are acting schools.

Dorothy Yes, there are.

Horace Do you know about acting schools?

Dorothy A little. How do your parents feel about this?

Horace I don't know. I haven't told them.

Dorothy I think you should tell them, Horace.

Horace I'm going to. I read in the *Chronicle* the other day that someone from Houston was studying acting in Pasadena, California.

Dorothy Yes, there is a school there. At the Pasadena Playhouse. They have summer courses, and as a matter of fact I was thinking of taking some courses this summer and I thought it might be interesting to go to an acting school that had a summer course. Pasadena was one and I was considering the American Academy as the other.

Horace Where is that?

Dorothy In New York City.

Horace Oh. Are they expensive, Miss Prather?

Dorothy They're not cheap. I have catalogues from both of them. Would you like to take them home and look them over? (*She opens a briefcase.*) I have them here. (*She hands them to Horace.*)

Horace Thank you so much.

Dorothy You're welcome, Horace. Think carefully about all of this, Horace. You are talented, certainly, but you are so very young.

Horace Yes, ma'am.

A section of the living room of the Robedaux house. There is an upright piano here and several chairs. Elizabeth, thirty-five, Horace's mother, is there playing 'Narcissus' on the piano. Jim, Horace's younger brother, nine, enters.

Jim Ma, can I go to the movies this afternoon?

She continues playing, not paying any attention to him. He walks over to her and says in a very loud voice, making himself heard over the piano.

Ma, can I go to the movies tonight? I've done all my homework.

Elizabeth stops playing and looks at him.

Elizabeth May I go to the movies tonight?
Jim May I? I've done all of my homework.
Elizabeth All of it?
Jim Every single bit of it.
Elizabeth What's playing?
Jim I don't know. It's a talking picture, I know that much.
Elizabeth Aren't they all talking pictures these days?
Jim No, ma'am. Some are just part talking and on Saturdays the serials are all silent.
Elizabeth Well call the theatre and see what's playing.
Jim I've done all my homework.
Elizabeth That's all well and good, but I still don't want you to go and see just any talking picture. Some pictures are not suitable, in my opinion, for children.

He goes. She continues playing 'Narcissus'. Jim comes in.

Jim Mama.

She continues playing.

Mama?
Elizabeth (*as she continues playing*) Yes?
Jim I know the name of the picture.
Elizabeth (*she continues playing*) What?
Jim *Weary River.*
Elizabeth *Weary River?* What's that about?
Jim I don't know. They said it was a love story.
Elizabeth A what?
Jim A love story.
Elizabeth Did they say it was suitable for children?
Jim I don't know. I didn't ask.
Elizabeth Who's in it?
Jim Lila Lee, Betty Compson and Richard Barthelmes.

Elizabeth I don't think so.

Jim Mom.

Elizabeth No, Jim. It all sounds too adult to me. Anyway, movies are expensive. You just can't go to the movies every time you turn around.

Jim You let Horace go to the tent show every night when it's in town.

Elizabeth But that's only for a week. Anyway, Mr Dude Arthur always trades at your daddy's store while he's in town. You could go to the tent show every night if you wanted to.

Jim I don't like tent shows. I like the movies. The movies only cost a dime for children.

Elizabeth Only a dime. Dimes don't grow on trees, you know.

Horace enters. He has school books.

Hello, son.

Horace Hello.

Elizabeth How was school?

Horace Okay. Miss Prather gave me a copy of the Senior play she's doing.

Jim Are you going to be in it?

Horace Yes.

Jim Are you going to play the lead?

Horace I don't know.

Jim I bet you do. All the kids say Miss Prather thinks you hung the moon.

Horace I'm going to go read the play.

Elizabeth Do you have homework?

Horace Not much.

He goes. She continues playing.

Jim I wonder if this one is going to be about a dope fiend too. Kids who saw the play in San Antonio said when he told roommates he was a dope fiend and

20

needed dope right at that moment he began to tremble and shake. They thought he was going to have a fit. I wish I could have seen it.

Horace Sr comes in.

Horace Sr Hello.
Elizabeth You're early.
Horace Sr I know. (*He kisses her on the cheek.*) Run on, Jim.
Jim Why?
Horace Sr I want to talk to your mother about something.
Jim About what?
Horace Sr Never mind about what. Just leave us alone for a while.

Jim goes.

Where's Horace?
Elizabeth He's in his room.
Horace Sr Studying?
Elizabeth I don't think so. Miss Prather gave him a copy today of the play they're doing as the Senior play.
Horace Sr Elizabeth, as you know I've always felt leaving school as I had to do in the sixth grade in order to go to work to support myself was a great disadvantage to me. I've always felt if I had only had a proper education, finished high school, gone to college . . .

A pause.

Well, I wouldn't always feel such a terrible failure. I haven't accomplished much, you know.
Elizabeth I don't agree. I think on the contrary you have managed very well in these terrible times. We have all the food we need, we have the clothes we need, and we have this house.
Horace Sr Which your papa gave us.

Elizabeth Never mind. We've never had to mortgage it. We –

Horace Sr I get no credit for that. I couldn't mortgage it even if I wanted to. You are not allowed to mortgage your homestead in the state of Texas. It's against the law. Anyway, it's not about me. It's about Horace Jr. I've been thinking more and more this last week about his graduation. Do you realise he'll be graduating in two months?

Elizabeth I know. Is it possible?

Horace Sr I was thinking all day yesterday and last night and again today, what would I most want to change about my life? And, of course, I would like to have been able to finish high school and go to college and get a profession like law or medicine, or engineering, but I was never good in Math, so I probably couldn't have been an engineer. Anyway, something to give me a proper education so I'd be equipped to do more than run a store. All that's too late for me now, of course, but I remember so well when Horace Junior was born I made a promise to myself I was going to see when he grew up he was going to have all the advantages my mama couldn't give me. I thought today, that's all well and good to remember promises, but what can I do about the promises? I can barely keep the store afloat these days, as you know. I've had to go to the bank twice and borrow money to pay current bills. I tell you I felt so sad and blue, and I thought, where in the world can I turn now? When Mr Beard came into the store I thought, it's not the first of the month, why is he here to pay his rent? And so I said, 'You're early. Your rent's not due for another week.' And then I thought to myself, something about the house needs fixing and he's here to get me to have it done, and I asked him if that's why he was here, or was he here to pay his rent early. 'No,' he said, 'I'm not here for either reason, but to talk to you about some business.' 'What kind of business?' I said. 'Have you ever thought about selling your rent house?' he asked. 'No, I haven't,' I said. 'You bought it from your father-in-law, didn't you?' he said. 'Yes,' I said, 'in 1918. Cotton was selling for forty cents a pound and the war was on and everybody had a little money then.' 'Do you remember what you paid for it?' 'Yes.' 'Well, would you be willing to sell it to me now if you made a profit?' 'Well, I'd certainly think about it. I have to talk it over with my wife first, of course.' 'I understand,' he said. 'I'll pay you three thousand dollars for the house.' 'Yes, sir,' I said. 'Let me talk to my wife.' And that's a thousand-dollar profit, you know, hon. And I figure the three thousand dollars will get Horace Jr into not a fancy college maybe, but a good one, and it will see him through four years. Of course, he won't be able to join a fraternity and he'll have to come back here and work with me in the store during summer vacations.

A pause.

What do you think?

Elizabeth Well . . .

Horace Sr I think it's a miracle, honey. The rent house is old and needs repairs. I've never been able to rent it for more than twenty dollars a month and . . .

Elizabeth Well, it's certainly alright with me. I'm sure Horace Jr will just be delighted.

Horace Sr Without saying anything about it, I've been sending off for catalogues of schools I knew were reasonable. I have some down at the store he can look at tonight.

Jim enters.

Where's Horace?

Jim He's in his room.

Elizabeth What's he doing?

Jim He's muttering to himself. I think he's reading aloud about that play they're doing.

Horace Sr Go tell him to come here.

Jim Yes, sir. (*He goes.*)

Horace Sr Shall I tell him or you?

Elizabeth You tell him.

Horace enters.

Horace Sr Horace?

Horace Yes, sir.

Horace Sr Sit down, son.

Horace Yes, sir.

A pause.

Horace Sr Son, you know our rent house the Beards are renting?

Horace Yes, sir.

Horace Sr I'm going to sell it.

Horace To whom?

Horace Sr Mr Beard. He came to the store today and offered to buy it.

Horace Do you want to sell it, Daddy?

Horace Sr Yes, I do. It's run-down, you know, and I'll never be able to get much rent the state it's in.

A pause.

You know why I'm so happy I can sell it?

Horace No, sir.

Horace Sr So I can do for you what my mama couldn't ever do for me.

Horace What's that, Daddy?

Horace Sr Send you to college. Of course, it will have to be a state school. And you won't be able to join a fraternity or anything fancy like that. I have been figuring ever since talking to Mr Beard and I can just about manage four years for what I'll get for the house.

Horace What are you selling it for?

Horace Sr Three thousand dollars.

Elizabeth Isn't it wonderful, Horace?

Horace Yes, ma'am.

Horace Sr And I have a lot of college catalogues at the store we could look over together, and after supper I'll go down and get them and bring them back here.

Horace Yes, sir.

Horace Sr looks at his watch.

Horace Sr What time is supper, Elizabeth?

Elizabeth In another hour.

Horace Sr I tell you what: I think I'll go down now and get those catalogues and we can begin looking at them before supper.

Horace Yes, sir.

A pause.

Daddy?

Horace Sr Yes, son.

Horace I feel terrible about this, but I have to tell you something.

Horace Sr Tell me what, son?

Horace I don't want to go to college.

Horace Sr What?

Horace I don't want to go to college.

Horace Sr You have to go to college, son. You'll regret it the rest of your life if you don't go to college. If you go to college you'll have all kinds of opportunities I never had. I want you to go to college.

Horace I don't want to go to college, Dad.

Elizabeth Why not, son?

Horace I don't know how to tell you, but I just don't.

25

Horace Sr You can tell me, son. I'm your father. Don't be afraid. I'll understand. Whatever it is.

Horace Yes, sir. I hope so.

A pause.

I don't want to go to college, because I want to be an actor and . . .

Horace Sr Good God Almighty! Did you hear that, Elizabeth? Am I dreaming, or did he say what I think he did? What did he say, Elizabeth?

Elizabeth You heard him correctly. He said he doesn't want to go to college, because he wants to be an actor.

Horace Sr An actor! An actor! What kind of an actor? Like Wallace Reid who died a dope fiend? Like Fatty Arbuckle arrested in a sex scandal? Like Charlie Chaplin seducing young innocent girls? Or maybe like Dude Arthur, with his tent show, half-drunk all the time. Talk to him about the life of an actor. You know what he told me? He said he'd rather a child of his would take a pistol and blow his brains out than be an actor.

Elizabeth Come on, honey. Just calm down now.

Horace Sr Where do such ideas come from? Where did he get such an idea here in Harrison, Texas? Did your teacher put all this in your head? Has she put you up to all this? What is the new play you're on about? More dope fiends?

Horace No, sir. It's a period piece about life in New York City. Eva Le Gallienne played in it in New York.

Horace Sr Who in the world is that?

Horace I don't really know, sir. I only know what Miss Prather told me. She said she is a great actress. She was in *Lilliom* in New York City.

Horace Sr In what?

Horace *Lilliom.*

Horace Sr What's that?

26

Horace What's what?

Horace Sr *Lilliomor* – whatever you said.

Horace That was a play in New York.

Horace Sr Is that about dope, too?

Horace No, sir. I don't think so. I don't know what it's about.

Horace Sr Well, where did all this foolishness come from if not from that teacher of yours?

Horace Do you remember old Mr Armstrong?

Horace Sr Yes.

Horace And you used to tell me he had a call to come to Texas to preach?

Horace Sr Yes.

Horace Well, one day I had a call just –

Horace Sr (*interrupting*) You had a what?

Horace A call.

Horace Sr What kind of a call?

Horace It's hard to describe, Daddy. It's just like something came to me and said, you want to be an actor.

Horace Sr I never heard of such thing. Did it say aloud, 'You want to be an actor?'

Horace No, sir. Not really, but I heard it.

Horace Sr I understand you heard it, but was it a man's voice or a woman's voice?

Horace No, sir. Come to think of it, it was more like a feeling, like . . .

Horace Sr Like what?

Horace I don't know, sir. It was like nothing I have ever experienced before, or since.

Horace Sr God Almighty. I never heard of such a thing.

A pause.

Well, what did you do after this whatever it was spoke to you?

27

Horace I went to Mother and I asked what Mr Armstrong
did after he got his call, and Mother said he probably
prayed and asked God to tell him what to do. So
I prayed and asked God to tell me what to do.

Horace Sr How long ago was this?

Horace About a year and a half ago.

Horace Sr Why didn't you tell your mother and me
about it?

Horace I thought you'd make fun of me, and tell me
I was foolish and crazy. Then soon after Miss Prather
came here to teach and began to put on plays, and
I thought maybe God sent her to help me be an actor,
and I prayed some more.

Elizabeth How did you pray, son?

Horace I just prayed. I prayed to know if I should tell
Miss Prather that I wanted to be an actor. But I was
afraid to just then, so I didn't. But it came to me to
write Mr Dude Arthur to see if I could see him next
time he was in Harrison and ask him how I could
go about being an actor. I wrote him, but he never
answered. The next time his show was in town I went
by his boarding house and he was there, but he was
drunk. I decided not to ask him anything then and
started to leave, but he kept asking me why I had
come there. I finally said I had written him a letter
and sent it to Tyler, Texas and had he gotten it. He
said no and what was the letter about. I said I wanted
advice on how to become an actor. He said why in the
name of God. I said because I wanted to know as I
wanted to spend my life when I got out of high school
acting. He said, well, you're a fool and get over it.
Mrs Arthur came in then and she yelled at him and
said he'd better start sobering up as he had a show
that night. I left and the next day while he was at the
store with Daddy, he came in and he told Daddy
about my visit to him and that I said I wanted to be

an actor. After he left Daddy yelled at me and said
he'd never heard of such a thing and to get over it.

Elizabeth Is that right, Horace?

Horace Sr Yes, it is.

Elizabeth You never told me about it.

Horace Sr I didn't see any use in worrying you, as I
knew he'd get over it. You remember George Rust
said he wanted to be a painter, and his family sent him
east to study and after two years he came back here
and built him a studio, so he could spend his time
painting and it lasted about six months and then he
got tired of it, so he ended up managing his family's
cotton farm.

Horace Anyway, since Daddy was so opposed to it and
Mr Arthur wasn't at all encouraging, I decided maybe
God hadn't spoken to me after all, and I wasn't going
to be an actor. But then Mother asked if I wanted to
go and see the Ben Greet Players. I said, yes, and
when I got to the theatre where they were playing,
I looked across the street where Florence Reed was
playing and something told me to go there instead
of to the Ben Greet Players. So I went to that instead
of the Ben Greet Players and when the play was over
I knew I had to be an actor for sure now and I told
Miss Prather what I wanted to do today. She wasn't
as encouraging as I thought she would surely be, but
she said if that's what I wanted to do, I should go to
school.

Elizabeth What kind of school, honey?

Horace A theatre school where they teach acting.

Elizabeth Are there such things? I didn't know that.

Horace Yes, ma'am. And she had sent away for
catalogues for a school in Pasadena and in New York
City, which is the one I like the best.

Elizabeth Why, honey?

Horace Because that's where Broadway is and they have lots of theatres there and . . .

Horace Sr (*interrupting*) Well, I'll tell you this: as sure as I'm standing here, you'll get over it. Mr Armstrong got over his call. He only preached for five years and when he saw he couldn't half-feed his family on a preacher's salary, he began to sell insurance.

A pause.

Horace Dad?

Horace Sr Yes?

Horace I have some catalogues in my room from acting schools. Would you look at them?

Horace Sr No. It's all a lot of foolishness.

Horace Daddy?

Horace Sr Yes?

Horace Help me, Daddy. I'll never ask you for anything again in my life, but just help me and send me someplace where I can learn to be an actor. I'll never ask you for anything else ever again. I swear. (*He begins to cry.*) I swear. I know it's crazy, Daddy. I don't expect you and Mother to understand, but . . . (*He's sobbing now. He controls himself.*) I'm sorry. I'm sorry.

He leaves his parents disturbed and troubled by his crying. There is silence for a moment.

Horace Sr Well . . .

Jim comes in.

Jim What's the matter with Horace?

Elizabeth Never mind. We'll talk about it later.

Jim He was crying.

Elizabeth We're aware of it.

Jim I never saw him cry before. He's sixteen. He shouldn't be crying at sixteen.

Elizabeth He's not sixteen yet.

Jim He will be in March.

Elizabeth It isn't March yet.

Horace Sr Go ask Horace Jr to give you the catalogues of the schools he was telling me about, and bring them to me.

Jim What schools?

Horace Sr I don't know the names of them. He'll know what I'm talking about.

Jim goes.

When I was in the bank I saw Louie Worthing. He's prospered, you know.

Elizabeth I know he has.

Horace Sr Made good investments.

Elizabeth I know.

Horace Sr He said he was investing in an oil pool, and that there was just one share left, and he didn't want to influence me, one way or the other, but he's investing in the oil pool, and he thinks whoever invests in the pool, can make quite a profit from their investment.

Elizabeth How much does the share cost?

Horace Sr Three thousand dollars, and I was tempted to invest the money I will get from Mr Beard, but I said to myself, if I lose the money, there goes Horace's college money.

Jim comes in with two catalogues. Horace Sr takes the catalogues and looks at them. Jim goes to the radio, turns it on and looks for a programme with music. The phone rings in another part of the house. Horace Sr goes to answer it. Jim finds a station with popular music.

Elizabeth Would you mind not playing that music now, Jim?

31

He looks around at her.

Just turn the radio off, please, Jim.
Jim Why is everybody so upset?

Horace Sr comes back in and picks up the catalogues he has been looking at.

Elizabeth Who was on the phone?
Horace Sr Louie Worthing. He says there is someone interested in that last share in the oil pool. He will have to give them an answer by nine tonight. He said he wanted me to understand he's putting no pressure on me, but he just thought I should know and I would have to decide before nine tonight. (*He looks at his watch.*)
Elizabeth What time is it, Horace?
Horace Sr Seven.

A pause.

Of course, if Horace refuses to go to college, I don't need the three thousand dollars right now. And if they strike oil, as Louie believes they will, our whole life could turn around. What should I do, Elizabeth?
Elizabeth I don't know.
Horace Sr Of course, I won't need money for Jim's college for another seven years. That is if he wants to go to college. (*to Jim*) I hope you don't wind up wanting to be an actor like your brother.
Jim No, sir. I'd like to be a crooner, but I know I can't be, because I can't carry a tune unless I'm singing along with somebody.
Horace Sr Thank God for small favours.

A pause.

I'm going to call Louie and tell him he can count me in on the pool.

He starts out of the room. He stops thinking for a beat. He comes back into the room.

I can't do it. As sure as I invest in that oil well and lose my money, Horace will come to me and say, 'I've changed my mind and I want to go to college.'

A pause. He picks up the catalogues and looks at them.

Jim Horace told me just now he'll never go to college. That he's going to be an actor. He says he had a call.

Horace Sr I know all about that call business.

Elizabeth If he goes to acting school, Pasadena is cheaper than New York.

Horace Sr I'll never help him to get to New York to school. Not a fifteen-year-old boy.

Jim He's almost sixteen.

Horace Sr You keep out of it, Jim. How much is Pasadena?

Elizabeth It's a two-year course. Seven hundred and fifty dollars for the first year and two hundred and fifty dollars for the second. Mama has two sisters out in California. Aunt Mag and Aunt Bobo.

Horace Sr I remember.

Elizabeth A thousand dollars for two years. That will still leave you two thousand dollars.

Horace Sr Not really. Does the thousand include board and room?

Elizabeth No, I guess not.

Horace Sr And there is the fare to California and back.

Elizabeth He could take the bus.

Horace Sr Even the bus costs money, Elizabeth. You see, it all adds up.

A pause.

And what worries me the most is, does a fifteen-year-old boy really know what he wants to do? What if we send him out there and he doesn't like it and wants to go to college? What then?

Elizabeth I don't know what then. I'm no fortune-teller.

A pause.

He was very upset, I only know that. I've never seen him so upset. Have you?

Horace Sr No.

A pause.

Here's what I think we should do. Make a bargain with him. Let him stay here next year after he graduates and work with me in the store, and if at the end of the year he still wants to go to acting school, we'll send him to Pasadena. Does that seem sensible to you?

Elizabeth Yes, it does. It sounds very sensible to me.

Horace Sr Of course, I think he'll change his mind while he waits out the year. He'll realise how chancy this whole acting business is and come to his senses and say, I was wrong, I want to go to college. In the meantime I'll leave all the college catalogues I sent for around the living room so he can see them and look at them if he wants to. (*calling*) Horace Junior.

Horace (*calling offstage*) Yes, sir.

Horace Sr Can you come here, please.

Horace Sr goes back to looking at the catalogues he has. Horace Jr enters.

Horace Yes, sir.

Horace Sr Sit down, son.

Horace Yes, sir.

Horace Sr We've been looking over the catalogues.

Horace Yes, sir.

Horace Sr Does either of these schools guarantee you a job when you finish their curriculum?

Horace I don't believe so, sir.

Jim No college guarantees you a job, Daddy.

Horace Sr You keep out of this, Jim, so I'll send you to your room.

Jim Yes, sir.

Horace Sr You see, I don't want you to think your daddy doesn't want to help you in any way I can, but we just want to be sure it's what you really want to do.

Horace I understand, Papa.

Horace Sr You know Mr George Rust?

Horace Yes, sir.

Horace Sr Well, when he was seventeen and graduated from high school he said he wanted to be a painter.

Jim What kind of painter? A house painter?

Horace No, not a house painter, Jim. An artist. He wanted to paint pictures of people and houses and cotton fields and God knows what all. That's all he would do from morning until night, and he got his family to send him east so he could study painting and off he went and stayed away for two years and studied painting and came back here and his family built him a studio and he painted night and day and then he got tired of it and quit and he's never painted a day since and manages his family's cotton farm.

Horace You told me about that earlier, Daddy.

Horace Sr Oh, did I? I guess I did.

Elizabeth And I had a cousin in Brazoria who was bound and determined to be an artist of some kind, and her family sent her to live in Greenwich Village where she could be an artist. She even got into O. O. McIntyre's column in *New York* about something she did in Greenwich Village like squirting some red ink on the monument in Washington Square, or something like that, and then she lost her mind, the poor thing, and they had to bring her back home and she wound up in the asylum.

Horace I'm not going to lose my mind, Mama. I'm going to work hard and make a success.

Elizabeth I'm sure you will, darling, but I just want you to know why we worry.

Horace Sr (*glancing at the Playhouse brochure*) Who is Gilmore Brown?

Horace It says there, he's the head of the Playhouse. The artistic director.

Horace Sr I see. And who is Charles Prickett?

Horace According to the brochure he's the business manager.

A pause.

Horace Sr Well, I'll make a bargain with you: wait a year until you're seventeen and work in the store with me in the meantime. If at the end of the year you still want to study acting, I'll help you go to Pasadena.

Horace is moved and relieved by their decision, but controls his emotions.

Horace Yes, sir. Thank you, sir. I appreciate it.

He goes.

Horace Sr Well, I bet you anything I have he'll come to his senses after a month or two here working in the store and he'll say, 'I've changed my mind. I want to go to college.'

A pause.

Do I have time to work in the garden a little before supper?

Elizabeth Yes, you do.

Jim What are we having?

Elizabeth Nothing special. A casserole. Horace, what if he doesn't change his mind?

Horace Sr Then I don't know. (*He goes.*)

Elizabeth Jim, in about half an hour set the table for me, will you?

Jim Yes, ma'am.

She goes. He picks up the Pasadena brochure and looks at it. Horace comes in.

Who are Onslow Stevens and Gloria Stewart?

Horace Why?

Jim It says here they are movie stars and went to the Pasadena Playhouse and were discovered there by Hollywood. Did you ever hear of them?

Horace Yes, I did.

Jim Well, I haven't. And Victor Jory. Did you ever hear of him?

Horace Yes, I did.

Jim Are you calmer now?

Horace Yes, I am.

Elizabeth enters. Horace takes the Pasadena brochure and starts to look at it. He begins to sing to himself.

'Once I built a railroad,
Made it run,
Made it run against time.
Once I built a railroad,
Now it's done,
Brother, can you spare a dime?'

Elizabeth Horace?

Horace Yes, ma'am.

Elizabeth Would you mind not singing that song around your father? He finds it depressing.

Horace Yes, ma'am.

He puts the brochure down. Jim picks it up and begins reading it. Elizabeth takes the American Academy

*brochure and begins to read that. Horace walks to
the front of the stage and addresses the audience.*

My father asked me not to tell anyone in town that
he was thinking of sending me to dramatic school
until it was time for me to go. Jim said he kept hoping
I'd change my mind and ask to go to college. At first
he left college catalogues all over the house. But when
he saw I wasn't going to change my mind they began
to disappear. A lot of my friends went off to college;
those that didn't mostly went to Houston looking for
jobs. Dude Arthur's tent show came for one last
summer and then it closed down for good. They did a
show in Harrison called *A Womanless Wedding* with
men from town playing all the parts. 'Dearie' Burtner,
who was big and fat and had been my scout master
when I was in Cub Scouts, was the bride and Mr
Piney, who was thin as a rake and only came up to
Dearie's shoulders was the groom. They asked me to
be in it, but I declined. People in town said that was
the kind of show they liked. Clean, wholesome and
fun. Vilma Banky and Rod LaRocque, two movie
stars that couldn't get work because of their accents
when talkies began, came to Houston in a play called,
Cherries Are Ripe. I went to see it, but I didn't like
it. The well Louie Worthing's pool invested in came
through and Louie Worthing and all his investors
became rich. Some said they made as much as fifty
thousand apiece. Anyway, the ones I knew all got new
cars for themselves and their wives and children. It
wasn't until years later my mother told me my daddy
could have been one of the investors, but was afraid
they would find no oil and the three thousand dollars
he had for me would be lost. When news got around
town that my folks were sending me off to dramatic
school, my daddy had many visitors. Mostly old men,

he said, came to the store to tell him he was making a
mistake and just throwing his money away. Most of
them he said used George Rust as an example of how
it would finally turn out. I was in the store when the
last one came in. An uncle on Daddy's side. I was in
the front of the store and Daddy was in the back at
his desk working on his accounts when this uncle
came in. He barely spoke to me and asked where
Daddy was and I pointed to the back of the store, and
I called out, 'Daddy, Uncle Albert is here to see you.'
He went on towards Daddy in the back of the store.
I could hear him say he was here as a concerned
member of the family to try and talk some sense into
Daddy. I heard Daddy say he would thank him to
mind his own business. Then his uncle brought up
George Rust one more time and they began to yell
at each other over that and his uncle left in a fury
without saying goodbye to Daddy or me. The night
I was to leave for California he and Mother went to
sit on the gallery after supper. I was in my room
packing my suitcase while listening to the radio, when
Daddy called and asked me to come out on the porch.
I went out and there was a moon, partly obscured by
a cloud, but high in the sky. Daddy gave me my bus
ticket and told me to be careful of pickpockets, and
I said I would. He gave me a twenty-dollar bill then,
which he said I should save in case an emergency
of some kind came up. I thanked him and Mother
began crying then and said they were going to miss
me. I said I would miss them too. Daddy said they
were both very proud of me and felt I would have
a wonderful success, but to always remember that
if things didn't work out in California or any other
place, I could always come back to my home and be
welcomed and there would be a place for me to work
in his store. I thanked him for telling me that. I never

did go back during their lifetime except on visits, though many a time when I was lonely and discouraged I wanted to. But then I remembered about my call and kept on going somehow.

The lights fade.

THE BEAR TABLE

Julian Garner

For Leoni, Natali and Maxim
And for Hanne, my reason for being in Finland

Characters

Harri
Ilona
Pekka
Pontus
all fourteen

Aleksi
twelve

A Bear

The play is set in the present.

Notes

Over 75 per cent of Finland is forested. In Helsinki, it is said to be possible to enter the forest at the edge of the city and walk to Siberia without once leaving the same forest. Bears are not uncommon, even in relatively settled areas, and will, on occasion, raid dustbins or attack joggers.

Finland has a long tradition of shamanism.

SCENE ONE

A derelict camp in the forest. Ilona and Harri enter. She takes the place in.

Harri Do you smoke?

Ilona It's not what I imagined.

Harri It's quite a few years since they actually lived here.

Ilona It's a bit spooky.

Harri This is where they slept. Do you want to come in and have a look?

Ilona Is this where they did their cooking?

Harri Well, made their wines, cooked their jams, yeah. They dug the trench to bring water from a pond over there. It's all dried up now. You know, like irrigation.

Ilona Not irrigation. They weren't irrigating anything.

Harri Whatever.

Ilona It's more like an aqueduct. Irrigation's something else.

Harri Yeah, well, whatever.

Ilona It's very cool, though.

Harri Yeah, pretty cool, considering they were just a bunch of piss-head winos. I mean, you don't think of winos digging ditches hundreds of metres through the forest, do you?

Ilona No.

Harri No, you think of Romans doing that. But these were really heavy-duty drunkheads. One of them, he was their leader actually, Bloodnut, my dad was at school with him, he used to be out of his head, in class, in the middle of the day, when he was ten! He had a bottle of cider under his desk, they had these

43

old-fashioned desks, with inkwells; he'd poke a straw
through the hole and have a good old slurp every time
the teacher's back was turned. He'd go through a
whole big bottle in a single maths lesson, evidently.

Ilona Wow.

Harri Yeah. I don't think he got much maths done,
though!

Ilona I never heard of winos living in the forest before.

Harri It's quite common, actually. It's not *un*common.
They move out here for the summer, you know, hang
out, get drunk, whatever. Then, when it gets cold
again, around October, they move back to the city,
for the hostels and that.

Ilona But not this lot?

Harri No. They disappeared.

Ilona Just like that?

Harri They Were Never Seen Or Heard Of Again.

Ilona Where are they supposed to have gone?

Harri No one knows. It's A Mystery.

Ilona Though this isn't really the forest, is it? It's so
close to the flats.

Harri It didn't used to be. The flats are pretty new.

Ilona Oh.

Harri This used to be quite deep forest, actually. Are
you gonna come in and sit down, it's quite nice in
here? We can have a drink, if you like, a chat.

Ilona We're having a chat, aren't we?

Harri A drink, then?

Ilona What have you got?

Harri Cider.

Ilona Pear?

Harri No, apple. It's stronger.

Ilona It's not, is it? I thought they were all the same?

Harri Wanna bet? This is much stronger, you can really
get pissed on this stuff. Aren't you gonna sit down?

Ilona It's wet.

Harri Sit on my bag, if you like. There used to be old armchairs but they got so manky we used them on the fire last year. Rats ran out of them! Cigarette? Lucky Strikes.

Ilona No thanks, I don't smoke.

Harri What, never?

Ilona I think it's a disgusting habit, to be honest.

Harri I like it. It relaxes me.

Ilona My father smoked.

Harri Yeah?

Ilona Every time he breathed in my face it made me want to puke.

Harri Yeah, but did he chew gum? I chew gum, me, stops you smelling like an old ashtray.

Ilona It wasn't an ashtray he smelt like.

Harri Do you want some gum? Your wish is my command! Whoops!

Ilona What's that?

Harri Condom! Be prepared, that's my motto! Ilona? Don't go. I'm sorry. The others'll be here soon. I'll introduce you, it'll be fine, they'll like you. I don't think there'll be any problem.

Ilona What do you mean?

Harri Well, you know, this is, like, our place; normally we don't let just anybody come here. But, you're with me, so it'll be fine.

Ilona When was all this? The winos?

Harri Oh, a few years ago. I'm not sure really. Quite a few years ago, I think it was.

Ilona And no one knows where they went?

Harri No one, no.

Ilona Perhaps – further in?

Harri It goes on for miles, hundreds of kilometres, thousands! Siberia's that way! It's true!

Ilona I expect there are bears there.

Harri Are you afraid of bears?

Ilona I'm not *afraid* of them –

Harri Only, there are bears here, according to Aleksi.

Ilona Who?

Harri Aleksi, he's one of us. He was sleeping here one night, and it came out of the forest, over there.

Ilona *Sleeping* here?

Harri I know, he does sometimes. It was digging things up, he said, old tins and stuff, like it was looking for something. Then, suddenly, he felt a sneeze coming on, Aleksi. He was in the bivvy, he held it as long as he could but then it came out like an explosion, the sneeze, and the bear ran away!

Ilona So close to the flats?

Harri I know, spooky, innit?

Ilona I don't believe that.

Harri Why not?

Ilona Bears don't come this close to civilisation.

Harri Yeah, well, this one did.

Ilona Well, I don't believe it.

Harri No? Well – Aleksi does exaggerate a bit, sometimes.

Ilona Sounds like it!

Harri He's a bit of a fruit, actually. I don't mean like a homo, you know, just weird, like an alien. Like, he's really small, he's twelve but he looks eight, and he's really, really thin, sometimes you can almost see through him! But, he's good at getting stuff – booze mainly, off his dad – so, we've got to put up with him.

Ilona I saw a bear once.

Harri Where? A real one?

Ilona On a lake near where I used to live. My dad had put a net under the ice and I went with him to get the fish. But when we got there he said, 'Still!' A bear had pulled up the net and was eating the fish, just their stomachs, throwing the rest on the ice. There was blood everywhere.

Harri What happened?

Ilona There was nothing we could do. If we'd had a gun we'd have fired it in the air, Dad said, to scare it. He'd never have shot a bear, though, you're not allowed to.

Harri You could've tried sneezing!

Ilona In the end it'd eaten over a hundred fish, just their stomachs. Our net was ruined. It was like there'd been a war. It wandered off across the lake and into the forest on the other side.

Harri Did anyone ever tell you you're really attractive, Ilona?

Ilona No.

Harri Well, they should've, 'cos you are.

Ilona How long do you reckon it took them to dig this trench?

Harri I thought it was an aqueduct?

Ilona Well, it's not now, is it? It's dry.

Harri That's 'cos the pond dried up. Drainage, or something. Can I ask you a question? Have you got a boyfriend?

Ilona Yes.

Harri Oh. What's his name?

Ilona Raimo, his name's Raimo. What do you want to know for?

Harri No, only – I was wondering, do you want to be *my* girlfriend? I mean it's up to you, but, you know, you've just moved here and you don't know anyone, and perhaps it'd be good to be, like, with someone who knows the area, who can show you round –

Ilona Alright.

Harri – introduce you to . . . What did you say?

Ilona I said, yeah, alright; that'd be cool.

Harri kisses her on the mouth. She neither resists nor responds.

Harri Do you want another drink?

Ilona If you like.
Harri Shall we go inside?

They do so.

Do you wanna lie down?
Ilona No.

They snog.

Harri It's alright here, don't you think?
Ilona It's alright.
Harri Don't look now, but here come Peks and Pontus.
Ilona Who?
Harri Let's pretend we haven't seen them!
Ilona Why?

Pekka and Pontus enter. Ilona has her back to them; they watch Harri fondling her. She pulls away.

Harri Hello, you're early! (*Comes out.*)
Pontus Are we? No, we're not.

Pekka elbows him.

What?
Harri It's alright, we were just – you know! This is Ilona, my girlfriend.

She comes out.

Ilona Hello.
Harri And this is Pekka and Pontus. Otherwise known as the Amazing Juggling Siamese Twins!
Pekka No, we're not.
Harri Mr Halonen, our maths teacher, calls them that.
Pekka Mr Halitosis.
Harri He reckons they're joined at the brain, but neither of them knows how to use it!

Pontus has put on a red nose.

What's the matter, Pont?

Pontus Nothing. (*Takes it off.*)

Pekka Numbskull!

Harri Pont's got this thing, you see, Ilona; every time he's stressed out, or something –

Pontus I'm not stressed out!

Harri – he puts on his little red nose. He doesn't even know he's doing it any more, it's become automatic!

Ilona You're not really twins, are you?

Pekka Of course not!

Ilona I didn't think so, somehow.

Pontus We're second cousins: his mum is my mum's –

Pekka She doesn't wanna know that!

Pontus Well, she *asked*.

Harri He also calls them Tom and Jerry, Mr Halonen, 'cos they're always fighting! Ilona just moved here – didn't you, darling? We met in the lift. Then we met at the shopping centre. Then we met on the bus, so I thought, better ask her what she's doing tonight. Anyway, one thing led to another, and – here we are!

Pontus has put the nose on again.

Okay, tell me; you haven't got any booze, right?

Pontus There was a store dectective!

Pekka Evidently.

Pontus You couldn't see her, she was more than ten metres away! She was weighing up the same bag of grapes for like ten minutes.

Pekka Ten minutes!

Pontus She was onto us, we couldn't risk it!

Pekka You mean *you* couldn't; chickenshit.

Pontus Chickenshit yourself! I've already been caught twice.

Harri Alright, alright. So what *did* you get? Did you get the Cokes?

Pekka One Coke. He didn't have any dosh.

Pontus My mum's at work!

Harri Shit.

Ilona Is there a problem?

Harri You could say that! The problem is, that Aleksi –
who I told you about – is gonna arrive any minute with
a litre of his dad's hooch, which is totally undrinkable
unless it's mixed at least fifty-fifty with Coke or Sprite.

Pekka It tastes like lighter fuel.

Harri It gets you pissed.

Pontus Aleksi's dad spilt some on the table once when
he was drunk and next morning it'd eaten a hole right
though the wood.

Harri Yeah, well, I think we can take that story with a
few salt mines actually, seeing as it's one of Aleksi's.

Pekka I'm not drinking it neat again, and that's that.

Pontus We've got to get pissed somehow.

Ilona We've got two bottles of cider.

Harri Yeah, but they're ours.

Ilona We can share, can't we?

Harri It's not enough. We'll have to draw lots.

Pekka What?

Harri Pick straws. Here you are; long straw wins.

Pontus Only three straws? But there are five of us.

Harri Yeah, but Aleksi don't count! And Ilona's not
gonna drink it neat, is she?

Pontus No one *wants* to.

Harri Well, she's not going to; end of discussion!

Pekka Take that stupid nose off!

Pontus It's not doing you any harm, is it?!

Pekka It's annoying me!

Pontus Take your glasses off, then, you won't see it!

Harri Just pick a straw!

Pekka I'm not drinking it neat, it makes me throw up!

Harri Pick a straw!

Ilona What if . . . what if you mixed it with the cider, as well as the coke? That way, nobody'd have to drink it neat, would they?

Pontus That is a brilliant idea, Harri.

Harri We can't do that.

Pekka Why not? Of course we can.

Harri Yeah, but – that's *our* cider!

Ilona They'd do the same for you, wouldn't they?

Pontus/Pekka Yeah. / Of course we would.

Harri Yeah, of course!

Pontus We would, honest!

Harri But – what are we going to do till Aleksi gets here?

Ilona Well, I noticed tons of mushrooms on the way here. If we picked them, we could do them on sticks, like kebabs.

Harri Then we've got to light a fire.

Ilona You've got a lighter, haven't you? You can't really have a party without something to eat.

Pontus That sounds great.

Ilona I'll go and pick the mushrooms, then.

Pekka But, aren't they dangerous?

Ilona Not if you know what you're doing.

Harri I'll come with you.

Ilona No. Erm. Actually I've got to do something else, too! (*Pecks him on the cheek and exits.*)

Harri Bags the bivvy tonight.

Pekka What?

Harri Yeah, Ilona and me have got some, er, business to take care of, as they say! Do you want some gum? (*Drops the condom.*) Sorry. Be prepared, that's my motto! Yeah, soon as I saw her, I thought, I know what *she* wants!

Pontus What about us? If you're in the bivvy –

Harri I don't know; the ditch?

Pekka What if it rains?

Harri Swim! But it won't rain. And even if it does, the trees'll keep you dry, the fire'll keep you warm. Everything's going to be very cool. You'd better get some wood. Make sure it's dry.

Pekka What about you?

Harri Just gotta texty Aleksi, I've run out of smokes. What are you waiting for? I'll be with you in a minute. Go on.

They exit. Harri quickly drinks some cider, then keys a message into his mobile. Aleksi enters: he keeps one hand in his pocket throughout the following.

Aleksi Hiya, Harri!

Harri You're early.

Aleksi A bit, yeah. How's it going?

Harri What's up?

Aleksi Nothing. Hiya, Pont. Hiya Peks!

They enter with wood.

Pontus Where's the booze?

Harri Yeah, what happened?

Aleksi Erm . . .

Pekka Haven't you got any?

Aleksi You see, there's been a . . .

Harri What? A what?

Aleksi A problem.

Pekka What problem?

Pontus What problem?

Harri 'What problem?'

Aleksi I got caught.

Pekka/Pontus What?

Aleksi I'm sorry, Harri, I –

Harri Caught? What do you mean?

Aleksi I – I, erm – I . . .

Ilona Look! (*Enters with mushrooms.*) There are so many
of these, it's like a mushroom supermarket here! Hello,
you must be Aleksi.

Pontus He got caught!

Harri How could you get *caught*?

Aleksi I thought he was asleep. He hadn't moved for ten
minutes, his head was resting on the table. I waited
and waited. He was breathing steady and everything.
Then, when I was pouring it over in a bottle, he – he
came round and he – he – erm . . .

Ilona What? He what?

Aleksi I'm really sorry, Harri!

Pontus We were relying on you!

Aleksi I know, I'm sorry –

Harri Stop keep saying that!

Ilona It's not his fault.

Harri Stay out of it, Ilona, it's none of your business!

Ilona I'm Ilona, by the way.

Harri All he had to do was wait for his dad to pass out!

Aleksi I thought he had!

Harri Shit! *Shit!*

Pontus What are we going to do now?

Pekka Go home. What else *can* we do, without booze?

Ilona They had a bit of bad luck, too!

Harri I said shut it!

Ilona Don't shout at me!

Harri I'll shout at who I fucking like!

Aleksi I'm sorry!

Harri If you say that once more I'll . . .!

Ilona Look –

Harri No, *you* look! Okay? We let him be here, we put
up with him! We look forward to this, all week!

Aleksi I'm really, really sorry!

Harri We don't want to know how sorry you are, we
want to get pissed!

Ilona I know what we can do!

Harri What?

Ilona You want to get pissed? Like, completely out of your heads? Stay where you are!

She exits, returns with a red agaric toadstool.

Pontus You're mad!

Pekka You'll die now you've touched that!

Ilona That's the white ones, Destroying Angels, they're like this only white. The old shamans used these, like E, they're fine. They're harmless. My dad used them, sometimes. Quite often, actually. He even let me, once.

Pontus What was it like?

Ilona That'd be telling, wouldn't it? No, if you want to know, you'll have to try it yourself. No? Oh, well, I'll just have to party on my own, I suppose! (*She eats some.*) Aleksi? It's nothing to be frightened of.

Aleksi takes some, Pontus also.

Pekka Don't!

Pontus She's done it, and Aleksi.

Pekka (*takes some*) Ugh, it tastes disgusting!

Ilona Have some cider with it, or Coke. So Harri, are you going to be the odd one out?

Harri takes some.

Now we just get comfortable and wait for it to kick in. It doesn't take long. We haven't lit a fire; never mind. This is going to be so cool, I think!

Pontus I can't feel my lips!

Ilona That means it's starting!

Pontus falls asleep. Then Pekka, then Harri.

What's wrong with your hand?

Aleksi shows her. Ilona is shocked but cannot stay awake. Aleksi eats the rest of the toadstool. When nothing happens, he exits.

SCENE TWO

Pekka and Harri wake up.

Pekka What happened?

Harri We must've fallen asleep. Shit! It's three o'clock in the morning! Ilona? Ilona?

Pekka I've got the worst headache in the whole world.

Harri Ilona! Ilona!

Pekka Pont? Wake up, mate. Pontus!

Pontus (*sits up*) What?

Pekka We've got to go home.

Pontus What happened?

Pekka We ate that stuff, remember? I feel so sick.

Pontus Where's Aleksi?

Harri He must've gone already. Little creep. She's out of it.

Pontus I had a dream about him.

Pekka About Aleksi?

Pontus He kept fading.

Harri What do you mean?

Pontus Fading – disappearing, you know. We asked him what was happening, but he said it was nothing, so we stopped asking. Then he faded clean away. Afterwards, we were talking about it, there were lots of theories, but in the end we decided it must've been done with mirrors.

Harri Mirrors?

Pontus It was your suggestion, actually. I don't remember the details, but in the end we agreed it must've been that. Sorry, I think I'm going to be sick! (*He vomits.*)

Pekka I dreamt about him, too.

Harri What?

Pekka We were in a field, and there was this balloon coming towards us, like a hot-air balloon, and as it got closer I saw that it looked like Aleksi, the balloon, like a giant Aleksi, coming slowly towards us through the air.

Pontus What happened?

Pekka It landed beside us and someone told us to get in.

Harri Who told us?

Pekka Someone in the gondola.

Pontus The basket-thing under the balloon.

Harri I know what a gondola is.

Pekka I couldn't see who it was, he had his back turned, but I think he was wearing a fur coat. Then, as we were getting in the basket, the gondola, he said: 'Whatever you do, don't touch the balloon; it's very fragile.' But, it was funny, as soon as he said it, none of us could get the idea of touching it out of our heads! We were desparate to touch it, and the higher we got, the more desparate we got. But at the same time we were really scared what might happen *if* we touched it.

Pontus And did we? Touch it?

Pekka Harri did.

Harri I did?

Pekka You climbed up on the ropes and touched it.

Pontus What happened?

Pekka I don't know, I woke up. (*Vomits.*)

Harri So, it's the Amazing *Dreaming* Siamese Twins, now, is it?! I can't wait to tell Mr Halonen about this!

Pontus You didn't dream about him, then?

Harri Of course not! I've got better things to dream about than that little wanker! Ilona, for instance! I dreamt we were having continuous simultaneous orgasms all night long! Perhaps that's why she's so exhausted!

Pontus I don't know how he sleeps here, do you? Aleksi.

Harri What's up, Pont, not spooked, are you?

Pontus I'm not spooked, but I wouldn't sleep here.

Harri Wouldn't you? I would.

Pekka I bet you wouldn't.

Harri Why not? It's only three hundred metres from the flats!

Pekka Even so.

Pontus I think we ought to be getting home, actually, Peks.

Harri You can't. Ilona's still out of it.

Pekka Can't you try and wake her again?

Harri She'll wake up when she's ready.

Pontus I hope she's ready soon, that's all I can say.

Harri Come on, it's only shadows. And moonlight. And the wind in the trees. And the small animals creeping about. And the not-so-small animals creeping about! And the bears! And the ghosts of dead winos! Ooooahhh!

Pontus Don't!

Pekka Seriously, why doesn't she wake up? *We* have.

Harri 'Cos she's a woman.

Pekka What's that got to do with it?

Harri Their bodies can't absorb as much as men's. It's why women get drunk more easily, for example.

Pekka Who told you that?

Harri My dad.

Pontus Is she alright, do you think?

Harri She's just a bit stoned, that's all. Aren't you, Ilona? Come on, darling, wake up; some of us want to go home tonight.

Pontus I feel so ill!

Harri And on with the nose!

Pontus takes it off.

I feel okay, actually. Shall we do it again? Only kidding.

Pontus Ilona, wake up. Please wake up. Ilona. Ilona!

Harri Leave her alone, she's mine! Ilona? Ilona! Ilona!
Pekka We'll be here all night.

Ilona wakes suddenly, making them jump.

Ilona Where's Aleksi?
Harri He's – not here.
Ilona Where is he?
Pekka Gone home, probably.
Ilona But, his hand . . . !
Pontus What about it?
Ilona Didn't you see it? Burnt?
Harri Burnt?
Ilona Red-raw, like a piece of meat! We've got to get
  him to a doctor, it's an emergency!
Pontus But – he's not here!
Pekka I was the first one awake, and he wasn't here,
  then. He must've gone home.
Ilona No, no, he wouldn't have gone home!
Harri Why not?
Ilona Because his father must have done it, don't you
  see? Held it in the fire, or something.
Pekka What?!
Ilona When he caught him! There was no skin left!
Pontus I want to go home!
Harri Wait! When did you see this?
Ilona What? When?
Harri When did you see his hand? I think – I think
  you've been dreaming. She's been dreaming, that's all.
Ilona Dreaming?
Harri We've all been dreaming about him. Well, they
  have.
Ilona No, no; he showed it to me, only I couldn't stay
  awake. And you'd already gone. And now he's gone –
Pontus His dad wouldn't do that!
Harri Of course he wouldn't.
Pontus He took us to the pictures that time, remember?

Ilona He was trying to tell you! But you wouldn't listen! You wouldn't – (*She vomits.*)

Harri She's off her box, if you ask me.

Pontus I'm going home! (*He runs off, downstage left.*)

Pekka Pontus!

Harri Peks! Don't go.

Ilona Aleksi! Aleksi!

Harri He's not here, my darling.

Ilona We've got to find him! I feel so sick!

Pekka What if you phoned him?

Harri What?

Pekka Then, we'd know where he was.

Harri Yeah, but – what if we wake his dad?

Pekka He'll be out of it till tomorrow afternoon, at the earliest.

Harri You reckon?

Ilona We've got to do something!

Harri Alright. We're going to phone him, Ilona. We're going to phone Alesksi, find out where he is.

Ilona Yes.

Harri (*gets out his mobile*) Shit!

Pekka Low battery?

Harri (*dials*) It's ringing.

Pekka Isn't he answering?

Harri It probably means – it probably means he's gone to bed and it's switched off. So's not to wake the whole house. I'm sure that's what it means. Aren't you, Peks?

Pekka Yeah, probably.

Ilona Don't we know where he is?

Harri He's not answering. But – Ilona, I'm *sure* you were dreaming, you know! Whatever's in that toadstool, it's made us all dream about him, for some reason. Ilona – Alexi's dad, he's a bit of a meathead, but – he wouldn't do anything like that, I'm sure he wouldn't. Would he, Peks?

Ilona So, what *would* he do? What's he done before?
Harri Well – nothing, necessarily –
Pekka Aleksi never talks about it . . .
Ilona About what?
Harri We don't know for sure, but . . .
Pekka He had a black eye, once.
Harri He fell downstairs –
Pekka He *said*, yeah, but . . .
Ilona What else?
Harri Nothing. A few bruises, little cuts . . .
Pekka A broken arm.
Harri When he fell off his bike, yeah.
Pekka He hasn't *got* a bike, Harri!
Harri He – he never wanted to talk about it – He
  wouldn't talk about it – We asked him –
Pekka No. We didn't! We never asked him anything.
  We just – We never asked him.

*Ilona vomits again. Pekka fetches the Coke from the
bivouac for her.*

Harri Let's go home. There's nothing we can do.
Ilona No! We've got to find him!
Harri How? He could be anywhere.
Ilona We've got to look for him!
Harri Ilona –

Pontus runs in, upstage right.

Pekka What are you doing?
Pontus I – I must've gone in a circle.
Harri What? You got lost? Between here and the flats?
Pontus I don't understand, I kept going straight.
Pekka You must've took a wrong turning.
Pontus There aren't any turnings!
Harri No, but you took them, anyway!
Ilona Did you see Aleksi?

Pontus No! He's gone home! (*He runs out, downstage left.*)

Pekka Pont! You shouldn't laugh at him!

Harri Does he need a map to get out of bed? Or a guide to take him to the toilet?!

Pekka He's *scared*, Harri! He's bloody scared!

Harri This is all your fault, bitch!

Ilona Ow!

Harri I felt sorry for you! I did you a favour, invited you along!

Pekka Harri, don't!

Ilona I was trying to stop you hurting Aleksi!

Harri What? I've never hurt him. None of us have. Peks, have we?

Ilona You hurt him all the time, you're just too stupid to see it!

Harri You'd better take that back! Take it back!

Pekka She's gonna puke, Harri.

Harri How have I hurt him? I've never hurt him! You hurt him, you could've killed him!

Pekka Let her puke.

Harri Yeah, I hope she pukes her guts out! Her brains, too, if she's got any! Who, with brains, would make people eat red fly toadstools?!

Pekka She didn't make us –

Harri She suggested it!

Pekka Leave her alone!

Harri Stop telling me what to do, she's my girlfriend!

They fight.

Pekka Wait! Wait, my glasses! Shit!

Harri Sorry, mate.

Pekka Where are they? Careful, you'll tread on them!

Harri They must be here somewhere.

Ilona What the matter?

Harri His glasses; can you help us?

61

Pekka My mum'll kill me, they're the only pair I've got! You bastard, why'd you have to start fighting me?
Harri Look, we'll find them, okay?
Pekka They cost more than a two hundred euros!

Pontus runs in, upstage right.

Pontus What's happening, why am I here?! There's no way I ran in a circle, I went straight the whole way!
Pekka You can't have done, Pont.
Pontus I did, I followed the path, there's only one, I fucking followed it! I should be at the flats, *why am I here?!*

Harri runs off, downstage right.

Ilona Harri, wait . . .!
Pontus Something's happening, I don't know what it is!
Pekka It's okay, Pont.
Pontus It's not okay! Don't you understand, we can't get home! Where are your glasses?
Pekka They're here, somewhere.
Pontus What happened?
Pekka It was Harri!
Pontus Has he gone mad? Your glasses?
Ilona He's a bastard, you all are! Why are you so horrible to Aleksi?
Pontus We're not.
Ilona I saw you!
Pontus That was Harri.
Ilona You didn't even notice he was in pain! You're supposed to be his friends! With friends like you, who needs enemies?
Pontus What's wrong with her?
Ilona I hate you, I hope you rot in hell!
Pontus We haven't done anything!
Pekka Quiet, quiet! Is that him?

They listen. Harri runs in, upstage right.

Pontus See, it's impossible! We're trapped!

Harri climbs a tree, off.

Pekka What are you doing? Harri?
Harri What does it look like I'm doing?
Pekka I don't know, I can't see you!
Pontus He's climbing a tree.
Ilona I hope he falls down and breaks his neck.
Harri If I can see the flats – get our bearings!
Pekka Help me look, will you?
Pontus Where were you?
Pekka I don't know, I don't where I am *now*!
Pontus It's so dark. Can't you help us?
Ilona Can you see anything? Harri? Harri?
Harri Shit!
Ilona What is it?
Pontus Harri? What's wrong?
Harri It's gone!
Pekka What has?
Harri The city! The flats! Everything!
Pekka Gone?
Harri (*climbing down*) It's all gone. The cathedral, the Olympic stadium, everything. All you can see is trees, everywhere!
Ilona What are you talking about?
Harri They've gone!
Pontus But, they can't have!
Harri Well, they have.
Pekka Gone?
Harri Gone. Gone!
Pontus What are we going to do?
Ilona Find Aleksi!
Harri Can't you shut up about fucking Aleksi?
Ilona He's out there, lost!

Harri So what?
Ilona So, we have to find him!
Harri *You* find him!
Ilona I will!
Pontus Please!
Pekka Shhh!
Harri What?
Pekka Quiet!

They listen.

Pontus I can't hear anything?
Pekka Shhhhhhhh.

Harri's mobile rings.

Harri It's Aleksi. (*Answers phone.*) Where are you?
What? What? Aleksi, what are you . . .? Speak
properly, can't you? Aleksi, what . . .? It's someone
mucking about, I think.
Ilona (*grabs the phone*) Aleksi, is it you? Where are
you? Aleksi, what . . .? Aleksi –

The phone beeps.

What are you trying to say? Aleksi, please, what are you –
where are you? What are you trying to *say*?

The phone beeps again and dies.

Harri Battery's gone.
Ilona It was him?
Harri It sounded like him. It was his number.
Ilona But, what was he saying?
Harri Nothing. Gibberish.
Pekka Why?
Harri I don't know. Taking the piss? Or, pissed: been at
his dad's hooch, I expect. Unless . . .
Pontus What?
Harri Why didn't I think of it before!

64

Pekka Think of what before?

Harri It's still working. The toadstool. We're out of our heads!

Ilona Hallucinating?

Harri It explains everything! It's like junkies, right? When they're coming off drugs, they see all these things, spiders and scorpions, but actually they're not there, it's just their minds playing tricks. Don't look so worried, Pont: we're just tripping! All we've got to do is sleep it off, and it'll all be over!

Ilona But where's Aleksi?

Harri He was still awake when you fell asleep, you said.

Ilona He showed me his hand.

Harri Or you dreamt he did? Or, he managed to get home before all this started. Or, it *didn't* start for him; for whatever reason, the toadstool didn't affect him in the same way. So, when we went to sleep, he went home to bed, switched off his phone –

Pontus But, he just phoned us!

Harri Hallucination. She said it.

Pekka How come we're all hallucinating the same thing at the same time, though?

Harri If we are.

Pekka Well, aren't we?

Harri Who knows? Who can honestly say they know anything? Perhaps you're just part of my hallucination and I'm part of yours; we're hallucinating completely different things at the same time? Or, the same thing at different times! How do we know? We can't know.

Ilona If I'm not hallucinating –

Harri I think you *are*.

Ilona But if I'm *not*, then he's out there, somewhere, in the forest, on his own, in terrible pain.

Harri Yeah, but what can we *do* about it?

Ilona Aleksi! Aleksi!

Pekka Aleksi!

Ilona/Pekka/Pontus Aleksi! Aleksi! Aleksi! (*etc.*)
Harri Well, you can give yourselves sore throats, if you like, I'm going to sleep it off in the bivvy.

He goes into the bivouac. The others continue shouting for Aleksi. After a while, Pontus goes into the bivouac, too.

Ilona/Pekka Aleksi! Aleksi!
Ilona Perhaps he's right.
Pekka Aleksi!
Ilona Perhaps we should just go to sleep and –
Pekka Listen! Can you hear that?
Ilona Aleksi? Aleksi, is that you?
Pekka It's not him.
Ilona It's a bear.
Pontus (*comes out of the bivouac*) Where?
Pekka Can't you smell it?
Harri Got your nose too near your arse again, Peks!
Ilona (*points*) It's there!
Pontus I can see it.

Harri comes out.

Can you see it, Harri?
Harri I can see it, it doesn't mean it's there.
Pekka Aleksi saw a bear here, once.
Harri Well, now we know what he was on, don't we!
Ilona It's coming this way. I think we should leave.
Pekka My glasses!
Ilona We'll find them later.
Pontus I'll help you, Peks.
Harri Look, look – we're out of our heads! Cities don't disappear. Bears don't come this close to civilisation.
Ilona Go very slowly. Whatever you do, don't run.
Harri Well, goodnight, everybody! I'm going to sleep!
Pontus Harri!

*Harri goes into the bivouac. The others leave. After a
while, a Bear enters.*

Harri Very subtle, Peks, I don't think! Wanker.

Harri comes out.

You're not real. You're only in my head. Bears don't
come this close to civilisation. Shoo, shoo; go away!
Smoke?

The Bear rears up. Roars. Blackout.

SCENE THREE

*Another, darker part of the forest. Ilona leads Pekka
across the stage. Pontus enters.*

Pontus Are we still hallucinating? Because if we are I wish
we'd stop!

Ilona and Pekka return.

Ilona If it looks like a bear and it sounds like a bear –
Pekka – and it even smells like a bear –
Ilona – then, as far as I'm concerned, it is a bear. At least
till we get some new information.
Pontus I can't smell it.
Ilona It's probably moved downwind of us. But it's still
out there, I can feel it.
Pontus I can't.
Pekka Perhaps it's stopped to eat, or something.
Ilona I guess we can take a few minutes.

They sit down.

Pontus I'm starving!
Ilona These are cranberries, I think? Are you gonna help
me pick some? There are loads.

Pontus No, thanks.

Ilona They're not poisonous.

Pontus What, like the toadstool wasn't poisonous or some other kind of not poisonous?

Pekka We're not dead yet, are we?

Pontus Might as well be. This is the worst Friday night of my entire life!

Ilona I'm sorry.

Pontus Yeah? Try saying that to Harri, sometime! (*Puts his nose on.*)

Ilona How does that work?

Pekka It doesn't work.

Pontus Yes it does! How do you know? You're not me!

Pekka Thank God.

Ilona Shhhh. So, what? You put it on when you're feeling depressed and someone smiles at you –

Pontus Something like that.

Pekka Smile Therapy, man!

Pontus Shut up! It was worth a try, my mum said!

Ilona Can I try?

Puts the nose on. Nobody smiles.

I guess we're not really in a smiling mood. I get that – depression.

Pontus Do you?

Ilona Since my dad died.

Pontus Oh. Sorry.

Ilona Do you take tablets?

Pontus They're addictive, my mum says.

Pekka What was it? Was it . . .?

Ilona Cancer.

Pontus Did he smoke?

Ilona Like a sauna!

Pontus My mum smokes.

Pekka So does mine.

Pontus So does Harri.

Ilona I'm never going to smoke.

Pekka Is that why you moved here?

Ilona Yeah. Well, *there*. We live with my nan. Why do you get it?

Pontus Oh, nothing. My weight and that.

Pekka Why don't you tell her?

Pontus Why should I?

Pekka He got fat after his dad left.

Pontus *Don't* tell her!

Pekka Why not? She told.

Ilona Shhhhh. You don't have to tell me.

Pontus Your dad left, too!

Pekka When I was two. I don't remember him.

Pontus I didn't get fat, anyway, I put on weight. I'm not fat like some people are fat, I don't take up two places on the bus or buy my clothes from the outsize shop.

Pekka Never said you did.

Ilona Where's he gone?

Pontus Norway.

Ilona Has he got a girlfriend there, or something?

Pontus Wife.

Ilona Do you see him much?

Pontus It's too expensive, he says.

Pekka He phones you, though.

Pontus Yeah, he phones me.

Ilona Well, that's good, innit?

Pontus Yeah. Except I don't know what to say to him.

Pekka I wouldn't know my dad if I passed him in the street. I wouldn't want to.

Pontus Just as well, innit, 'cos you wouldn't see him without your glasses!

Pekka My mum's gonna kill me!

Pontus Unless the bear gets you first!

Pekka I'd sooner face a bear than my mum in a strop.

Pontus She's alright, your mum.

Pekka Sometimes. When she's asleep.

Pontus Better than my mum. My mum's such a stress-head.

Pekka I like her.

Pontus Only 'cos she likes you.

Pekka Wanna swap?

Pontus Alright.

Pekka Sorted.

Ilona It's so quiet. I wish I could hear a road.

Pekka If we found a road, we could hitch a lift. Or just follow it.

Pontus I'm not allowed to hitch. Since that kid got killed in Sweden.

Ilona Which one?

Pontus All of them.

Pekka They don't *know* they're dead.

Pontus Of course they're dead.

Pekka They never found any bodies. I bet they're alive somewhere and living as princes and princesses, eating anything they want. Chips, ice cream.

Pontus Pizza.

Pekka Sausages.

Pontus Meatballs and macaroni.

Ilona Fish, from the lake, fried in butter, with new potatoes.

Pontus I'm starving.

Pekka So am I.

Ilona What couldn't you eat, right now?

Pontus What *couldn't* I eat?

Pekka I couldn't eat a block of flats. That's all. I could eat anything else.

Pontus A dog?

Pekka In a bun, mate, with all the relishes!

Pontus Could you eat, er . . .

Pekka Yes!

They laugh.

Ilona There's a bloke who eats cars, evidently.

Pekka Where?

Ilona Belgium. He saws them up into tiny bits and eats them over a six-month period.

Pontus Why?

Ilona Probably the only way he can get them down!

Pontus Why does he eat them?

Pekka Perhaps they haven't got MacDonald's in Belgium?

Ilona A Ford Escort takes him about six months, but he's also eaten a Ferrari. He said it tasted better, but it took him almost a year. They took him in for an X-ray – he had stomach strouble –

Pekka No, really?!

Ilona He broke the machine.

Pontus Seriously?

Ilona It was in one of my dad's magazines.

Pekka Wasn't a car magazine, by any chance, was it?

Pontus No, it was a cooking magazine!

Ilona I'm so hungry, I could eat a horse between two mattresses.

Pontus Who said that?

Ilona I did, I just said it!

Pekka Who said it first?

Ilona It was a film, I forget which one. Did you ever see that film about the people eating themselves to death?

Pekka What was it called?

Pontus Do you see them actually eating themselves?

Ilona Not that sort of eating themselves! Eating too much. So their stomachs explode.

Pekka Do you see that, then?

Ilona I don't know, I never *saw* it.

Pekka I never saw a great film once.

Pontus Didn't you?

Pekka No. It was about a bloke who gave his son a birthday cake –

Ilona Who didn't give him a birthday cake, you mean?

Pekka That's right, not shaped like a Mercedes.

Pontus Oh, I never saw that one.

Ilona Didn't you? Nor did I!

Pekka Any other great films you haven't seen?

Ilona Well, I never saw a great film starring Robin Williams.

Pontus Nor did anyone else!

Aleksi runs in, backwards, his clothes are all on inside out and back to front. He glows slightly in the gloom.

Ilona Aleksi?

Pekka Is it?

Ilona Why are you dressed like that?

Pekka What?

Pontus He's wearing all his clothes inside out and back to front.

Ilona Are you alright?

Aleksi ?tnorf ot kcab lla sehtolc ruoy gniraew uoy era yhW

Pontus What?

Aleksi ?tnorf ot kcab lla sehtolc ruoy gniraew uoy era yhW

Pekka What's he saying?

Aleksi ?sdrawkcab gniklat uoy era yhW

Pekka Say it again.

Aleksi !?sdrawkcab gniklat uoy era yhW

Ilona Aleksi.

Aleksi !yawa nur t'noD (*Runs out, backwards.*)

Ilona Don't run away! (*Gives chase.*)

Pontus Wait for us!

Pekka Pont!

Pontus Come on, then!

He leads Pekka off. Their voices calling after Ilona, and hers calling after Aleksi, echo through the forest.

Aleksi runs on, backwards. He listens to their voices coming closer. He runs off, backwards. Ilona runs on, followed by Pontus and Pekka.

Pontus Can't you wait for us?!

Ilona I don't understand it. I'm much bigger than he is, and he's running backwards, but the faster I run the further he seems to get away from me. It doesn't make sense.

Pekka It's no good running after him.

Pontus I can taste blood!

Ilona We've got to catch him!

Pekka We won't. It's all back to front, inside out. He's talking backwards. I *think* he was saying, 'Don't run away.'

Ilona *I* was saying that.

Pekka So was he. Only backwards. Yawa: away. Nur: run. T'nod: don't. Don't run away. That's what he was saying.

Ilona How do you know?

Pekka I heard him. He repeated it. I don't know, I just heard it. He said don't run away! He said something else, but I didn't get that, too many words.

Pontus But – he was the one running away, why tell *us* not to run away?

Pekka I don't know.

Ilona I think I do. If everything's back to front – if he's back to front to us and we're back to front to him . . .

Pontus What?

Ilona Well, don't you see?

Pontus I don't see anything!

Pekka It makes sense! Back to front, inside out, fast is slow, slow fast.

Ilona Quick: turn all your clothes back to front and inside out!

Pontus Why?

Pekka Do it!

They're all changing throughout the following.

We'll have to talk backwards, too!

Ilona What shall we say?

Pontus Oh, I get it!

Pekka 'Don't run away from us!' Su. Morf. Yawa. Nur t'nod.

Pontus We'll never remember it.

Ilona Write it on our hands.

Pekka su morf yawa nur t'noD! su morf yawa nur t'noD!

The others practise, too.

Pontus Should we do his name?

Ilona !iskelA

Pekka !iskelA, su morf yawa nur t'noD

They practise this.

Ilona Are we ready?

Pontus Backwards, we've got to walk backwards.

Pekka It's hard enough walking forwards!

Pontus I'll help you.

They practise walking and talking backwards.

Ilona Isn't that him? Aleksi!

Pekka !iskelA

Ilona !iskelA, iskelA, yawa nur t'noD

They exit, backwards, shouting. Their voices recede and echo in the forest. In the darkness, their sentences gradually turn round, so the words are clear. Aleksi enters, dressed and walking normally. Ilona, Pontus and Pekka enter also dressed and walking normally. This part of the forest is very dark, only the occasional beam penetrates the canopy of trees.

Ilona It worked.
Pontus Well done, Peks.
Pekka No, we all did it.
Pontus No good trying to get away from us!
Pekka Not likely!
Ilona How are you feeling. Aleksi? How's your hand?
Aleksi Where's Harri?
Pontus He –
Aleksi Where is he?
Ilona You see, the bear –
Pekka – we heard it roar –
Pontus – then, Harri screamed –
Aleksi What bear?
Ilona At the camp –
Aleksi You left him?
Pontus We didn't leave him –
Ilona – he wouldn't come. We told him to come.
Pekka He didn't think it was really happening.
Pontus There was nothing we could do.
Ilona Can I see your hand? You ought to go to a doctor
with it, really.
Aleksi Why did you keep running away?
Ilona We didn't, it just seemed that way to you.
Pontus We thought *you* were running away.
Aleksi Why were you wearing your clothes back to front
and inside out?
Pontus We weren't.
Pekka We are now, though.
Ilona But you are too, so it seems as if we're not.
Pekka It's a bit weird, but it sort of makes sense, if you
think about it.
Pontus Or if you *don't* think about it!
Aleksi Is that why the trees are growing downwards,
too?
Pontus Shit!
Pekka What? Growing downwards?

Ilona How long have they been like this?

Aleksi Ever since I left you at the camp. You all went to sleep, so I thought I'd go home but I couldn't find the flats. After a while, I noticed the trees were growing downwards.

Ilona How could you go home? I mean, your dad . . .? Your hand . . .? Didn't he . . .?

Aleksi He didn't mean it.

Pontus What happened?

Aleksi He put it in the fire.

Pekka How couldn't he mean it, Aleksi?

Aleksi He was drunk. He'll have forgotten it in the morning.

Ilona Will you, though, that's the question?

Aleksi Where else should I go?

Pekka Where is this? Siberia, do you think?

Pontus Or Australia!

Ilona How do we get out of here?

Pekka If we climbed a tree –

Pontus What for?

Pekka We'd be where the ground is.

Ilona And, what? Walk around upside down, like flies on the ceiling?

Pontus I used to think Australians had sticky feet, like flies! I can remember thinking, it must be really weird, don't they get headaches?

Pekka I know!

Ilona Go on.

Pekka We're the ones upside down, right? Not the trees, not the forest?

Ilona So?

Pekka So, if we get dressed properly again –

Pontus You mean back to front, inside out?

Pekka No, that's what we are *now*.

Pontus No, we're not.

Pekka We are. Remember?

Pontus Oh, yeah. But, that doesn't make sense!

Pekka It makes sense *here*.

Ilona Let's do it, then.

Aleksi What about Harri?

Ilona Aleksi, you know, Harri's –

Pontus We told you, he's dead.

Aleksi You told me the bear roared.

Pekka Then Harri screamed.

Aleksi Of course he did, he was scared. But did you see him dead? Did you even go back?

Ilona It was too dangerous. The bear –

Aleksi So you didn't actually see him? Then, I think we should go and check, at least.

Ilona But, Aleksi –

Aleksi I don't think the bear would've killed him, not if it's the one I saw. It ran away when I sneezed!

Pekka But listen, listen – we'll never find our way back there. We've been walking for hours through the forest –

Pontus Hours and hours, the bear was chasing us, all the time!

Pekka We don't know where we are. We don't even know what direction we've come from.

Ilona They're right, Aleksi.

Aleksi Well, you can do what you want. I'm gonna look for Harri. (*He exits.*)

Ilona Aleksi! Shit!

Pekka What are we gonna do?

Ilona We can't lose him now. (*She exits.*)

Pontus But –

Pekka Come on.

Pontus But –

Pekka Come on!

They exit, Pontus leading.

SCENE FOUR

Harri at the bottom of a dark pit. His clothes are in tatters. He wakes, suddenly, grabs his mobile phone, which is not ringing:

Harri Dad? Dad, is that you? I've fallen down an old well in the forest, I've broken some ribs, I think, I was running from a bear, it's freezing, Dad, I can't get out, I've tried, I'm starving, Dad, please, Dad, come and get me, it's near the old camp, Bloodnut's old camp, you know, there's a shark like a rock, I mean a rock like a shark, can you hear me? Dad? Dad? Can you hear me? I'm stuck here, you are there, aren't you? Dad? Dad? Dad! Dad! Dad! Dad! Dad!

The phone rings.

Shut up! You're not really ringing, it's just a dream. Shut up! Shut up! Your battery's flat, you can't be ringing! I said, shut up! Shut up! SHUT UP! SHUT UP! SHUT UP! SHUT UP!

He answers it.

Hello? Aleksi? But – You're at the camp? I'm in a well, I think it's a well, I fell down it. It's about two hundred metres from where the flats used to be, two, three hundred metres. There's a rock that looks like a shark, I never saw it before, near there. Like a shark, yes, bursting out of the ground, there's trees on its back, but it looks like a shark. Are you really there, is it really you, Aleksi? It's so good to hear your voice, you know, I – Hello? Hello, Aleksi –? You're breaking up. Hello? Your voice – Can you see it? Really, you can see it?! Like a shark, yeah, it's there, near there, be careful, it's very deep! I'll shout, perhaps you'll hear

78

me. ALEKSI, THIS WAY! THIS WAY! DOWN HERE!
ALEKSI! ALEKSI! HERE I AM! OVER HERE, DOWN
HERE, OVER HERE! CAN'T YOU FIND IT? IT'S HERE!
HERE! ALEKSI! ALEKSI?! HELP! HELP!

Aleksi (*above*) Harri?

Harri Yes! Yes! I'm here, you've found me, I can't
believe it! Oh my God, I can't believe it!

Aleksi (*above*) We're. Going. To. Try. And. Get. You.
Out.

Harri Okay. That's wonderful, fantastic! That's fantastic!

Aleksi (*above*) Wait. There.

Harri Well, of course I'll wait here, where else am I
gonna wait?! This is fantastic! I can't believe it, I was
sure I was dead, you know, I thought I was going to
die down here! Aleksi? Aleksi, are you there?

Ilona (*above*) Harri?

Harri Ilona!

Ilona (*above*) We're. Fixing. A. Rope. We'll. Be. There.
Soon.

Pontus (*above*) Hello. Harri.

Harri Pontus!

Pekka (*above*) Hello. Harri.

Harri Pekka! I can't believe it! I can't believe it. Hello?
Hello? ARE YOU UP THERE? HELLO?

Aleksi (*above*) We'll. Be. With. You. Soon. Harri.

Harri This isn't happening, it can't be happening, my
battery's flat, they're not really there, they didn't ring,
how could they? Why are they talking so strangely?
I'm dreaming, it's all a dream. Perhaps I'm dead? Then
this is hell. Or I'm hallucinating.

*Aleksi is lowered into the pit. His clothes are on back
to front and inside out.*

Aleksi Hello. Harri.

Harri Aleksi? Is it you?

Aleksi It's. Me. Yes.

Harri How did you find me?
Aleksi We. Phoned. You.
Harri But, my phone doesn't work. The battery's flat.
Aleksi It's. Complicated. We'll. Explain.
Harri Why are you talking like that? Why are you
    dressed like that? Aleksi, your hand, I – I'm sorry –
    I was a bastard, a complete shit, I –
Aleksi It's. Fine. Really.
Harri Why are you talking like that?
Aleksi We'll. Explain. Later.

Pontus climbs down, also dressed in reverse.

Aleksi ?rettam eht s'tahW
Harri Huh?
Pontus !gnimoc si raeb ehT
Harri What? What?

Ilona and then Pekka come down the rope.

Aleksi The. Bear. Is. Coming!
Pontus !epor eht nwod emoc ll'tI
Ilona !od nac ew gnihton s'erehT
Pekka !hhhhhhhhhS !su rarh lliw tI
Harri This *isn't* happening! You *aren't* real!
Aleksi We. Are. It. Is.
Ilona !su raeh lliw tI .hhhhhhhhS
Harri It's climbing down!

*The rope thrashes around. They notice a small dark
opening at the back of the pit.*

Ilona !ereht nI
Pontus ?tahW
Harri What?

They crawl into the tunnel. The Bear roars. Blackout.

SCENE FIVE

Sunlight and birdsong.

Pontus *(off)* I'm so hungry, I could eat a horse between two mattresses!

Ilona *(off)* Shhhh.

They all enter, attired and walking normally.

A house!

Aleksi Someone lives there. Smoke.

Ilona Yes, but who?

Pontus Why don't we knock on the door and find out?

Ilona There's a window. We need to find out who it is.

Aleksi Where are you going?

Ilona To look in.

Aleksi I'll go.

Harri I'll go.

Pekka I'll go.

Pontus You can't see! I'll go.

Aleksi Let's all go.

Pontus What if we're caught?

Aleksi If we're all there, we can fight him off.

Ilona Or her.

Harri Or it.

Ilona Okay. Quietly.

Harri No, really?

They look in the window. Freeze in terror, speak in whispers.

Pontus How'd that get there?

Ilona Shhhh.

Pontus It was behind us!

Pekka Is it the bear?

Ilona Yes.

Pontus Perhaps it's a different one?
Aleksi No, it's the same one.
Pontus How do you know?
Pekka Quiet, Pontus!
Aleksi I recognise it.
Harri So do I.
Pekka What's it doing?
Ilona Sitting at a table.
Pekka What?
Aleksi Its back's to us. It hasn't moved.
Pontus I never saw so much food in my life!
Ilona Don't move!
Pontus I'm so hungry.
Pekka We're all hungry.
Ilona Perhaps *it's* hungry!
Pekka Perhaps it's dead?
Aleksi It's very still.
Ilona Like a statue.
Harri Perhaps it's waiting for us?
Ilona To do what with us?
Pekka Do you think it's a trap?
Aleksi I don't think so.
Harri Nor do I.
Ilona We can't be sure.
Pontus We can't stand here for ever!
Aleksi Let's go in.
Harri What?
Aleksi What's there to lose?
Ilona Aleksi, wait!
Aleksi I'm going.

*They freeze. A man wearing a bearskin enters. He has
red hair. He lays a blanket on the floor and spreads a
feast on it – loaves, cheese, apples, game. They turn to
him.*

Bearman Welcome to my house. You may eat at my
table if you wish. You need never be hungry, or cold,
or frightened again. Stay as long as you like, there's
room for everybody. First, though, you must put on
these bearskins. Only then can you sit at the table.

*They put on the bearskins then take their places. The
Bearman sits at the head, with Harri, Ilona and Aleksi
to one side of him, Pekka and Pontus to the other.
At a sign from the Bearman they begin passing dishes
to each other. Pontus helps Pekka. The Bearman
hands Harri a pair of glasses, which are then passed
round to Pekka. He puts them on.*

Pekka Wow.
Bearman How is your hand?
Aleksi Better.

They begin eating.

THE EXAM

Andy Hamilton

Characters

Mr A, Andrew's dad
Mrs A, Andrew's mum
Mr B, Bea's dad
Mrs B, Bea's mum
Mrs C, Chas's mum
Andrew, sixteen years old
Bea, sixteen years old
Chas, sixteen years old
BSE, Geography teacher
Biggs, PE teacher
Ex, voice of the exam
Dad, Chas's dad
Jean, Bea's auntie

SCENE ONE

A tight spotlight picks out a cluster of adults.

Mr and Mrs A (well dressed, moneyed, Telegraph readers who probably spend a lot of time at the gym), Mr and Mrs B (clothing from C & A, like to stay in and watch Inspector Morse) and Mrs C (chaotic, single mother of four, bit heavy on the make-up, prone to leopard skin, hectic social life).

Physically, these five characters are in a tight group, but the eyelines of the two couples and single mum are all trained in slightly different directions. For a moment they form a still tableau, but then Mr A kicks them into a rat-tat-tat barrage of parental 'support'. (Mr A is dynamic, comically so, Mrs A is relentlessly positive, Mr and Mrs B are a two-headed, smothering pride-fest and Mrs C is cursory and getting ready to go out.)

Mr A *Always* read the question.

Mrs A Always.

Mr A And read it carefully.

Mrs A Very carefully.

Mr B We know you'll do well.

Mrs B You always do well.

Mrs C Just try not to cock it up.

Mr A Keep an eye on the time.

Mrs A Don't spend too long . . .

Mr *and* Mrs A *(louder)* . . . on one question.

Mr B You're bound to do well.

Mrs B You're so good at exams.

Mr B Mr Pringle said so.

Mrs B At the parents' evening.

Mr B 'She's brilliant at exams.'

Mrs B That's what he said.

Mr B 'But then she's brilliant at everything.'

Mrs B His very words.

Mrs C I won't be in when you get back.

Mrs B 'She's my star,' he said.

Mrs C You'll have to make tea for the others.

Mr A Take plenty of pens.

Mrs C I'm out line-dancing.

Mrs A Lots of pens.

Mr A You never know when a pen might let you down.

Mrs A True.

Mr A Pens are like that.

Mr B We'll be thinking of you.

Mrs B I've got eclairs for tea.

Mr B Celebration eclairs.

Mrs C Not sure what time I'll be back.

Mr B Good luck, dear.

Mrs C Don't let Ashley near the light sockets.

Mrs B Good luck, dear.

Mrs C He might not be so lucky next time.

Mr A I know exams are tough.

Mrs A He does know, dear.

Mr A Life is tough.

Mrs A But exciting.

Mr A It's a jungle.

Mrs A An exciting jungle.

Mr A And if you're in the jungle . . .

Mrs A . . . the vibrant jungle . . .

Mr A . . . you want to be a cheetah, not a limping wildebeest.

Mrs C Just do your best.

Mr B We're so proud of you.

Mrs C You can only do your best.

Mrs B So very proud.

Mrs C And if your best is still rubbish, well, there you go.

Mr A Remember, don't panic.

Mrs A Panic never helps.

Mr B Don't worry.

Mrs B We're not worried.

Mrs C Don't piss about.

Mr A Don't freeze.

Mrs A Don't rush.

Mr B Don't worry.

Mrs B Don't hurry.

All And don't get nervous!

Snap blackout.

Slowly the lights come up on three schoolchildren sitting side by side on three chairs.

Andrew is sixteen, bookish, his school uniform is immaculate and he is relentlessly studying his notes as he crams in some last minute revision. He is a martyr to teenage spots. Next to him is Bea, also sixteen, a little self-conscious, but very bright. She is looking out into space, trying to stay calm, but she throws a tell-tale glance at her watch. Next to her is Chas, also sixteen. His school uniform is chaotic and his left arm is in a sling. He looks around, bored. This is a guy with a short attention span. He looks at Bea, trying to make eye contact, but she keeps looking out straight. He makes a quiet popping sound with his lips. Neither of the other two respond. He leans back a bit and stares at the ceiling for a while, then sits up again.

Chas (*suddenly breaking into a Murray Walker impersonation*) And the tension here is unbelievable. You could, quite literally, cut it with a knife.

He gets no reaction from the other two, apart from Bea shifting her body-weight and angling herself away from him slightly. Another awkward silence develops. Chas hunts for an ice-breaking topic.

So . . . how would you defeat global terrorism, then?

Slowly Bea turns and looks at him with withering disdain.

Just trying to make conversation.
Bea Well don't.

Bea angles herself away from him again. Another awkward silence. Chas slaps his thighs to a rhythm, puffs his cheeks, stares at the ceiling and generally tries various displacement activities before chancing his next gambit.

Chas Adults are such prossocks, aren't they?

Again, no flicker of a response. The statement just hangs in the air.

. . . Yup . . . total prossocks.
Bea 'Prossocks'?
Chas Yeah.
Bea What sort of a word is 'prossock'?
Chas . . . It's one of my words.
Bea You have your own words?
Chas Yeah, how cool is that?

Bea shakes her head and quietly mutters something as she turns her back on Chas. For the first time, Andrew looks up from his notes.

Andrew (*sounding unnaturally middle-aged*) Jesus wept, where has that bloody woman got to? It's a disgrace.
Bea I know.
Andrew I mean, where's she gone to find this key, Vladivostok? She's taken – (*Checks watch.*) – fourteen and a half minutes. The woman's a nightmare.

Chas She's a prossock.

Andrew What's a prossock?

Chas A prat, a tosser and a pillock rolled into one. Prossock. I have my own slang, see, because normal slang dates really quick, doesn't it?

Bea (*trying to be aloof*) Is that right?

Chas Oh yeah, like, the other day Terry Doyle came out with 'wick-ed' and everyone just stared at him like he was a complete twonklet, have you got a boyfriend?

Bea (*with lawyer-like precision*) No I do not have a boyfriend. I do not want or need a boyfriend, but if I do decide to have a boyfriend he won't be someone who says things like 'twonklet'.

Chas It's your loss, baby.

Bea gets up and walks away, muttering something uncomplimentary.

Andrew Where has the woman got to? We should have started these exams – (*Checks watch.*) – fifteen and a half minutes ago.

Chas What are you taking?

Andrew Resitting History GCSE . . . I, um . . . well, there was a bit of a hiccup.

Chas (*sensing there's a story behind this*) Oh . . . I see. I'm doing Maths GCSE. Should have been last Thursday, but I was down the hospital having my collarbone seen to. (*Indicates his arm in a sling.*) Maths is the only one I stand a chance of getting, really. I'm not bad with numbers. But anything that involves writing words, well I've got this problem, y'see.

Andrew Dyslexic?

Chas No, just thick as pigshit. What exam are you taking, Two-Brains?

Bea (*icy*) Please don't call me that.

Chas Don't get in a strop, they only call you Two-Brains on account of you being a genius. It's a compliment. And anyway there are worse nicknames, aren't there, Zitboy?

Andrew stiffens at the use of his nickname.

That's what they call you, isn't it? Zitboy? I heard Toby Pearce calling you that in the playground. Mind you, he can talk, his face looks like it's been pebble-dashed. What's your real name?

Andrew Andrew.

Chas Classy.

Andrew (*looking at watch*) Where has she got to?

Chas And-rew. Not Andy. And-rew.

Bea Oh, she'll be ages yet. You saw how she went to pieces when she discovered the room was locked. She'll have gone into one of her flaps. I've seen her do it hundreds of times. She's my form mistress. We call her BSE.

Andrew BSE?

Bea 'Cos she's a dizzy cow.

Andrew Oh, right.

Chas (*apropos of nothing in particular*) Biggsy's my form teacher.

Bea She's shagging him.

Chas I know. Gary Spackman took a Polaroid of the pair of them playing tongue-hockey behind the CCF hut . . . (*Worries.*) Funny bloke, Gary.

Andrew . . . But Mr Biggs is married, isn't he?

Bea Oh yes.

Andrew Well then, they shouldn't be having a relationship, I mean, that's totally unprofessional.

Chas No, it's only unprofessional if the shagging affects the quality of their work. (*to Andrew*) Who's your form teacher?

Andrew We haven't got one at the moment. It was Henderson. Till he had that breakdown.

Chas (*remembering*) Oh . . . yeah . . . he looked quite funny naked, didn't he? . . . Had sort of sticky-out nipples.

Andrew Look at the time. This is scandalous. (*He starts to pace.*)

Chas The man's right.

There is another pause as they think their own thoughts, till Chas punctures it.

(*to Bea*) How old were you . . . the day you first realised that adults were useless?

She doesn't answer.

I worked out you couldn't rely on them when I was six. My dad bet his mate that tortoises could swim and, well, that's how I lost my pet tortoise.

Andrew (*checks watch*) Seventeen minutes! I mean this is our future she's jeopardising. My mental preparation for this exam is completely shot now, I was pacing myself . . . Mental preparation is the key.

Hard cut to a tight spotlight where Mr A (Andrew's dad) is giving a pep talk.

Mr A Mental preparation is the key, son. That's a fact. It's what gives you the edge. It's probably where you went wrong last time when you . . . (*He stops himself.*) Come here.

Andrew crosses and enters the tight spot. Mr A wraps his arms around Andrew and hugs him hard with possessive affection.

Listen, tiger, this isn't just one more exam, this . . . this is when you find out about yourself.

Mrs A joins them to form a group hug.

It's about character. About bouncing back from disaster
and proving something to yourself. About walking
back into the sunlight, having stared down into the
abyss.

Mrs A Think of it as an adventure.

Mr A Now, let's see you bounce, eh, tiger?

*Immediate lights-up as Andrew crosses to rejoin Bea
and Chas.*

Andrew I mean, is it really so much to ask? That
candidates for exams should be able to access the exam
room? Jesus! (*Andrew winces slightly.*) . . . Um . . . I'll
be back in a minute. (*Exits.*)

Bea I wish he wouldn't shout 'Jesus' all the time.

Chas Are you a Christian?

Bea No, I just believe all religious faiths should be
respected.

Chas What, even Jehovah's Witnesses?

Bea Yes.

Chas Oh right. 'Jesus' is just something people say
though, isn't it? Doesn't mean anything. I mean, when
you say 'Jesus' you're not actually mentally picturing
Jesus, are you? Just like if you say 'bollocks' you
don't picture a pair of testicles . . . Well, not usually
anyway.

Bea (*mocking*) Don't you have your own word for
bollocks?

Chas No, bollocks is too good a word not to use. Are
you sure you don't want a boyfriend?

Bea I told you.

Chas Only I've always quite rated you.

Bea I am so not interested in this conversation.

Chas Every time you go up on stage to get one of your
prizes I say to my mates, 'I quite rate her.'

Bea I feel honoured.

Chas And rightly so. Mind you, I preferred you before you got skinny.

Bea I haven't 'got skinny'.

Chas You have. I mean, granted, you're not as skinny as some of the other girls in your form have got . . . not yet anyway.

Bea I'm not obsessing about my diet, if that's what you're saying.

Chas Pleased to hear it.

Bea I'm merely aiming to achieve my ideal body-weight.

Chas Fair enough, do you want some Kit-Kat?
(*producing Kit-Kat*)

Bea No, thank you.

Hard lighting change to Mr and Mrs B (her parents).

Mrs B Some cake, then?

Bea (*crossing to join them*) I don't want cake, Mum.

Mrs B Well you've got to eat something.

Bea I eat plenty.

Mr B We've got eclairs. You deserve an eclair. All that revision you've been doing.

Mrs B And chocolate's good for the brain. It was on *Richard and Judy*.

Bea (*with a hint of snobbery*) *Richard and Judy*?

Mrs B Yes.

Bea I'm going up to my room. (*Exits.*)

Mr B (*calling after her*) I'll bring you up a cocoa.

Mr and Mrs B exchange a look. They wish they could bridge the distance between themselves and their daughter.
The lights pick out Bea and Chas, as before.

Chas (*eating*) How many calories in a Kit-Kat, then?

Bea About 320.

Chas But who's counting, eh, Two-Brains?

Bea looks at him as he pops the last bit of Kit-Kat into his mouth. She is just not sure what to make of him. Andrew re-enters, looking a little pale.

You okay?

Andrew Nervous tummy.

Rather gingerly, Andrew picks up his revision notes and tries to concentrate on them.

Chas I wouldn't bother with any last-minute swotting if I was you . . .

Andrew Really.

Chas Yeah, in my experience, if you don't know it by now, you never will.

Bea Oh, so you're an expert on passing exams then, are you?

Chas I never said I'd passed any. I just said that in my experience, if you don't know it by now, you never will. And my results bear that out.

Andrew suddenly closes his revision notes.

Andrew You're probably right . . . making me feel nauseous . . . (*Looks around, hunting for a topic.*) How did you break your collarbone?

Chas Very painfully. Do you know Spike Morton?

Andrew Morton? Is he the one with the tattoo saying 'Babe Magnet'?

Chas That's right, on his left buttock.

There's a mutter of disdain from Bea.

Spike lives near me, so we go home together after school. Anyway, we've got this game we like to play where I shout abuse at passers-by and then he tells them that I suffer from Tourette's syndrome. It's great fun. You can get away with murder. My favourite was when

I saw this bunch of nuns and I started yelling that they were 'giant nympho killer penguins'.

Andrew laughs, a kind of kinship is springing up between them. Bea, meanwhile, is working very hard at pretending not to listen.

So, last Wednesday this chubby bloke walked past and I shouted, 'You big fat git,' and . . . well, he didn't take it very well, got a bit upset. But then Spike weighs in and goes, 'Calm down, mate, no offence, he didn't mean it, he's got Tourette's.' And so this fat bloke goes, 'Oh, right, okay, no problem,' and starts to back off, and Spike goes, 'He didn't mean to call you a big fat git, mister, he meant to call you an ugly fat git.' Then we both legged it as fast as we could up the High Street.

Andrew So, what happened then?

Chas Well . . . you know fat people aren't supposed to be very good at running?

Andrew He caught up with you.

Chas Well, he would have done, if we hadn't had the brains to climb up this scaffolding, 'cos both me and Spike are shit-hot at climbing, so we ended up two storeys high with the Michelin man down below, puffing and wheezing, shaking his fist and stuff. So, we taunted him a bit more about . . . y'know . . . about his . . . not having achieved his ideal body-weight. (*We feel Bea stiffen.*) Then, and with hindsight this was a mistake, we started singing. (*Sings.*) 'Who ate all the pies? Who ate all the pies? You fat bastard, you fat bastard, you ate all the pies.'

Andrew Then what?

Chas Well . . . you know fat people aren't supposed to be any good at climbing?

Andrew Oh no.

Chas Like a sodding monkey he was. Coming straight for us. Well, Spike was panicking, but I spotted this way down, namely one of those sort of orange waste chutes that hang down off scaffolding into skips . . .

Andrew (*realising*) You prat.

Chas I've seen people do it on the telly. That girl, Caroline Thingy, she jumped down one in an episode of *Jonathan Creek*, and all that happened to her was she got a bit dusty. I just thought it'd be like, I dunno, like a helter-skelter at the fairground, only maybe a bit quicker. Anyway, it was, um, well it was quite a lot quicker, actually. The bloke in Casualty said I'm lucky I didn't kill myself. Then he said something I didn't quite catch but it ended with the words 'stupid cretin'.

Andrew Jesus, what did your parents say?

Chas My mum got a bit emotional . . .

Snap lighting transition to the parental zone where Mrs C (Chas's mum) is getting ready to go out. Chas crosses to join her as she talks. Every now and then she shouts over her shoulder to invisible offspring.

Mrs C Well, this is bloody inconvenient. How are you going to help me out with one arm? (*Shouts off.*) Ashley, get your fingers away from that socket! (*to Chas*) What you've done is stupid, reckless and unhelpful. (*Shouts.*) Sacha! Come down here, I'm sending you up the chip shop! (*to Chas*) What the hell were you . . . (*Shouts.*) Ashley, I won't tell you again. (*to Chas*) What the hell were you doing? You could have killed yourself. What would I have done then? (*Shouts.*) Ashley, if you don't get your fingers away from that socket I'll chop them off, so help me God! (*to Chas*) Oh, and now he starts crying, brilliant. (*Shouts.*) Sacha!! I'm leaving the money on the table! (*to Chas*) Alright, you take it easy, you silly sod. (*She* *brushes her hand against his cheek*.) You are such a silly sod . . . Okay, gotta dash, can you help Gary with his homework? It's algebra or something. (*Shouts.*) Ashley, stop crying.

Chas He's going purple, Mum.

Mrs C Ignore him, that's just an attention thing. I might be late, so don't put the bolt on. Be good, you silly sod, try not to fling yourself down the stairs, don't wait up. (*She kisses him on the cheek and then is gone.*)

Lighting transition as Chas crosses stage to rejoin Bea and Andrew.

Chas So . . . that was Mum's reaction. (*A thought dawns.*) At least . . . that's how I remember her reaction . . . It was something like that.

Andrew And what did your dad say?

Chas Not a lot, he's dead.

Andrew Oh . . . I'm sorry.

Chas Yeah, well . . . there you go. Four years ago now.

Bea What happened?

Chas Well, he was always a bit of a vague person, y'know, daydreamer, forgetful and um . . . well one day he forgot to look and got hit by a bus.

Bea Oh . . .

Chas Yeah.

Andrew Where did the bus hit him?

Chas looks at Andrew in bewilderment.

Chas . . . All over . . .

Andrew No, sorry, I didn't mean where on his body, I meant where? What street?

Chas Oh right, sorry, Cambridge Circus. It's a well-known black spot, only the victims are usually just tourists.

Andrew Do you miss him?

Chas 'Course, but I still see him a fair bit, y'know.

Bea You still see him?

Chas Yeah, his ghost comes to visit me.

Bea Your dad's ghost?

Chas Yeah.

Bea This is a wind-up, right?

Chas No.

Bea (*certain it's a wind-up*) So, when your dad's ghost appears to you . . . what does he look like?

Chas Like Dad.

Bea I mean, what does he wear?

Chas Well, white stuff obviously, he's a ghost.

Bea (*laughs, mocking*) Oh right, white stuff, yeah, 'course.

Chas You don't believe me, do you, Two-Brains?

Bea I am a rational person, I don't believe in ghosts.

Andrew People do see things, though, don't they? My mum saw the shape of a woman at a B and B in Margate.

Bea People convince themselves they see things. It's just projections from their subconscious mind. He doesn't have a ghost, he's having you on. Look, he's smirking.

From offstage we hear an approaching apologetic voice. It is Miss Baxendale, or BSE, as she's known. She is as nervous as a small bird and her self-confidence is brittle. She is carrying a Polaroid camera.

BSE Sorry, sorry everybody, sorry to take so long, but everything's under control, sorry.

Andrew Have you got the key?

BSE Well, it seems our beloved caretaker has wandered off with the keys, he's always doing that, gives him a sense of power, but *nil desperandum*, the trusty Mr Biggs is locating the spare. So all shall be well. Sorry about this, you'll get your full allotted time, of course, but I'm sorry about the . . . Sorry. (*She starts to look out for Mr Biggs. She clears her throat with a nervous cough.*)

Chas Why are you holding a polaroid, miss?

BSE Eh? Oh, um, I confiscated this off, oh whatsisname, Gary Spackman. He's always bringing this in, he's been warned. Anyway, I gave him a week's worth of detentions.

Chas I'm not sure that was a good idea, miss.

BSE (*still looking out for Mr Biggs*) What?

Chas Well I just don't think Gary Spackman is someone you want to get the wrong side of.

BSE What are you talking about, you strange boy?

Andrew (*looks as if he's really suffering*) Where's Mr Biggs gone to get this spare key?

BSE Don't fret, he's . . . Are you okay, Andrew, are you in pain?

Andrew I'm okay.

BSE Is it the ulcer?

Andrew (*irritated by her indiscretion*) I'm okay.

BSE Well say if you're not.

Andrew I will.

BSE Because you don't have to sit this, y'know, given what you –

Andrew (*cuts her off*) I'm okay! . . . Okay?

BSE Okay.

There is an awkward pause as they wait for Mr Biggs.

Mr Biggs will be here in a mo . . . He's a good man in a crisis . . .

The kids just watch her. She becomes self-conscious. She does some more involuntary nervous throat-clearing.

(*referring to camera*) Just going to dump this in the staff room.

She exits busily. Bea and Chas look at Andrew.

Chas You've got an ulcer?

Andrew Yes.

Bea A stomach ulcer?

Andrew Yes.

Chas (*disbelief*) You're sixteen years old and you've got an ulcer?

Andrew Yes.

Chas You have to be middle-aged at least to get an ulcer. What, have you got a mortgage as well? And a wide selection of cardigans?

Andrew I can't help it. Ulcers run in the family. It's to do with tension. When I'm tense, I make acid.

Chas Then don't get tense. Learn to hang loose. (*Starts jive-talking and moonwalking.*) Stay cool, babe, find your groove.

Bea Ignore him, he's a twat.

Andrew (*to Bea*) I try not to get tense. I try so hard. Hardly slept for months.

Bea You have to learn to unwind. What do you do for fun?

Andrew (*thinks hard*) Erm . . . nothing really. (*Remembers.*) Oh, I read biking magazines. I love Harley Davidsons, see. They're fantastic things. I know every inch of a Harley Davidson. I'm going to own one some day. And the leathers, with the eagle's-wings badge, and my name picked out in studs. (*His face is bright with enthusiasm, but suddenly all the confidence seems to drain out of him.*) . . . Well, that's if everything goes okay and I can afford it and I pass the driving test and stuff . . . Got to get through this first. (*He slumps with his head in his hands.*) . . . You heard what happened to me I suppose?

Chas No.

Andrew (*surprised*) Oh, funny, I just presumed everyone would have heard.

Bea Why, what did happen to you?

Andrew (*very depressed*) I humiliated myself.

Chas (*trying to make him feel better*) Oh, we've all done that. (*Looks to Bea for support.*) Eh? . . . Actually you probably haven't, have you? (*Throws it back to Andrew.*) But I have. Made a pratt of myself dozens of times. It's not important. People forget.

Bea (*to Andrew*) What happened?

Andrew I was supposed to sit this with the rest of my History set last Thursday, and I was all ready, I'd been up most of the night, memorising all my notes about Palmerston and Disraeli and the Tolpuddle sodding Martyrs . . . but the moment I turned over my exam paper . . . none of the words seemed to join up . . . and it wasn't just the words . . . nothing looked joined up . . . even the legs of the chairs didn't seem to be connected to the floor. Everything seemed . . . dislocated . . . and everyone's faces looked sort of jagged, with mouths like . . . like the mouths of broken bottles. Then everything started to spin and I woke up in the Nurse's Room.

Chas Bloo-dy hell. That is major-league scary.

Andrew What's really scary is I've no way of knowing if it'll happen again.

Bea But, why are you resitting this today?

Andrew Well my dad persuaded the Head to ask if I could resit. He got them to say I'd reacted adversely to some hay-fever medicine.

Bea No, I meant why the hell are you resitting it today? You're obviously still in a state. Why put yourself through this? You could resit next term.

Andrew No . . . no, I have to face it now.

Bea Says who?

*Hard lighting transition to Mr A on his feet, animated,
with Mrs A hovering nervously behind. As he talks,
Andrew crosses to join him.*

Mr A You have to face this now. You can't run away.
Alright, you lost it, you panicked, you fell off the
horse, but the answer is to jump straight back on the
horse . . . It's the only way . . . otherwise you'll just
spend your whole life . . . (*runs out of metaphor*) . . .
scared of horses.

Andrew . . . I'm allergic to horses.

Mr A No, look, the horses are just a . . . Forget the
horses, look it's about . . . it's about mental strength,
son . . . because . . . look, let me tell you something . . .
You're feeling the pressure with all these exams, that's
normal, of course it is, and you blew a bit of a fuse,
that can happen, and you're probably looking forward
to the day when you can wave school goodbye and
not have to go through any more exams, am I right?

Andrew Yes, absolutely right.

Mr A Yeah, well, get this . . . the exams never stop . . .
life is an exam. I face an exam every day at work . . .
I have to achieve a pass mark . . . maintain good grades,
outperform my fellow examinees, or colleagues, I have
an invigilator, my immediate boss, Hugh Steepleton,
and an Examining Board . . . Head Office. And
everyone in the adult world is sitting this continuous
exam . . . and it's that pressure that makes us stronger,
helps us compete . . . and you have to compete
because believe me, son, it is brutal out there . . . it's
a piranha-filled river . . . and if you live in a piranha-
filled river . . . you're better off being a piranha.

*Both Andrew and Mrs A look bewildered, even a little
scared, by Mr A's bleak take on life.*

Mrs A Who fancies a cup of tea?

Andrew Piranha don't compete, though, do they?

Mr A What?

Andrew Well, at least, a piranha doesn't compete with other piranha.

Mr A Look . . .

Andrew Piranha are successful because they hunt communally in shoals.

Mr A Yes, but they have to compete with the, the crocodiles and the alligators and look, forget the piranha, okay? That was just . . . (*to Mrs A*) The boy is so literal . . . Look, tiger . . . (*He puts his hands affectionately, if a little firmly, on Andrew's shoulders.*) I'm not asking you to do this for me . . . You have to do it for yourself.

Mrs A (*tentatively*) He could resit it next term.

Mr A Yes, he could. (*to Andrew*) But you'd know you'd chickened out . . . you'd carry that sense of shame inside for ever . . . and it'll eat away at you . . . Believe me . . , shame is corrosive . . . Now you're at a cross-roads here . . . there's a path marked 'weak' and a path marked 'strong' . . . Which are you going to choose?

Snap lighting transition to Bea and Chas.

Bea Does your dad really talk like that?

Andrew Yeah. (*He crosses back to Bea and Chas.*) He's a bit . . . um . . .

Chas (*trying to be helpful*) Full of shit?

Andrew But he's not, though, is he? He's right. I have to face up to things, I don't want everyone knowing I bottled out . . . *I* don't want to know that . . .

Bea But –

Andrew And if I wimp out again I'll just spend my whole life wimping out and being even more of a failure.

Bea Yes, but what if it happens ag –

Andrew Look, just leave me alone, okay! I can do this! (*He walks away with his fingers pressed to his temples.*) It is simply a question of staying focused.

Andrew has now put some distance between himself and the other two. There is a pause, an awkward pause. Chas slaps out a rhythm on his thighs, stares at the ceiling for a bit . . .

Chas Are you *sure* you don't want to go on a date with me?

Bea I said no, didn't I?

Chas I know, I just couldn't believe it. (*Looks off to one side.*) Not now, Dad.

Bea . . . What?

Chas Oh, my dad's ghost just appeared. Over there. You can't see him, of course. He often pops up when I'm talking to a girl. He likes to coach me on when to make my move and stuff.

Bea That isn't funny. Just tacky.

Chas (*talking off again*) Look, Dad, later, okay? This is a bit of a bad moment. Yeah – (*thumbs up*) – cheers.

Bea Do I look like a gullible idiot?

Chas No, but then looks can be deceiving, can't they?

We hear some nervy twittering from offstage and BSE enters with a rather taciturn Mr Biggs. Mr Biggs is wearing a tracksuit and has the unmistakeably sarcastic bent of a PE teacher.

BSE Sorry, sorry kids, crisis over, our knight in shining armour is here with the key, tra-la. Sorry to muck you about. Mr Biggs had trouble locating the key to the cupboard with the spare keys in.

Mr Biggs is a long way downstage, miming trying the key in the door.

Biggs It's that joke of a caretaker, he should be fired.

BSE Yes, Michael . . . sorry.

Biggs (*having some difficulty with the key*) I shouldn't have to waste time doing this, I'm supposed to be overseeing 3B's trampolining. Damn and blast!

BSE Is there a problem?

BSE comes downstage next to Biggs.

Biggs This key's a crap key, surprise surprise, like every crap thing in this crappy place.

BSE and Biggs are now physically very close together downstage. She drops her voice to try to prevent Andrew, Bea and Chas (behind) overhearing.

BSE Have you told her yet?

Biggs (*also sotto*) Now's not the time, Emily.

BSE turns to the kids and gives them a reassuring smile.

BSE Sorry about this silly old key, kids. (*She turns back to Biggs and drops her voice again.*) You said you were going to tell her.

Biggs I said not now.

BSE Or maybe you don't want to tell her.

Biggs Please, Emily, don't crowd me.

BSE You said you'd tell her.

Biggs (*snaps, raising his voice*) I said don't crowd me!

They become aware that Bea, Andrew and Chas are listening in. But when they turn to look, the kids feign casual disinterest, study their shoes etc.

(*thrown*) I . . . I can't turn this key if you crowd me.

BSE Oh . . . sorry. (*She backs off a few paces.*)

Biggs In fact (*still trying the key*) I can't turn this key . . . because, joy of joys, it's the wrong bloody key, isn't it.

BSE (*approaching*) Oh, you're kidding.

Biggs This is Room 6 and, *voilà*, a key labelled 6, but is it the right one? Oh no, that would be too much to expect. Heaven forfend, we can't have that.

Bea Perhaps it's a nine.

Biggs (*stopped in his tracks*) . . . What?

Bea Perhaps it isn't a six, perhaps it's a nine.

BSE (*examining the label on the key*) You know I think she might be right, I think it's a nine.

Biggs (*even more scornful*) Well, I'm sorry, but that is totally pathetic. Are you telling me you can tell that *that's* a nine and not a six just from looking at it?

BSE Well I . . .

Biggs There should be a little line scored under or over the digit, shouldn't there? Because, funnily enough, nine and six resembling each other is not a recently observed phenomenon.

BSE (*a bit upset*) Well, never mind, it's an easy mistake to make.

Biggs (*now in sarcasm overdrive*) Yes, it is an easy mistake, especially when nobody bothers to denote whether it's a six or a nine, either with a little line or with the number spelt out in brackets alongside, which is what they would do in an establishment that wasn't run by total bloody amateurs!

BSE (*her eyes welling with tears*) I'm not responsible for numbering the keys, Michael.

Biggs Yes, yes, I know.

BSE (*starting to lose it*) It's really not my area, I'm just a Geography teacher.

Biggs Yes, yes, alright.

BSE Just a small cog in a very big wheel. (*She bursts into tears.*)

Wearily Biggs takes her in his arms.

Biggs Alright, alright.

Andrew (*under his breath*) Bloody hell, I don't believe this.

Biggs (*with BSE still crying on his shoulder*) Come on, old girl . . . (*Biggs is thoroughly embarrassed by this show of emotion and very aware of being watched.*) Come on, fruitdrop . . . chin up, eh?

BSE . . . I'm sorry, Michael . . . I've, um, I've been feeling a bit fragile.

Biggs Alright, alright, let's get you to the staff room and give you a cup of tea while I sort out this key nonsense. (*As he leads her off, he casually calls over his shoulder.*) Okay, you lot, I'll be back in a tick, in the meantime, just . . . relax.

Biggs leads BSE off. Andrew stands open-mouthed with disbelief.

Andrew We could sue them for this, y'know. This is mental torture. We could take them to the European Court of Human Rights.

Bea Try not to get too worked up. At the end of the day, it is just an exam.

Andrew (*feeling patronised*) Yeah, well, that's easy for you to say, isn't it, Two-Brains? You just have to fart and you get an A.

Bea That is so gross.

Chas Very vulgar.

Bea Yes.

Chas True, though.

Bea What?

Chas Well, it is sort of revolting how easy you find exams. How do you manage that? What's your secret?

Bea I don't have a secret.

Chas You don't feel pressure, right?

Bea Of course I feel pressure, I'm not a robot.

Chas Well then, how do you do it?

Bea Well, um, basically, I suppose I just approach the exam as if . . . well, as if it was a sort of . . . big game.

Andrew turns and stares at her, appalled.

Andrew . . . A *game*?

Bea Yes.

Andrew (*sits, demoralised*) She treats it as a game.

Bea For instance, when I read the questions on the exam paper, I imagine I hear them in a voice. And the voice is a smooth, slightly sinister voice, y'know, like a baddie in a James Bond movie.

Chas Oh what, like Goldfinger? (*as Sean Connery*) Do you exshpect me to talk? (*as Goldfinger*) No, Mr Bond, I expect you to die!

Bea Well no, the voice I hear is more like Christopher Lee in *The Man With the Golden Gun*, or whatsisname, the one in *Thunderball*, Blofeld. Anyway, this 'voice' is my adversary and my job in the exam is to come up with the right answers and generally outwit and confound him.

Andrew (*to himself*) . . . A game . . . She treats it as a game . . . (*Suddenly his face lengthens.*) . . . Oh no.

Chas What is it?

Andrew I think I'm going to be sick.

Bea You *think* you're going to?

Andrew Yeah, not sure . . . Could go either way . . . Oh, God.

Bea Think of something nice.

Andrew (*distressed*) Oooh.

Bea Think of Harley Davidsons.

Chas He might feel better if he throws up.

Andrew Oh, hang on . . . wait . . . I think it's going to pass . . . (*Turns queasy again.*) . . . Maybe not . . . it's borderline . . . I hate this feeling.

Chas Think of school custard.

Andrew stiffens, very tense, on the brink.

Think of the lumps.

Andrew bolts offstage.

Bea That wasn't very kind.

Chas Yes it was. Better he throws up now than over his cxam. Examiners don't like marking papers with little bits of carrot stuck to them.

Bea Oh p-lease. I do *so* not want to hear this.

Chas Why do you talk like that?

Bea Like what?

Chas Like you're in an episode of *Friends*.

Bea Well why do you talk like you're in an episode of *The Cocky Moron Show*?

Chas Very good . . . I hate *Friends*.

Bea Well, I like it.

Chas What, 'cos it's full of skinny girls? I suppose you like *Ally McBeal* as well.

Bea My taste in television programmes is none of your business, actually.

Chas Yeah, you do like it.

Bea Ally McBeal is a complex, funny . . . modern female character.

Chas She's an X-ray with lips.

Bea (*hunts for a put-down*) Oh . . . go plummet down a chute.

She turns away from Chas to freeze him out. He sits down two chairs away from her.

Chas You never told me how you'd solve global terrorism.

She pointedly doesn't respond.

Look, I'm sorry I wound you up, I'm a wind-up merchant. Can't help myself . . . I'm a bit wound up too . . . Maths is the only paper I stand a chance of doing well in . . . and it'd be nice to do well . . . if only for the novelty value.

Bea gives him half a smile.

Are you resitting like him, then? Or did you miss one or something?

Bea (*a little self-conscious*) No, I'm . . . I'm sitting an A-Level.

Chas What, two years early?

Bea Yeah, Mr Pringle said I need to stretch myself.

Chas Did he? What's the subject?

Bea Sociology.

Chas clearly has no idea what Sociology is. (And who has?)

Chas Ah, right, yeah, Sociology . . . the study of . . . sociologs.

Bea laughs.

Yeah, well, 'course I nearly chose Sociology, but in the end I opted for the intellectual challenge of Woodwork.

The ice is now broken between them.

Why aren't you sitting it with the Sixth Formers?

Bea None of them are doing Sociology.

Chas So it's just you on your own then.

Bea Yeah . . . Still, I'm used to that.

Bea looks at the floor. A cloud has descended. Chas isn't quite sure how to respond.

Chas Do sociologists earn big money?

Bca No, you're confusing them with footballers.

Chas Oh yeah, I'm always doing that.

There is now the definite beginning of a spark between them. But the moment is ruptured by the return of Andrew.

Andrew I didn't make it to the toilet.

Chas Oh no.

Andrew Just suddenly realised I wasn't going to make it, so I had to choose between chucking up in the corridor or nipping into the games cupboard and doing it with a bit of privacy. Still, managed to miss my trousers, just splashed my shoes a bit.

Chas Which bit of the games cupboard did you throw up in?

Andrew Mostly over the cricket pads.

Bea Did you clean it up?

Andrew No, just did a runner. (*He sits with his head in his hands.*) I feel so ashamed.

Chas Don't be ashamed. Be proud. You threw up in Biggsy's games cupboard. Most of us can only dream of achieving something like that.

Bea Listen, you've been ill. That's a bona fide reason not to put yourself through this. You don't have to face it today.

Andrew I do have to face it. Otherwise I have to face him.

Bea Never mind him. What do *you* want to do?

Andrew I want to be in Orpington.

This complete non sequitur stops everyone in their tracks.

Bea What?

Andrew The train I catch every morning terminates at a place called Orpington. And every morning I think, wouldn't it be wonderful to just not get off the train? To sit there until Orpington . . . then get off . . . and have a look around Orpington, in my own time, then jump on another train, maybe to Brighton, throw stones into the sea . . . Have you ever felt like that?

Bea Of course I have, everyone has. We'd all like to stay on the train. Lose ourselves. But we can't, so forget bloody Orpington, ignore your dad –

Andrew (*interrupts*) Oh yeah, like that's really possible.

Bea Of course it's possible.

Andrew You just don't understand what it's like, Two-Brains. You're a star. No one has you down as a mental weakling, you have it easy.

Bea Oh here we go, you think it's easy, do you? Easy to deal with that endless, excruciating chorus of . . .

Snap transition to Mr and Mrs B.

Mr and Mrs B We are so very proud of you.

Mrs B Very proud.

Mr B You've done so brilliantly.

Mrs B Amazingly brilliantly.

Mr B Your Auntie Jean's very proud as well.

Mrs B She's coming round later.

Mr B For tea.

Mrs B With eclairs.

Mr B And to make plans.

Mrs B For the party.

Mr B Your big party.

Mrs B You will play your violin for her if she asks, won't you?

Mr B Only she loves to hear you play.

Mrs B And she was so disappointed last time.

Mr B When you . . . didn't want to.

Hard cut to Bea who is now in full, aggressive sarcasm mode.

Bea Oh yes, I'm really looking forward to being force-fed chocolate eclairs and being paraded like a show pony. Oh and lucky me, they want to throw a party for me, where Mum can tell everyone how I've done 'amazingly brilliantly' and generally double up her adverbs like some poxy disc jockey. And, if I'm *really* lucky, they might even get up and dance!

Hard lighting and music cut as Abba's 'Dancing Queen' booms out and we see Mr and Mrs B doing their embarrassing parental dancing.
   Abba: 'You can dance
   You can jive
   Having the time of your life . . .'
The lights and music disappear as suddenly as they began.

Bea (*continues*) That's something to look forward to. Yes, it's just great . . . being suffocated and . . . and smothered with . . . with (*can't find the word*) . . . treacle.
Andrew Treacle?
Bea (*shouts*) Yes! . . . Toxic treacle!

Andrew has been taken aback by the vehemence of her feelings. The silence is broken by Chas.

Chas (*as Murray Walker or any prototype sports commentator*) And you join us here live for the World Heavyweight Whingeing Championships.

Bea and Andrew look at Chas, whose manner turns serious and quiet.

You don't know you're born . . . At least you've each got two parents who give a toss . . . I've just got the one . . . and she barely notices I'm there.

Andrew and Bea feel shamed. Suddenly BSE flutters in.

BSE Sorry about that, found the key. On the wrong hook and in the wrong cupboard but heigh-ho, such is life. I'm so sorry about the delay, sorry, and sorry about the silly scene earlier. Been a bit under the weather, sorry. (*She mimes opening the door.*) Aha!

Open sesame, in you go. Are you okay, Andrew? You
don't look very good.

Andrew Um, I'm fine, miss. Thanks.

BSE Okay, you three go in and get yourselves settled. I'll
be in to hand out your exam papers shortly. (*She
starts to move off.*)

Bea (*exasperation*) Where are you going now, miss?

BSE I promised Mr Biggs I'd just give him a quick hand.
Someone's had a bit of an accident in his games
cupboard. (*as she leaves*) Go on, go on, go through,
make yourselves at home, shan't be a tick. (*She exits.*)

*Hesitantly Bea and Chas move towards the exam
room. Andrew stands frozen to the spot.*

Bea Are you coming?

Blackout.

SCENE TWO

*In the blackout the actors portraying the parents are
stagehands as they position three desks (with chairs) in
a triangle. One chair is in the foreground, two slightly
further upstage. Another chair is placed at the front of
the stage off to one side.*

*As they move this furniture into place the parents
quietly deliver a 'round' of parental advice, each line
beginning before the previous one ends, as follows:*

Mr A Always read the question.

Mrs A And read it carefully.

Mr A Always very carefully.

Mr B We know you'll do well.

Mrs B You always do so well.

Mr B We are so proud of you.

Mrs C Just try not to cock it up.

Mr A Always check what you've done.

Mrs C You're such a silly sod.

Mr A Allow time, at the end –

Mrs A – to check what you've done.

Mr A Don't get panicky.

Mrs A Treat it as a challenge.

Mr A Don't flake.

Mrs A An exciting challenge.

Mrs B There'll be an eclair.

Mr B Many eclairs.

Mrs B Ready and waiting.

Mr B And Auntie Jean.

Mrs B She's so proud of you.

Mr B Everyone is.

Mrs C For God's sake concentrate.

Mrs B So very proud.

Mrs C That's all I ask.

Mr A Remember, tiger . . .

Mrs A All the best.

Mr A . . . don't let yourself down.

Mrs A The very best.

Mr A Just up to you.

Mrs B We're all so proud.

Mr A This is where you find out . . .

Mr B You're our star.

Mr A . . . find out about yourself.

When the lights come up there are three desks centre-stage with Andrew sitting at the front desk, the apex of the triangle, and Bea and Chas at the two desks behind.

The exam papers are face down on the desks. Andrew is looking horribly tense as BSE walks between the desks giving them a final briefing. The chair she will sit in is off to the side.

BSE Remember to keep an eye on the time. If anyone
has a problem, just put up your hand. Very well. (*She
heads towards her invigilator's chair.*) You may now
turn over your . . . Oh sorry, sorry, forgot something,
sorry . . .

*Bea and Chas stop half way through the act of
turning over their exam papers. They look at each
other in exasperation. Andrew, by contrast, has not
moved a muscle and seems to be almost in a trance.*

Sorry. I meant to say make sure what you write is neat
and legible. There's no point getting something right if
no one can read it. Right, okay . . . sorry, just wanted
to say that. And now – (*She walks towards her chair.*)
– you may turn over your papers.

*She sits down, takes a paperback out of her bag and
starts to read.*
*Meanwhile, Bea and Chas turn over their papers
and start to avidly read the rubric. Slowly they
become aware of the fact that ahead of them Andrew
has still not moved a muscle. They share looks of
concern. Bea gives Chas a look as if to say 'Do
something.' Chas isn't sure what to do. Eventually
he leans forward and gently lobs a rubber that hits
Andrew on the shoulder, but Andrew doesn't register
it at all. Bea and Chas share another look, then Chas
raises his arm in the air. BSE doesn't notice him,
just keeps her nose in her book and does her nervous
throat-clearing cough. Chas starts to click his fingers
to get her attention. She looks up.*

BSE Yes?
Chas Um, I've dropped my rubber, can I go and pick it
up please, miss?
BSE (*a little perplexed*) Yes.

Chas comes forward and kneels down next to Andrew under the pretext of retrieving his rubber.

Chas Are you okay? (*no response*) . . . My mouth doesn't look like a broken bottle, does it? (*Still Andrew doesn't respond.*) Andrew . . .
BSE No whispering.

Slowly Chas heads back towards his desk. As he does so, BSE initiates another irritating flurry of throat-clearing coughs.

Chas I've got some throat sweets, miss, if you'd like one.
BSE What?
Chas Throat sweets . . . for that cough.
BSE (*mystified*) What cough?

Chas and Bea share a look of exasperation.

Chas (*mutters*) Doesn't matter, miss.

BSE notices the inert Andrew.

BSE Andrew . . . (*She approaches him.*) Andrew . . . (*He looks at her.*) Is there a problem?
Andrew (*robotically*) . . . No, miss.
BSE Only you don't seem to have turned your paper over.
Andrew Don't I?

Andrew stares at the untouched exam paper for a few moments. Then suddenly turns it over.
  As he does so, the rest of the stage goes dark as his face is picked out exclusively in a tight, single spot. There is a feeling that we are now inside Andrew's head.

(*reading the instructions to himself with occasional moments of hesitancy*) 'In the boxes above, write your centre number, candidate number, surname and initials, signature . . .'

The spot suddenly transfers to Chas, as the only lit figure on stage. He too is scanning the rubric.

Chas '. . . and the date. Show all stages in any calculation. Supplementary . . .'

Again, the spot switches across to Bea as she reads the rubric. Her audio heartbeat is now barely audible. She is calm and collected.

Bea '. . . answer sheets may be used. Work steadily through . . .'

Suddenly her mouth is miming the words but the words are spoken by an elegant, smooth male voice, her imagined voice of the exam – 'Ex'.

Slowly another spotlight comes up on a chair positioned preferably quite high on a rostrum upstage. The chair is a swivel chair, with the back towards us. We cannot see the occupant, just his sinister arm stroking a stuffed white cat. His voice should be miked, so that it fills the theatre smoothly. (If the resource is available, the voice could be synchronised to the lighting.)

Ex '. . . the paper. Do not spend too long on one question.' So, my dear . . . we meet again.

Bea (*with relish*) Let's have your first question, loser.

Ex Very well. 'Is the family a social or biological grouping?'

Bea Is that your best shot? You're dead meat. (*Busily she starts to write her first essay, ignoring the voice of Ex.*)

Ex It looks like you have thwarted me again. No doubt this will be yet another starred A grade . . . You will become even more of a high-flier . . . even more of a prodigy . . . even more . . . separate.

Bea stops writing.

Bea . . . Separate?

Ex Yes, separate. As in 'set apart'. Different, detached . . . (*with sinister, slow relish*) . . . i-so-lated.

Bea (*defensive*) Why should I become isolated?

Ex Because you are Two-Brains. An alien life form. Everyone is intimidated by you.

Bea (*pauses for a moment, then resumes writing her essay*) You're talking nonsense.

Ex Am I, my dear? Count your school friends. Do you have as many as last year? Or the year before?

Bea (*it's beginning to get to her, but she keeps her head down and carries on writing*) Just shut up, okay?

Ex How often do you get included in things these days, um?

Bea (*still head down*) I said shut up.

Ex The party invitations have rather dried up, haven't they?

She doesn't respond, just writes even more furiously.

I bet Anne Widdecombe gets more invites than you do.

Bea (*still writing*) I don't have to listen to you.

Ex Why not?

Bea Because you're imaginary. I created you and I can blot you out any time I like.

Ex Some voices are harder to blot out than others, though, aren't they?

Bea Not really.

She screws her eyes tight shut as she concentrates hard on banishing him from her mind. The spot on Ex fades to darkness.

There, gone.

She pauses apprehensively for a moment, as if half-expecting him to answer. Then she gives a little smile and gets stuck into her essay again.

As she turns a page the general lighting comes up on our three exam candidates and BSE, who is reading her paperback. Bea and Chas are writing busily, but Andrew is still just staring at his paper. BSE does a short burst of her involuntary throat-clearing. She looks up and notices Andrew.

BSE Are you alright, Andrew?
Andrew I'm thinking, miss.

Suddenly a spot picks out Andrew's face amid a general blackness.

No I'm not. What I'm doing is the opposite of thinking . . . Thinking joins things up. (*He stares at his exam paper.*) These are just individual words . . . forming a queue . . . a pointless queue . . . Got to do something . . . Perhaps if I try it her way . . . turn it into a game . . . (*He looks at his exam paper and falteringly starts to read the first question.*) 'Palmerston's foreign policy of imperial . . .'

As with Bea, the voice of Ex insidiously takes over as he appears upstage, as before, in his chair, with his back towards us. This time he has a glass of brandy instead of the white cat.

Ex . . . 'expansionism ended in failure.' Discuss . . . You don't even know where to begin, do you? . . . You haven't the foggiest . . . Oh yes, you've studied Palmerston, you know all about Palmerston, but it's just a swirl of dates and facts, you can't possibly bring a shape to any of it. That's far too difficult for a dim little plodder like you. It's too much for you. Any moment now, you'll snap. Like a dry twig.
Andrew Yeah? Well, maybe I'll surprise you.
Ex I don't think so, twig-boy.
Andrew Listen you, I'm . . . (*He starts to flounder.*) . . . I'm . . . I'm considerably stronger than a twig.

Mysteriously, as Ex speaks, his voice turns into Mr A.

Ex/Mr A Then prove it. Make a start. Write something. You can't. You're going to fail again, aren't you? You've chosen the path marked 'weak'.

Andrew (*suddenly jumps to his feet shouting*) Oh shut your face, you stupid git!!!

During this exclamation, the lights have snapped up and Andrew finds himself on his feet being stared at by Bea, Chas and a shocked BSE.

BSE Are you *sure* you're alright, Andrew?

Andrew Um, sorry, miss, I . . . um . . .

BSE Who were you shouting at?

Andrew Well, you see it was . . . (*Realises he can't explain it without being sectioned.*) It was . . . me . . . I was shouting at myself, miss. Sorry.

BSE I can't tolerate shouting in an exam.

Andrew No, miss, permission to go and be sick, miss.

BSE Oh, of course, yes, go.

Andrew bolts off. BSE watches him go, rather concerned. She does some throat-clearing. She notices Chas and Bea watching her.

Alright, drama over, carry on.

The spot switches to Chas, who goes back to his calculation of a tricky maths problem.

Chas 78 point 4 . . . No that doesn't look right . . . Start again . . . 369 divided by 4 . . . 4s into 36 go 9 . . . 4s into 9 go . . . 2 carry 1 . . .

As Chas goes back over his figures a figure in a white suit appears behind him and watches over his shoulder. Chas keeps working.

(*without turning round*) Not now, Dad, I'm in the middle of a long division.

Dad Oh, right, sorry. (*Dad hovers nervously.*) Maths, eh? Can't help you there. Never my strong point . . . and it's all that new maths now, isn't it? In my day we . . .

Chas (*stops his wittering*) Look, Dad, I don't mean to be rude . . . It's lovely to see you and everything, but Maths is probably the only GCSE I can pass and I really want to . . .

Dad (*interrupts*) Nope, it's okay, I understand, your old dad's in the way. I'm always in the way. Just ask that bus driver. (*Laughs self-consciously.*)

Chas You're not in the way, it's just . . . Well, why are you here?

Dad (*goes to say something, then dries*) . . . Do you know it's gone completely out of my head. I know there was something . . .

Chas You've chosen a really bad moment.

Dad Have I? Maybe the moment chose me.

Chas Eh?

Dad Well, I think it's whenever you get really anxious that . . . somehow . . . I get sort of summoned.

Chas Oh, I see, so does that make you (*remembering Bea's words*) a projection of my subconscious mind?

Dad Could be.

Chas Or are you a . . . y'know, a proper supernatural being from another world?

Dad I wish I knew.

Chas (*annoyed*) You must have some bloody idea!

Dad Why? I'm not management, I've no idea what I am. Or why.

Chas (*going back to his exam*) Look, I really need to get on.

Dad I don't understand any of this. I mean, why am I all in white? I've never liked white. White makes me look fat. Always has done.

Chas (*still working*) Dad, please.

Dad And I certainly wasn't wearing white when that bus hit me . . . Perhaps I should have been . . . maybe he'd have spotted me earlier.

Chas Look, Dad, I really want to do well in this.

Dad I know, I know, I'm just saying none of this makes any sense to me either, that's all. I mean, how come you're the only one who can see me? Why can't this lot hear you talking to me?

Chas Dad, I'm trying to concentrate.

Dad I know, I know, I'll shut up, sorry, it just gets to me sometimes.

Chas cracks on with his calculation, muttering occasional numbers, but he becomes increasingly aware of his dad's ghost, standing self-consciously behind him.

Chas (*without turning round*) Why haven't you gone?

Dad . . . I'm lending moral support.

Chas Dad, I don't need your support.

Dad Well, that's not what you said when you were on that date last month, is it, eh? You appreciated my support then, didn't you?

Chas Dad . . .

Dad When I gave you the advice about that bra strap . . .

Chas Yes, but . . .

Dad You'd have been fumbling away for hours. And then there was the useful tip about how sensitive their nipples are!

Chas (*exasperated*) Dad! Leave me alone! I really want to do well in this!

Dad Right, sorry. (*He motions to leave.*)

Chas Could be important for my future.

Dad (*stops, as he sets off*) Oh that's what it was, I remember now.

Chas Eh?

Dad Your future. I just came to tell you that everything's going to be alright.

Chas (*thrown*) Everything's going to be alright?

Dad (*quick and casual*) Yeah, your future's going to be really happy, just thought you might like to know, 'cos you seemed a bit worried about it, anyway, see ya!

Chas But wait a minute, I want . . .

Too late. Dad has disappeared, leaving Chas frustrated.

That is so bloody typical . . . always buggering off when I need him . . .

We hear BSE's raised voice, which brings up the general lighting.

BSE You have one hour fifteen minutes remaining. (*couple of throat-clears*)

Bea turns over a page and the tight spot returns to her. She continues to write with impressive speed. Ex's voice returns, but this time he is not lit (or barely lit).

Ex (*voice only*) I'm still here.

Bea (*continues writing*) I'm not listening. You're just the voice of self-doubt.

Ex Are you sure you're right about that?

Bea (*still writing*) I'm not listening . . . and I'm not imagining you in the chair with the cat any more. In fact I'm not picturing you at all.

Ex Oh dear, I can see I'm no match for you.

Bea That's right, pal.

Ex You're one of life's winners, aren't you? You're going to be a huge success . . . probably very rich . . . and very thin . . .

She stops writing for a beat as he's hit a nerve.

You'll probably own a lovely big house . . . a long way
away from your parents . . . You'd rather like that,
wouldn't you? . . . It'd save all those uncomfortable
conversations.

Bea For your information, I love my parents, actually.

Ex You love them.

Bea Yes.

Ex But you're deeply embarrassed by them.

Bea (*losing confidence*) I don't know what you're talking
about.

Ex Yes you do, they make you cringe.

Bea You're talking out of your arse.

Ex I'm a disembodied voice, I don't have an arse.

Bea My parents and I are . . . are just fine, okay?

Ex Then why won't you allow them to be proud of you?

Bea (*genuinely lost for an answer*) Well I . . . I . . .

Ex They are so proud, poor dears, they've placed you
up on that very high pedestal . . . Trouble is, from
up there, they do look so awfully small to you, don't
they? And getting smaller all the time. And further
away. Like your friends. Everyone's drifting further
away as you get higher and higher . . . and lonelier
and . . .

Bea (*briskly cutting him off*) Right, that's enough.
(*Covers her ears.*) I'm not listening.

Again BSE's voice throws the lighting wide.

BSE Andrew? . . . Are you alright now?

*Andrew is hesitating on the edge of the lit area. BSE
approaches him, lowers her voice.*

You don't look right. Do you still feel sick?

Andrew No . . . I made it to the toilets.

BSE Good. That's good . . . well done. (*She looks at him compassionately.*) It's not worth making yourself ill over, y'know . . . You've got nothing to prove.

Andrew Yes I have.

He trudges a little weakly to his desk and sits down. The others watch him with concern.

The ghost of Dad materialises behind Chas. The lighting homes in on them.

Dad There was something else.

Chas What?

Dad Something else I meant to say, what was it now?

Chas You know you said my future's a happy one?

Dad Eh? . . . Oh, yeah.

Chas Well how can you possibly know that?

Dad Well I can see into the future, can't I? (*Chas looks dumbstruck.*) Sorry, haven't I mentioned that before?

Chas No, I don't think you have.

Dad Oh, right, I lose track.

Chas How can you see into the future?

Dad Well I don't know, do I? I told you, I don't understand how any of this stuff works. Now, what was the other thing I wanted to say? My memory never used to be this bad, or did it?

Chas (*frustrated*) So what is this happy future then?

Dad Well I can't tell you any details, can I? If I tell you your future that would probably influence your future and disturb the space–time continuum. That's basic *Star Trek* stuff. Besides, knowing what's going to happen takes the fun out of it. Like watching the highlights when someone's told you the score. I mean, admittedly, I did consider warning you not to dive down that orange chute-thing, but then I thought, no, it'd be wrong to deprive him of the experience.

Chas Oh, cheers.

Dad (*still trying to remember*) Damn, what was it now?

Chas At least give me some idea. Will I have a wife and kids and stuff?

Dad (*still trying to recall*) Yeah, yeah, all of that.

Chas And a house?

Dad Yeah, yeah, nice house, with a garden, and a water feature. Don't go telling anyone I gave you all this info. People might think you're a nutter. Mum's the word. (*Recalls.*) That's it!

Chas That's what?

Dad Mum! The other thing. I just wanted to say, try not to be too hard on your mother. I know she's a crap mum, but she means well. She can't help being a shambles. Which of us can, eh? I know I can't.

Chas Was that it?

Dad Yup, I'll let you get on with your maths. (*He starts to leave.*)

Chas Hang on, um, listen, could you do me a favour? You see that kid over there? (*Indicates Andrew.*)

Dad What, the sort of zombie-looking one?

Chas Yeah, well, could you just go over and tell him not to worry because everything will be alright.

Dad I'm exclusive to you, son. I can't see into his future.

Chas No, but he wouldn't know that. *Please*, he just really needs someone to tell him that everything's going to be alright.

Dad (*uncomfortable*) Well, why do *I* have to do it? Hasn't he got a dead dad of his own?

Chas (*pointedly*) No, he's not as lucky as me.

Dad He won't even be able to see me. You're the only one who can see me.

Chas Try and make him see you.

Dad If I do manage it I'll probably scare the shit out of him. And I mean that literally.

Chas Just try. Please. And I'll forget about the four birthday presents you owe me . . . and the incident with . . .

Dad (*cuts him off*) Alright, alright, don't drag the drowned tortoise into it.

Reluctantly Dad walks across to where Andrew is sitting, still transfixed. He stands behind Andrew and taps him on the shoulder. Andrew does not register it at all. Dad gestures in a 'told you so' manner to Chas. Chas gestures for him to try again. Dad stands diagonally in front of Andrew. Again, not a flicker of a response. Dad launches into a little tap dance. Nothing. He lifts his arms and emits a ghost-like 'Woooo'. Nothing. He sticks his face right up close to Andrew's and gibbers. Still there is not a flicker. Dad gives up and crosses back to Chas, pausing briefly to try a cursory 'woo' on Bea. She too doesn't flicker.

Dad Told you. Whatever I am, you're the only one who can see me.

Chas Yeah, trouble is, if you are a product of my imagination, then all that stuff about my happy future is just imaginary bollocks as well, isn't it?

Dad 'Fraid so. Mind you, does it matter?

Chas Eh?

Dad Well, is there any difference between something that feels real and something that is real?

Chas (*ponders this*) I don't know . . . maybe not . . . What do you . . . (*He looks around. Dad has gone.*) Oh for . . .

In the distance the bell rings for change of period and we hear the familiar tumult as kids change classes. At the same time the lights come up on the three exam candidates again. BSE develops a nervous little throat-clearing cough, which she finds increasingly difficult to clear. It bothers Chas and Bea, but Andrew doesn't notice it. Suddenly we hear a stage whisper from

Mr Biggs as he hovers awkwardly on the edge of the lit area.

Biggs Um . . . Miss Baxendale?

She looks up from her book. He gestures that he needs to talk to her in private. She indicates that she can't leave her post. He beckons her more forcefully. Reluctantly, with some throat-clearing, she crosses to join him.

BSE I'm invigilating.

Biggs I know but, um . . . look, can we step outside and talk for a moment.

BSE I can't, I'm invigilating.

Biggs (*suppressing his irritation*) Yes, you've said that, Emily, it's just . . . well this is rather urgent . . . extremely urgent in fact.

She casts a furtive glance over her shoulder. Bea and Chas, who've been earwigging, pretend to get on with their work. Biggs and BSE exit together. Chas glances across to Andrew, who is still motionless.

Chas (*to Bea*) He still hasn't written anything.

Now Chas notices that Bea has put down her pen and is sitting with her head in her hands.

Are you okay?

Bea Sure. Just trying to come up with a rhyme.

Chas A rhyme?

Bea For this limerick. 'There was a young woman from Putney, who stuffed both her nostrils with chutney . . .' But now I've lumbered myself with this 'utney' thing for the last line.

Chas (*interrupts*) You're writing limericks?

Bea Yeah.

Chas Is that part of the Sociology exam then?

Bea (*chuckles*) No.

Chas Don't waste time pissing about. It'll affect your pass mark.

Bea I'm not after a pass mark.

Chas Eh?

Bea leans back in her chair and clasps her hands behind her head in a slightly forced show of relaxation.

Bea I've decided to fail for once. I'm tired of being 'Two-Brains'.

Chas For someone so bright, you're really stupid, do you know that?

Bea I beg your pardon.

Chas You can't just deliberately fail an exam.

Bea Why not?

Chas Because it's an insult.

Bea An insult?

Chas Yes, it's an insult to all us thickos and plodders, who have to work like mad just to scrape an E, if someone with brains and ability deliberately fails just as some . . . some wanky, selfish, cheap thrill. (*He turns to Andrew for support.*) That's right isn't it, Andy?

No response.

Bloody hell, he's really off with the fairies.

Bea (*inflating with rage*) It is not a wanky, selfish, cheap thrill.

Chas So, you fail in Sociology, ooh how daring. Like that's really going to put a dent in your prospects.

Bea My prospects are –

Chas – brilliant. Doors will always open for you. You're clever. Life'll be a doddle.

Bea (*getting upset*) That's rubbish, life's hard when you're clever.

Chas Oh yeah? How's that then?

Bea Because clever people are never free. You're always (*Hunts.*) . . . hedged in by expectations . . . always having your story written for you . . . always waiting to disappoint people.

Chas There are worse things.

Bea Clever people are misfits. They're . . . they're afflicted with thinking, so they never have that knack of just . . . *being*, just surrendering to the moment and feeling happy. They analyse and mentally pick away at all their scabs until they end up in therapy groups spilling their guts out to total strangers.

Chas So what are you saying? That stupid people are lucky because they're too stupid to realise they're miserable, is that what you're saying?

Bea No, no, I . . .

Chas Because we stupid people get stressed as well, y'know, we just can't afford the therapy.

Bea You're not stupid. You just pretend to be. (*Her tone becomes more glum.*) And, anyway . . . you're the one whose life is going to be a doddle . . . because you can talk to people. That's better than being clever any day. Everyone likes you.

Chas Oh right, so everyone likes me, do they?

Bea Yes.

Chas And I suppose that's your roundabout way of asking me out for a date?

Bea is completely thrown by Chas's ingenious change of tack.

Bea Well, I . . .

Chas Alright, you suckered me into it. I'd have caved in sooner or later. Those beautiful eyes would have got me in the end.

Bea tucks her hair behind her ears and starts to turn very girly.

Bea You like my eyes then?

Chas Of course I do. Any bloke would. They're gorgeous.
How about Saturday?

Bea Um . . . okay, yeah . . . that'll be nice.

Chas Yes, it will. There's just one thing, though. I only
go out with winners. I don't date twonkpots who
think it's cool to take a dive in an exam.

*Bea breaks into a smile. She realises what Chas has
been up to. And she likes it.*

Bea Fair enough.

*She turns round, scrunches up her limerick and starts
tackling her exam proper.*

'Twonkpot'?

Chas No more talking, please, I've got an E to get.

*They resume work on their exam, but become aware
of Biggs and BSE offstage having an increasingly
animated conversation. We can't quite pick out
exactly what Biggs is saying, but BSE is getting
clearer, louder and angrier.*

BSE (*off*) Well it's understandable if I'm getting a tad
upset, Michael.

Anxious male mumbling.

Yes, well, I resent the word 'hysterical', I don't see why it's
'hysterical' to expect someone to keep their promises.

*Now we can discern Biggs, and by now even Andrew
is aware of the row.*

Biggs Emily, calm down.

BSE I will not calm down, what does it matter if she
knows? If everyone knows? You've always said your
marriage was a sham.

Some disgruntled mumblings from Biggs.

You did say that, Michael, you *did*, in the Holiday Inn in Slough, on one of our Tuesdays, I have a distinct memory of you saying your marriage was a sham and that you wished you could be with me all of the time. Well, now that can happen, can't it?

Biggs mumbles what sounds like an evasive answer but the words aren't quite clear. The three kids all lean to that side to try to pick more of it up. Suddenly we hear a slap.

You lying two-faced shitbag! How could I be so totally stupid! I thought I meant something to you, but now I realise I was just your . . . your occasional willy-warmer! I hate myself for being such an imbecile. I hope you rot in hell, Michael Biggs. I've been humiliated.
Chas See? Happens to everyone.

All of a sudden BSE stomps back into the exam room. For a few moments she paces up and down in a febrile emotional state. Then she stops, aware of being watched. With a huge effort of will, she pulls herself together.

BSE (*glances at her watch*) . . . You have one hour ten minutes remaining.

Blackout.

SCENE THREE

*The lights come up, but in a subdued state. The parents
again become stagehands, each taking a desk and a chair
and laying them out in a straightish line across the front
of the stage. Each set of parents arrange themselves
around the desk as if it was a kitchen table. They do this
scene-shifting in turn, starting with Mr and Mrs A.*

Mr A So then I said to him, I said, what is the point of
having a business plan if we keep changing it all the
time? It's a farce. A total fiasco.

Mrs A Well, try not to worry about it.

Mr A I have to worry about it, that's my job. Comes
with the territory. And it's pretty rough territory, I can
tell you. Apache country.

Mrs A I know dear, you've said.

Mr A (*exhales with stress*) I don't know. It just never
gets any easier . . . What time should he get back?

*Mr and Mrs B and Auntie Jean do their desk and
chair shifting.*

Mrs B So what did the hospital say?

Mr B Do we want ordinary tea or Earl Grey?

Jean I'm not fussed, as long as it's wet and warm.

Mrs B So what did the hospital say? Only you have to
hold them to what they say, otherwise they'll just keep
fobbing him off and he'll never see the plastic knee,
poor love.

Jean They said it'd be before Christmas.

Mrs B But when? You need a date. In writing.

Mr B Our little star will be home soon.

Jean Yes, bless her.

*By the time they finish there's a plate of chocolate
eclairs in evidence.*

Mrs C quietly sings Ricky Martin's 'La Vida Loca'
to herself and practises the occasional dance step as
she shifts her desk and chair.

When all is in position there's a few moments
silence. Then the lights come up on the stage-right
table where Mrs C, dressed up and ready to go out, is
counting out some money and leaving it on the table.
As she does this she shouts over her shoulder. She
talks fast. Mentally she is already on her way out of
the door.

Mrs C Sacha! It's a take-away for tea! I'm leaving the
money on the table. Don't let Ashley have cutlery and
keep him away from the electrics!

Meanwhile, Chas has trudged in. He plonks his satchel
on the floor and sits down.

Oh, hello, love, didn't hear you come in, how did it go?
(*She gets out a mirror and starts to freshen her make-*
up.)

Chas They couldn't find the key to the exam room.

Mrs C Oh no.

Chas And then, when we finally got in, the teacher who
was invigilating kept going outside and bursting into
tears.

Mrs C (*still applying make-up*) Honestly . . . that school
. . . teachers are always having breakdowns. (*Starts to*
pack her make-up away.)

Chas She should never have confiscated Gary Spackman's
camera. Gary got the hump and took his Polaroids of
her snogging Mr Biggs straight round to Mrs Biggs,
who took them straight to the Headmaster, who
suspended them both, pending a meeting of the
governors. 'Least, that's the rumour.

Mrs C (*hasn't really listened to a word*) How did you
get on in your Maths?

Chas Well, alright, I think, in the end.

Mrs C You think you did alright?

Chas Yeah, maybe better than alright.

Mrs C Oh, thank God for that, I've been worrying about you all day.

Chas (*taken aback*) . . . You have?

Mrs C Yeah . . . 'course I have. Just 'cos I'm all over the place doesn't mean I don't worry about you. (*She hugs him close and kisses him affectionately on the top of his head.*) You're my baby boy. (*She sets off.*) Okay, I'm off to salsa classes, don't wait up. Catch you later.

She exits at speed. Chas is left with a rueful, relaxed smile on his face.

Chas Yeah . . . have a good time. (*He chuckles to himself.*)

The ghost of Dad appears. Chas looks at him, pleased to see him.

Hi, Dad . . . what can I do for you?

Dad I just popped by to say . . . No, it's gone.

The lights fade down on this scene and fade up on the table positioned stage left, where Mr and Mrs B are sitting, drinking tea. They have a guest, Auntie Jean, and there is a plate of chocolate eclairs on the table. Bea comes home from school. She is humming quietly to herself and seems far more carefree than the girl we saw in the previous scenes.

Bea Hi, Mum, hi, Dad . . . oh hi, Auntie Jean, how's Uncle Bob?

Jean Oh fine, still waiting for a new knee, but, well, there's always someone worse off than yourself, isn't there?

Bea Yup. Although statistically somewhere in the world there *must* be someone who *is* worse off than everyone else and so can't say that.

They laugh.

Mrs B She's right, y'know.

Mr B She's always right. How did it go today?

Bea It went fine.

Mr B Well done, love.

Mrs B Do you want an eclair?

Bea I'm trying to watch my weight.

Jean Oh listen to her, she's a lovely size. Perfect.

Mrs B (*proffering the plate*) Go on, have one.

Mr B We got them in your honour.

Bea hesitates for a moment.

Bea . . . Cut me half of one.

Mrs B starts to cut one.

Jean Now then, young lady, you know what I'm going to ask, don't you?

Bea Yes, I do.

Bea turns and exits.
As she goes, the lights fade up on the table centre stage, where Mr and Mrs A sit, waiting anxiously.

Mrs A He's a bit late.

Mr A (*worried*) He's late sometimes, it's nothing to worry about. Besides, the trains are a nightmare at the moment. I blame Richard Branson.

Mrs A I thought you blamed Gordon Brown.

Mr A Well yes, him as well. They're as bad as each other. (*He interrupts himself when he spots his son arriving.*) Hi there, tiger, how did it go?

Andrew Oh, um, yeah, okay really.

Mr A It went okay?

Andrew Yeah.

Mr A Good man, good man.

Mrs A You're a bit late, we were worried.

Mr A I wasn't worried.

Mrs A Were the trains bad?

Andrew No, I came home the long way round. Caught the train down to Orpington and then waited for it to turn round and come back up.

Mr and Mrs A exchange a worried look.

Mr A You went to Orpington?

Andrew Yeah.

Mr A Why did you go to Orpington?

Andrew (*shrugs*) Because it's there.

His parents are bewildered . . . and concerned.

Mrs A You didn't have any problems today, did you, darling?

Andrew Well, it didn't start well. For a while I just sat there, not being able to think. But then, after about half an hour, I felt the fog in my brain just clear. I worked out what I should do and from that moment on I was okay.

Mr A So you got through it? You lasted the exam?

Andrew Oh yes. Right to the end.

Mr A And you left time to check over what you'd done?

Andrew Yes.

Mr A And you were pleased with what you'd done?

Andrew Yeah, pretty pleased.

Mr A Good.

Andrew (*fishing in his satchel*) You can look at it if you like.

Mr A What?

Andrew I bought it home with me.

Mrs A You brought it home?

Andrew Yeah.

Mr A But . . . but why didn't you hand it in?

Andrew (*producing a sheet of A4*) Well there was no point handing it in. (*He hands the sheet to his dad.*) Not in a History exam.

Mr A is now standing transfixed by the sheet of paper he's holding. Mrs A watches her husband apprehensively.

Mrs A What is it?
Mr A It's, um . . . it's a detailed drawing of a Harley Davidson.

He turns the sheet round so that she and the audience can see it. It's an impressive and lovingly done drawing.

Andrew (*proudly*) Not bad is it? I'm starving, can I raid the fridge, Mum?
Mrs A Erm . . . yeah, sure.

Andrew exits cheerfully. Mrs A approaches Mr A. Together they look at Andrew's opus, both stunned.

Well . . . you have to admit it is rather good.

Mr A doesn't respond, just keeps staring at the picture.

You used to like Harley Davidsons, didn't you?

Slowly Mr A looks at Mrs A.
    We switch stage left where Bea enters carrying her violin.

Mrs B Your eclair's ready and waiting.
Bea Okay, after this. I've got a date on Saturday, by the way.
Mrs A Oh good. Someone nice?
Bea He's a maniac who hurls himself off scaffolding and makes up his own words.
Mrs A . . . Right.
Bea Any requests, Auntie Jean?
Jean No, dear, you choose.
Bea All right.
Jean You don't mind playing for us, do you?

Bea (*at peace with herself*) No, it's okay . . . I don't mind.

Jauntily, she tucks the violin under her chin and shapes to draw the bow across the strings.
Black out.

A beat. Then we hear Abba's 'Dancing Queen'.
The lights come up. The cast take the curtain call.
After the curtain call we hear the voice of Ex.

Ex Goodbye . . . until we meet again.

GOLD

Book and Lyrics by Timothy Mason

Music by Mel Marvin

In honour of Reidar Dittman of the Resistance

Characters

Mikkel
Thea
Hjalmar
Leif
Bjorn
Inga
Kirsti
Anna
Peder
Haakon
Mari
Lars
Anders
Siri

A young man emerges from the dark, clutching a book.
And from the pages of his diary, a crowd of remembered
young people emerge from the past.

Ensemble
No one remembers our names
But names aren't the point
Names come and go
No one remembers our war
Wars aren't the point
They come and go . . .

Mikkel I wrote it all down. Who we were and what
we did.

Ensemble
Maybe the point is a mark on the page
A flame in the dark, to light up an age
Maybe an instant – we rise above
The everyday fears, the push and the shove

Maybe a once-upon-moment exists
You open the door, whatever the risks
Maybe the whole is assembled from parts
Maybe we're more than the sum of our hearts.

Mikkel April the 9th, 1940. The Nazis thought they
could take Oslo without a struggle. After all . . .
Norwegians? I think the Nazis were forgetting the
Vikings.

Ensemble
No one who lived through this war
No one who lived through this war

Says wars aren't the point
Says wars aren't the point
Wars come and go
Wars come and go
Wars come and go . . .

There's a sound of an explosion, Mikkel ducks.

Mikkel We shot at them with ancient artillery as they sailed up the Oslo Fjord, I think even *we* were surprised the guns still worked. Something that showed up on the German maps as a museum sank their biggest cruiser.
Ensemble
Wars come and go . . .

Light on Thea and Hjalmar.

Thea What!
Hjalmar I'm sorry, sir, but it's true.
Thea You're sorry? A 'museum' just sank the *Blücher*!
Mikkel That's Thea. She's not really a Nazi commandant, we're painting a picture here. That's Hjalmar.
Hjalmar (*to us*) Hi.
Mikkel It all started with three kids in Oslo.

Leif grabs Bjorn, shakes him awake. Inga watches.

Leif Bjorn, wake up! I need to borrow your lorry!
Bjorn (*barely awake*) What? It's not my lorry, it's my uncle's lorry. Leif?
Leif We need it. We've got to transport eighty-five tons of gold before dawn.
Bjorn It's not very big, my uncle's lorry.
Leif Not all of it goes on your uncle's bleeding lorry! Come on, Bjorn, wake up!
Bjorn It's more a van, really. (*noticing Inga*) Do I know you?
Inga I'm Inga.

Leif She's with me.

Bjorn Oh. Well, in that case . . . Eighty tons of *what*?

Leif We're rounding up all the trucks we can find, we're meeting at the Bank of Norway right now.

A distant explosion, the lights flicker.

Bjorn What was that?

Leif Bjorn, the Nazis have invaded, the Germans are sailing up Oslo Fjord.

Bjorn No.

Leif The King and the Crown Prince have escaped, they're on the run. We're driving Norway's gold over the mountains, the entire gold bullion reserve, we're driving the gold to the sea!

Bjorn What time is it?

Leif (*to us*) It's April the 9th, 1940.

Bjorn (*to us*) My uncle never saw his lorry again. Of course, my uncle never saw *me* again, either.

Inga (*to us*) We were young. In a terrible time.

Ensemble

No one remembers our names . . .

No one remembers our names . . .

Lights shift, night on the streets of Oslo, headlights, searchlights. A cacophony of car horns erupts: people shouting, babies crying, brakes screeching, horns, horns, horns. And the Ensemble become the citizens of Oslo in a panic. Mikkel steps out of it all to address us.

Mikkel April the 9th, 1940. That's the population of Oslo trying to get out of Oslo. The Norwegian traitor, Quisling, he got on the radio, said the British were going to bomb Oslo at two p.m. tomorrow. The British!

Kirsti, runs on, followed by Thea. Mikkel grabs Kirsti.

Kirsti Let me go, let me go!

Thea Kirsti, you little twit, it's a lie!

Mikkel The Germans want us to fear the British, it's a trick!

Thea Nobody's going to bomb Oslo!

But Kirsti runs off.

Ensemble
Maybe the whole is assembled from parts
Maybe we're more than the sum of our hearts!

Mikkel (*to us*) April the 9th, 1940. We didn't live there, we were in Oslo on a school trip, my friends and I.

Thea (*to us*) To the National Gallery. I was going to be a painter.

Mikkel We went to school in Ottestad, a little town in the mountains.

Thea You sound like you're proud of it.

Mikkel I am. On that bus, from Ottestad to Oslo, we were children for the last time.

And the kids are instantly 'on a bus'. Hjalmar stands and starts singing a simple old Norwegian folk song.

Hjalmar
'I'm forever bound to Norway . . .'

Groans from the others.

Lars Not again, Hjalmar!

Hjalmar
'Wheresoever I might roam
Every road is just a doorway
Leading back to my first home . . .'

Thea (*overlapping*) No more songs, Hjalmar, please!

Anders (*overlapping*) Hjalmar, sit down!

But Anna stands and joins Hjalmar.

Anna *and* **Hjalmar**
'Every road becomes a doorway
Leading me to my first home . . .'

Anders makes kissing noises, someone whistles.
But Hjalmar and Anna prevail, and eventually others
join in.

Anna *and* **Hjalmar**
'Here the fjord divides the mountain
Here it journeys to the sea
Here's the birthplace and the fountain –
Norway's children, strong and free
This, the birthplace and the . . .'

And it's beautifully, painfully innocent – so much so
that Thea finally can't bear it and cuts it off:

Thea Stop! Please! Mikkel, it's all so long ago!
Mikkel Twenty-four hours later the world had changed
for each of us for ever. Riding the bus back to school,
we were still young, but we would never be children
again.
Thea Why bring it up now?
Mikkel Remember my diary? I finally finished it.
Thea A diary is something people write from one day to
the next, Mikkel, not fifty years later. Nobody cares
any more.
Mikkel Precisely! That's my point! How are your grand-
children?
Thea Distant. You didn't come to my exhibition.
Mikkel I was there, you just didn't see me. Story of my
life.
Thea (*affectionate*) Hush. Do you ever hear from any of
the others?

Members of the ensemble approach.

Ensemble
No one remembers our names . . .
No one remembers our names . . .
Leif Hello, Thea. Mikkel.
Thea Leif!
Leif You thought I was dead, how could you think I was dead?
Inga How could we think he was dead? I'm Inga.
Peder I went back to the farm. You remember me – Peder?
Kirsti Kirsti. (*indicating Peder*) I ended up with him.
Peder Thank God.
Haakon (*running on*) My name is Haakon, am I late? Did I miss anything? I don't come into the story until later.
Mari I'm Mari, hi.
Anna My name is Anna. I got into parliament, and then I got out again.
Hjalmar Anna!
Anna Hjalmar . . .
Hjalmar I always wanted . . . I never got to tell you . . .
Anna I know, Hjalmar. And I have thought about you every day of my life.
Lars I'm Lars.
Bjorn Bjorn. I guess you all remember what happened to me.
Inga This is difficult, Mikkel.
Leif Very.
Anders Siri?
Siri Anders? Oh God.
Anders Siri, look at me. Look at me!
Siri Mikkel, is this absolutely necessary?
Mikkel It's important!
Thea Why, Mikkel, why?

THE SUM OF OUR HEARTS

Mikkel
No one who lived through this war
Says wars aren't the point
Wars come and go
No one who knew what we did
Could ever forget
Ever let go . . .
Ensemble
Maybe the point is the point where we touch
I give you my life, it isn't so much
All that I've got and it all goes to you
You give me your life, it's all we can do
Listen! Remember the mark on the page
Remember the flame, it lit up an age
Don't let the memory of 'us' ever fade
Always remember the role that we played
Listen! 'Cause this is how history starts –
It's lit by the flame of the sum of our hearts!

*Lars and Thea step out of whatever tableau the
ensemble has ended in, and suddenly they are Nazi
soldiers.*

Lars *Sei still!*
Thea Silence!
Lars *Wo gehen Sie?*
Mikkel We're going back to our school bus, sir.
Thea And then?
Mikkel We're travelling back to Ottestad.
Thea What is that, Ottestad?
Mikkel A town. Our school. Is there.
Hjalmar (*sotto voce*) Nazi pigs.
Thea You there, step out.
Mari We're schoolchildren.

Anna He didn't mean anything.
Lars (*to Hjalmar*) You! Step out!

Hjalmar steps out, Thea puts a hand on his shoulder.

Thea Don't worry, son. We're just talking about civility
here. The rest of you, go to your coach.
Mikkel But sir . . .
Thea Don't worry.
Lars Go!

The rest of the ensemble goes.

Thea Boy, what is your name?
Hjalmar Hjalmar.
Thea (*to Lars*) Hjalmar.
Lars Hjalmar.

*Lars puts his finger to Hjalmar's head and pulls the
trigger. Gunshot. Hjalmar drops to the pavement,
dead. Lars drags him off by his feet. Thea turns to us.*

Thea (*to us*) They did that. Again and again. Honest.

She goes off, Mikkel comes on.

Mikkel It would be that bad and worse for the next five
years, but we didn't know it yet. We waited for
Hjalmar as long as we could and then the driver said,
'We're going,' and we drove through the night, into
the mountains and home. But in Oslo there were three
kids who were busy bringing the war to us.

*Half a dozen ensemble members enter and cross,
carrying heavy wooden crates. One ensemble member,
the boy who played Hjalmar, enters as a Norwegian
Officer.*

Officer (*in great haste*) The Germans will make for the
Bank here as soon as they arrive in Oslo, they want
this gold, they need it desperately. Our job is to get it

to Lillehammer. There'll be a train there, we hope, that will take the cargo over the mountains, to the sea and then to England. Now, gentlemen, it's absolutely crucial that the convoy stay together. Whatever you do, stay together. Look sharp now!

The Officer trots off after the others. Bjorn and Leif enter carrying a heavy crate, Inga follows.

Bjorn Leif, we're the youngest here by far.
Leif So keep your mouth shut, nobody'll notice.
Inga How much do you think it's worth, just what we've got in this crate?
Leif God knows.

Not-so-distant explosion.

Bjorn I'm a little scared.
Inga Me, too, Leif.
Leif Come on, they're starting their engines, they're leaving without us.

Bjorn and Inga still hesitate. Leif indicates the crate.

This is our country in here. The one bit of it we can protect.

Bjorn picks up the crate and heads off. Leif and Inga stare at each other.

So who isn't scared?

Inga heads off and Leif follows. Mikkel, Thea, Siri, Anders, Lars, Kirsti and Peder enter – Siri and Anders as a couple.

Mikkel (*offering his diary*) One of you, do Quisling on the radio.
Thea (*stepping up to a 'microphone'*) Citizens of Norway. This is Major Vidkun Quisling. I speak to you tonight as your new Prime Minister. We welcome

153

our German comrades, fellows-at-arms in the Great
Struggle. King Haakon has abdicated his throne, he
has fled the capital like a coward. The King is wanted:
dead or alive!

THE TRAITOR WITHIN

Group
How could it be? How could it be him?
This weak little man with his weak little chin?
How could he open the door to the dark?
Open the door to the traitor within?

Lars (*to us*) At that point they didn't know about the
gold. Wait till they find out about the gold!

Anders (*as the German Major Falkenhorst*) It's been
what?!

Thea Herr Major, I regret to inform you that the Bank
of Norway has been looted.

Anders The gold?

Thea (*as Quisling*) Gone, all of it. Tracks in the snow,
lorries, lots of them, headed north.

Anders Get that gold, Quisling!

Group
How could it be? How could it be him?
This weak little man with his weak little chin?
How could he open the door to the dark?
Open the door to the traitor within?
What did he give you? What did he flash?
The weak little man with the Chaplin moustache?
Hey, did he promise you power and rank?
Hey, did the Austrian offer you cash?
I refuse to believe
There are people like this!
Countrymen willing to kowtow to Hitler,
To Quisling!
Don't want to believe a Norwegian existing

Is willing to forfeit his soul for this shit!
[Is willing to forfeit his birthright for this!]
Group
When did it start to start to creep in?
What could make Oslo a little Berlin?
How did it open, the door to the dark?
How did it get here, the traitor within?
I don't want to believe
There are people like this!
Countrymen willing to goosestep for Hitler,
For Quisling!
Don't want to believe a Norwegian existing
Is willing to forfeit his soul for this shit!
[Is willing to forfeit his birthright for this!]

*In another space we see Leif, Inga and Bjorn in Bjorn's
uncle's van, squinting into the night – with 'Traitor
Within' instrumental under. Bjorn is at the wheel, Inga
in the middle, wiping down the windscreen, and Leif
peers out of the passenger window.*

Bjorn I can't see their lights through the snow. Can you
see any lights?
Leif Look out, you're almost off the road!
Inga It's been half an hour since I saw anything.
Leif Can't this damn thing go any faster?
Bjorn It's overheating already, Leif, it doesn't do well in
the mountains.
Leif Well, why the hell didn't you say so?
Inga Leif, shut up.
Leif We've lost the convoy, dammit, God knows how far
ahead of us they are.
Inga What's that . . .? Oh Lord, it *is* overheating.
Bjorn Is that a light?

Lights out on them.

Ensemble
How could it be . . . how could it be . . .?

Mikkel April the 10th, 1940. The mountain roads were choked with traffic. Our school bus didn't get home until two a.m., but to our great relief we found Headmaster waiting up for us. Lars – be Headmaster?

Lars Right.

Mikkel Someone else – Peder – be Mr Neissen – (*to us*) – one of our teachers.

Anna Headmaster, the Nazi soldiers took Hjalmar away and we don't know where he is.

Lars (*as Headmaster*) Yes?

Anna He didn't do anything, Headmaster, you know how Hjalmar is, he's just a little saucy sometimes.

Kirsti He's a boy.

Mikkel Sir, there are German troops everywhere.

Thea Please, sir, we've got to do something.

Lars That's quite enough, all of you. I shall notify Hjalmar's parents in the morning, we'll see what we can do. But as to Hjalmar, it may be that this is the best thing that ever happened to him. It might just put him right with his country, and his God, it might just wake him up.

Mikkel But sir . . .

As he speaks, Lars puts on a swastika armband.

Lars (*as Headmaster*) Understand me: this country wants order, it wants discipline, it wants setting to rights – you young people especially. The Germans are our neighbours, our allies and our comrades. Mr Neissen, unlock the kitchens, give these children a sandwich and get them to bed.

Peder Yes, sir, Headmaster.

Lars moves off. Peder, as Mr Neissen, hesitates.

Peder (*furtively, to the kids*) Don't trust anyone. The school, the town . . . It's not everyone, of course, but . . . I didn't know, I didn't know it was going to be like this.

Mikkel What can we do?

Peder, as Mr Neissen, pulls on a swastika armband.

Peder You're on your own.

Lars and Peder rip off their armbands and become kids again.

THE TRAITOR WITHIN

Ensemble
When did it start to start to creep in?
What could make Oslo a little Berlin?
How did it open, the door to the dark?
How did it get here, the traitor within?

I don't want to believe
There are people like this!
Countrymen willing to goosestep for Hitler,
For Quisling!
Don't want to believe a Norwegian existing
Is willing to forfeit his soul for this shit!
[Is willing to forfeit his birthright for this!]

Lars Hey, believe it.

In another space, Leif lights a cigarette lighter to read a road map, and we see him, Inga and Bjorn standing in the snow on the side of a mountain road in the middle of the night.

Bjorn Sorry. About my uncle's van and all.

Inga (*going through a bag*) We've less than half a sandwich left.

Leif Where the hell are we? (*realising*) It's a map of
Paris, it's a goddamned map of Paris!

Leif furiously rips the map in two.

Inga I'm cold.

Leif Inga! There's two things you don't want to talk
about right now – cold! and hunger!

Bjorn I make it we're not too far from Ottestad. (*Bjorn
goes off.*)

Leif What the hell's Ottestad? How far are we from
Lillehammer, that's the question.

Inga Maybe we could hitch a ride?

Leif In the middle of the night? And leave the gold by
the side of the road, with the German army coming
along behind?

Inga Stop! Right now! I don't know what we should do,
Leif, I'm at a loss. But last time I checked, I wasn't the
enemy. So you can stop treating me like one right this
minute!

*There's a silence. Bjorn comes skiing on (roller-
blades?), carrying ski-poles and wearing a rucksack.*

Bjorn We've got our skis. Leif? I've a cousin goes to
school in Ottestad, it's not too far from Lillehammer,
maybe she'd help. Listen, we're going to have to leave
the gold for now because we can't very well guard it
if we're frozen to death, we'll just have to trust to
luck. Her name is Thea, my cousin, you'll like her.

Inga (*to Leif, only half-joking*) Why can't you be more
like Bjorn?

*Leif stomps off a few paces, then freezes. First we
hear the sound of a car, shifting gears, straining to
climb the mountain. Then we see headlights.*

Leif Get down.

*They drop to the snow: the sound of the car and the
headlights grow, pass and fade.*

(*finally*) A German staff car. On the road to Lillehammer.
Inga I'm cold.

Leif goes to her, holds Inga.

Leif Let's get the skis on and go.
Bjorn Maybe we could go with the gold. I mean, if the
Nazis don't get it. To England. I had a cousin went to
England, he said it was like Paradise.
Inga Right now I'd settle for warm, is it warm?
Bjorn Oh, ever so.

*And while Inga and Leif go off to the van for skis and
rucksacks, Bjorn assumes a stance that tells us his
whole history as a choirboy.*

HOW WARM IT IS IN ENGLAND!

Bjorn
Oh, how warm it is in England!
Oh, how safe and snug and dry!
People's lives are lit by glory,
And a splendour fills the sky.

There's a bar that glows like fire
When you put your shillings in.
Even teapots there wear cosies,
Even beer is warm, and gin.

*And Bjorn is joined, one by one, by a chorus of some
or all of the following idealised Englishmen and
women: a young woman in tennis flannels with racket;
an Oxford undergrad in commoner's gown; a boy in
cricket whites; and, by the final stanza, Lord Nelson,
Queen Victoria and Sherlock Holmes.*

Bjorn *and the* **All-British Chorus**
And to bed they take a bladder
Filled with water piping hot.
It performs a warming function
That a married spouse cannot.
It's what makes a Briton British,
It's what people mean by 'form'.
Yes, their lives are lit by glory
'Cause the population's warm!

It's the secret of their greatness,
Simple British common sense:
Where the sun is always shining
Honi soit qui mal y pense!

The chorus retreat into Bjorn's imagination as Leif
and Inga re-enter with ski-poles and skis.

Leif Ready?
Bjorn Ready.
Inga Let's go.
Young Man Halt!

A Young Man – played by Hjalmar – shines a torch on
them and approaches. He wears a military greatcoat.

Young Man What are you doing here?

They don't answer.

Who are you people?
Leif Who are you?
Young Man I'm a Norwegian, like you. Whose van is
that?
Bjorn It's my uncle's. It doesn't go.
Young Man Then it's not much good, is it? Give me
your papers.
Leif Why should we?
Inga Leif . . .

Young Man pulls out his pistol.

Young Man What are you, a cowboy?

The kids fumble for their identification papers and hand them over to the Young Man. He shines the torch on the van.

What's in it?

When the kids hesitate, Young Man starts off to approach the van.

Bjorn (*finally*) Pig manure, sir.

Young Man stops.

Leif For his uncle's farm.

Young Man So you are in a pickle, ja?

Leif You're not a Norwegian.

Young Man *Vieleicht nicht.* But I speak it like a native. (*re their papers*) I will keep these. If we ever need any shit, we will know how to reach you.

The Young Man strides off toward his car, the kids breathe for the first time. Then they thrust their ski-poles into the snow and ski off.

Mikkel walks toward us with his diary. Lars enters carrying a bulky portable radio and wearing a headset; the other kids enter.

Mikkel You know that moment? When you wake up and everything's pretty much okay and then a moment later your stomach knots up and you remember that nothing's even remotely okay, the world is changed for ever, and it isn't good?

Peder I should be able to enlist, I'm old enough to fight, I'm sixteen!

Lars The wireless says the Germans have taken every port south of the Romsdal Valley.

Siri What about the King?

Lars Some say he's right here somewhere, in the mountains, heading for the coast. Some say he's already been taken and killed.

Mikkel Lars?

Lars gives Mikkel the headset, Mikkel listens to the wireless.

Siri I'm telephoning my parents, I want to go home. Anders, you come too.

Anders What if they've, you know, gone over?

Siri My parents . . .? Quislings? Anders, never.

Anders Why not? Siri?

Siri Because then nothing would make sense.

Peder There's got to be others like us, lots of them.

Kirsti Of course there are, never mind what a few fools get up to, this is Norway, we're Norwegians!

Mikkel The wireless says that Oslo switchboards are flooded with calls from all over the country, people everywhere calling to report that they've seen the King and his party.

Anders There, you see? The whole country's gone over to the Germans!

Mikkel Don't you understand, Anders? They're phoning in false reports. It's brilliant – people everywhere, they're sending the Germans on wild-goose chases all over, they're giving the King a chance to escape. Ordinary Norwegians. It makes me proud. It makes me want to help.

Thea has entered with Leif, Inga and Bjorn.

Thea Everybody? This is Bjorn.

Bjorn Hi.

Thea He needs our help.

The kids gather around Thea and the newcomers, while Mikkel approaches us.

Mikkel It wasn't easy to believe. Norwegian gold? And what could *we* do, we were just kids?

Leif We just need to get it as far as Lillehammer, there's a train there to take it to the coast.

Mikkel Lillehammer's not far.

Peder I'm good with motors.

Lars We could even take it by sledge, it'd be a lark!

Anders I think we should tell somebody.

Thea Who, Anders? Headmaster?

Siri Won't they send somebody for it? The army?

Inga We lost the convoy, nobody knows the gold is missing.

Anders We've got our exams, we've got our lives . . .

Bjorn I'm afraid we don't, exactly, not like we used to.

Anders It can't be all up to us – you're talking about the nation's gold bullion reserve!

Leif Just one little bit of it, the bit that's ours to protect.

A silence.

Mikkel Listen. Those who feel they can, will help. Those who can't – well, we're not judging here.

Thea The hell we aren't!

Mari enters, supporting Anna.

Anna He's dead.

Mikkel (*to us*) Anna was in love with Hjalmar.

Anna They killed him.

Mari Someone rang his parents, they said he was resisting arrest and they shot him. Hjalmar's dead.

There's a stunned silence. This is inconceivable, this is one of them. This is what it is to be young in a terrible time. Finally Thea begins the Anthem. She is joined, one by one, voice by voice.

FOR YOUR FRIENDS

Thea
>There comes a time in every life
>You've got to make a stand.
>There's some who want to save the world
>Or just to lend a hand.
>Some do it for a bit of fun
>To make us proud of what they've done.
>Some are desperate to belong
>To dance the dance, to sing the song,
>And others do it for their land.
>But finally this is all there is,
>And this is where it ends:
>It isn't for your God or flag –
>We'll do it for our friends.

>*And Hjalmar appears from nowhere – as Hjalmar.*

Hjalmar
>Not your nation's glory
>Not your own life story
>There's a job to finish for our friends.

>*Adding a voice or two at a time.*

Lars There comes a time in every life
>You've got to make a choice
and **Siri**
>There's some who want to run and hide,
>There's some who say 'Rejoice!'
and **Kirsti**
>There's some who never dared to dare
and **Peder**
>And those who never cared to care
and **All**
>And others still who never spoke

Now it's as though they just awoke
To find they have a voice.

Ensemble

But this is what it really means
And this is where it ends:
It's isn't for your God or flag –
We'll do it for our friends.

Hjalmar

Not your nation's glory
Not your own life story

Ensemble

There's a job to finish for our friends.

Hjalmar disappears. Suddenly there's the two-tone wailing of a police siren.

Leif We've got to go!

Thea No, we've got to think. If they haven't found the van yet, we're alright. If they have, they'll have found the gold and they'll be watching the van, the van will be a trap. Someone's got to make a reconnaissance.

Kirsti I'll go.

Everyone looks at her in amazement.

I'll just ski by, nobody ever suspects me of anything.

Mikkel (*to us*) The war taught me this: people have things in them you'd never guess.

Kirsti I can get away with almost anything, I don't know what it is about me.

Peder (*to Kirsti*) Nonsense, you're not going anywhere. I'll go.

Leif I started all this, the gold is my responsibility, I'm going!

Inga Actually, Leif, Hitler started it. Who are you trying to impress?

A moment, Leif looking between Inga and Bjorn.

Leif Not you, that's clear. Let me know what you all decide, what's the diff anyway?

Mikkel Kirsti, Peder – if the van is watched, come straight back. Otherwise wait there – we'll come for you and the gold after dusk.

Kirsti Come along, Peder.

Peder Oh, you're funny, you are.

The two of them exit.

Thea Right, then. Let's get organised. One party needs to go ahead to Lillehammer to let the convoy know we're coming . . .

Leif I'll go. If I'm lucky the 11.03 is still running.

Mari Anna – are you sure?

Anna You're damn right I'm sure.

Thea Right. Someone else needs to borrow a car from somewhere . . .

Lars And a sledge, we may need a sledge.

And the others follow Thea off. Only Mikkel, Anna and Mari remain.

Anna I never got to tell him how I felt.

Mikkel He knew. Anna? Hjalmar knew.

Anna It's his birthday in two weeks' time.

Anna exits, Mari follows.

Mikkel (*to us*) And from that moment to the last, pretty much nothing worked out the way we planned it.

Lights change, Mikkel runs off and Kirsti and Peder ski on in swirling light.

Kirsti (*to us*) We skied the entire mountainside, nobody was watching that van. That was the good news.

Peder (*to us*) Then it started to snow.

Kirsti (*to Peder*) It's not going to stop anytime soon, is it?

Peder (*to Kirsti*) The van'll be covered in an hour if the
wind keeps up. Nobody's going to be able to find us
up here tonight.

*The swirling light on them flickers and crossfades with
Lars crossing with Bjorn and Leif and Inga.*

Lars Dammit, I was sure he'd lend us his car, to hell
with him! Bastard wouldn't even let me borrow his
damned sledge!
Leif We'll get a car. I'll just take one, what's the diff?
Lars Really? Wow. Steal one? No. Honest? Listen. Leif.
This isn't Oslo.

*As this group exits together, Thea, Siri, Anders and
Mikkel enter together.*

Siri Thea . . .
Thea I hate him!
Siri Thea . . .
Thea 'Headmaster, Hjalmar was our friend, sir, some of
us just aren't able to come to class.' I told Headmaster
the *truth* and he didn't believe me!
Mikkel Thea . . .
Siri Thea, you told Headmaster to . . . Well, you know
what you told him to do.
Thea Well, I'm through with this damned school!
Mikkel I think, Thea, in point of fact, you actually are.
(*to us*) And then Headmaster walked right in on us.

Hjalmar enters as Headmaster.

Headmaster I understand one of you has a radio set in
his possession.
Mikkel Sir?
Headmaster This is now illegal, you will give me the
radio.
Mikkel I couldn't believe my ears.
Headmaster This instant!

Mikkel gives the radio to Headmaster.

Headmaster (*to Thea*) Are you still here? Pack your things and get out.

Headmaster goes.

Anders Wonderful, Thea. You've put us all in danger of being thrown out.
Mikkel You can do whatever you want, Anders. I'm leaving with Thea.
Siri Anders . . .

Siri steers Anders to a place apart; Mikkel takes Thea by the arm and finds a private place with her.

Thea Sorry. I guess I lost control in there. Just like me.
Mikkel I like you when you're 'just like you'.
Thea Mikkel . . . don't.
Mikkel We'll pack. We'll go.

Lights for Anders and Siri.

Anders For God's sake, Siri! I'm studying to be a doctor, I can't afford to be expelled!
Siri Anders, this is war.
Anders No, dammit, this is you! This career, all my work, my whole life, it's for you!
Siri I know that, Anders. I love you for it.
Anders It just seems a bit much, that's all.
Siri What does?
Anders That we should give up everything for a bunch of . . . I mean, the Jews run almost everything as it is, and the communists are taking over everything else . . .

Siri backs away from Anders in horror.

You know it's true! What are you doing? Wait, now. Siri?

Mikkel and Thea approach Siri and Anders.

Mikkel Each of us should pack a small bag, just the bare essentials.
Siri Anders won't be going.
Thea Anders – are you sure?
Siri He's sure.

A moment. Anders abruptly turns and leaves. Thea puts her arms around Siri and holds her. Mikkel stands awkwardly by.
Lights change: we see Inga and Leif together, Leif whittling off the insulation from the end of a length of flex.

Inga You think you can get it started?
Leif I don't want to lose you in all this.
Inga What? Leif, what are you talking about?
Leif I don't know what I'd do if I lost you.

Bjorn and Lars run on wearing rucksacks.

Bjorn We got the food.
Lars We nearly cleaned out the school kitchens, I never stole anything before.
Bjorn Have you found a car?
Inga The silver-grey one, this end of the row.
Lars Oh, no – no, no, no – that's Headmaster's car!
Inga So?
Leif So?
Bjorn So?
Lars (*a moment*) I get to drive.
Leif (*gives the length of flex to Bjorn*) Here you go, Bjorn. (*meaning one thing*) I can trust you, can't I?
Bjorn (*understanding another*) Leif, it'll be a snap! (*to Lars*) Watch, and learn!

Bjorn runs off to the car, followed by Lars. Leif and Inga look at each other. School bell rings.

Lights for Thea and Siri and Mikkel, Thea still holding Siri.

Thea Are you going to be all right, Siri?
Siri I'm going to pack.

Siri walks off. Thea and Mikkel look at each other.

JUST OUR LUCK

Mikkel
  The world is tumbling down about us
  The tempest broke – the lightning struck
  The ship we wanted sailed without us
  And here we are – it's just our luck.
Thea
  The plaster's crashing round our shoulders
  The ceiling fell – forgot to duck
  The world just keeps on growing colder
  And here we are – I call that luck.
Leif *and* **Inga**
  There's no more room for love or laughter
  There isn't time to touch, to kiss
  We go from ruin to disaster
  And that's just perfect – luck like this.
Leif, Inga, Mikkel *and* **Thea**
  I thought I had a map to follow
  I had a plan, I made a list
  Now all the hopes I had seem hollow
  And everything I aimed at missed.
Leif, Inga, Mikkel *and* **Thea**
  So maybe this is known as 'history'
  And maybe history isn't fair
  And maybe why we're here's a mystery
  And maybe history doesn't care!

We hear a car engine start, squeal out, then brake, screeching to a halt. Lars runs on.

170

Lars He's got it started!
Mikkel That's Headmaster's car!
Inga Run! Run! Go!

*Lars, Mikkel, Thea, Siri run off to the car, Inga and
Leif run after them. We hear the car screeching off.
It fades into the distance.*
   *Crossfade to mountain. Kirsti and Peder huddle
together inside an eerie blue light. Kirsti holds a bar
of gold bullion.*

Kirsti So this is gold. It's heavy.
Peder That's . . .'cause of its high atomic number.
Kirsti Oh. Of course.
Peder I don't . . . know what that means, actually.
Kirsti I wish it were a loaf of bread.
Peder We shouldn't talk, there's not much oxygen in
  here.
Kirsti It's so quiet.
Peder It is.
Kirsti How many feet under are we, do you reckon?

This is too frightening to consider.

Peder I'm going to be a farmer, I'm going to take over
  my grandfather's dairy farm when I'm done with
  school. I don't even know why they sent me to this
  damn school, I'm no scholar, I'm a farmer, what's the
  point? I belong back there.
Kirsti This is the longest conversation we've had in the
  past two years. Or, actually, ever.
Peder I don't . . . always feel . . .
Kirsti . . . comfortable?
Peder Yes.
Kirsti . . . talking?
Peder That's it.
Kirsti Well, no. Who does? Except. Me, I guess. I talk,
  Peder. It's something I do.

Peder They'll see us, won't they? They'll see the mound
the van makes in the snow?

Kirsti Hope so.

Peder I'll dig us out with my fingers if I have to, I'll do
something . . .

WHAT DO YOU DO?

Kirsti
What do you do when the roll-call is through
And your name isn't there on the list?
What if it's true, they forgot about you
And you're missing without being missed?
What do you do when the world that you knew
Is erased, is a myth, is a lie?
How do you act when the numbers come back
And the odds make it your day to die?
The odds make it your day to die?

Peder
What do you do when you're scared through and
through
Till you choke on your spit, on your breath?
What do you do when the caller's for you
And the bastard who's calling is death?

Peder *and* **Kirsti**
How do you live with a knot in your gut
And it's taken the place of your hope?
What do you say when the hangman goes hey!
Got a great price today on some rope?
There's a special today on the rope . . .

Peder Kirsti . . . Listen! Do you hear something?

Kirsti It's them. They're digging for us! Peder, this whole
time I never stopped praying and now God has sent
our friends to save us!

Peder Kirsti . . .

Kirsti Hello! Hello! We're down here!

Peder Kirsti, hush! What if it's not them?

And suddenly the two of them are motionless and frightened, and all we hear is the rhythmic sound of a shovel, digging.
 Lights fade on them; rise on Mikkel, walking towards us with diary in hand.

Mikkel The snowstorm made it rough going, but it probably helped us elude the police. Elude the police, me, Mikkel. The day before I'd been struggling with the 'floral imagery in Keats'. We felt so bold, such rebels, so courageous, packed into the Headmaster's stolen car. And then it stopped snowing and the moon came out, and there was the van on the mountain, drifted high with snow, and we were so happy. That's when we saw that someone had been there before us, with a shovel. They weren't there, Kirsti and Peder. Our friends were gone and so was the gold.

Sound of a small plane overhead.

There was only one thing to do, of course: we had to follow the tracks that led away from the van, wherever they might lead us.

Train whistle blows. Crossfade: Anna and Mari enter, each clutching a bag, each frightened.

Train Conductor's Voice Lillehammer! The station is Lillehammer!

We hear the sounds of a commuter train station, the hiss of air brakes, and the train starting up again. Mari and Anna are at a loss.

Mari Where do we go, who do we talk to?
Anna I have no idea, I didn't think this through.

Mari We have to be sure of who we're talking to. The Germans are bound to be looking for the gold, we have to find someone we can trust.

Anna Hush, people are watching.

Mari But how will we know?

WHAT DO YOU DO (REPRISE)

Anna
What do you do when the world that you knew
Is erased, is a myth, is a lie?
How do you act when the numbers come back
And the odds make it your day to die?

Anna *and* **Mari**
How do you live with a knot in your gut
And it's taken the place of your hope?
What do you say when the hangman goes hey!
Got a great price today on some rope?
I can give you a deal on the rope . . .

They sink onto a bench. And a moment later a Young Man approaches them – Hjalmar, playing the German spy we've already met.

Young Man Excuse me . . .

Anna gasps.

Forgive me, but you look a little lost, am I right? You're in some sort of distress?

Mari We're fine.

Young Man I see. I'm glad to hear it, sorry to trouble you.

He starts to move off.

Anna No!

He stops.

Please.

Mari Anna . . . All right, all right, I don't know what
else to do, either.

Anna We have . . . some information to convey. And we
don't quite know who we can turn to.

Young Man Well, I'm a Norwegian. Like you.

Anna It's . . . It's about some gold.

Young Man I see. Gold. You know, I *thought* you were
in a pickle. Come. Walk with me. Tell me all about it.

*Anna and Mari look at each other, uncertain. The
Young Man goes, the girls follow him off. Lights fade
quickly.*

    *In moonlight, a wary procession comes into view:
Mikkel and Thea, Lars and Bjorn, Inga and Leif, and
Siri.*

Leif There's a light in at least one window.

Bjorn They've got a fire going, you can smell it.

Inga There's the truck they used – see the tracks leading
up to the house?

Thea People actually live here? The buildings are
collapsing.

Haakon It's nicer in the barn.

*Everyone whirls around, nearly jumping out of their
skins, and now we see that they are being followed by
a boy with a rifle – Haakon – and the rifle is trained
on them . . .*

I got it fixed up in the barn. Do you like music?

No one moves, staring at the rifle.

The BBC says the Allies are going to invade Norway,
they're going to take Norway back from the Nazis!
Oh, ja, this is my grandfather's. I had to make sure of
you. (*Haakon lowers the rifle.*) Grandfather goes away
winters. He works for the railroad. I listen to the
radio. Come in the barn, I got it fixed up nice.

*And a warm, flickering light rises on Kirsti and Peder,
wrapped in blankets and drinking something hot from
mugs and sitting on the crate of gold.*

Peder Hi.

Kirsti Do you want coffee or hot chocolate? This is
Haakon. We've got the gold.

*While everyone else moves to encircle Peder and
Kirsti, Mikkel moves down to us.*

Mikkel (*to us*) In all the years of the war, there was so
much I hoped for and didn't get, and so much I never
dreamed of, and received. Haakon was, I think, the
strangest gift I never wanted, and one of the best.

Haakon Who likes Swing? The BBC says the
Reichsführer has declared that Swing is evil and
barbaric and decadent, thereby proving that the
Reichsführer is decadent and barbaric and evil. Let's
dance!

Mikkel (*to us*) He was either crazy, I thought at the
time, or he was fourteen years old. Today I'd say –
split the difference.

Haakon (*rapidly, to Siri*) You like Duke Ellington?
Benny Goodman? Tommy Dorsey? Louis Armstrong?
Bix Beiderbecke? Charlie Parker? Count Basie? Basie?
You do love Basie, don't you?

Siri Ah, probably . . .

Haakon They're not taking away *my* radio. You ready?

Siri No! Yes! For what?

*Haakon grabs Siri by the hand, pulls her to the barn's
'dance floor'. He turns up the volume on his radio and
bang! Haakon is dancing . . . but Siri is not.*

BEASTLY MUSIC (INSTRUMENTAL)

Siri No. No, I'm sorry.

But Haakon is persistent. Siri is sort of going through the motions now . . .

This makes no sense. Hey, Strange Boy! I don't want to . . . Oh, what the hell.

And she's full out!

Who *are* you?
Kirsti (*shouting over the music*) Peder?

Everyone looks at Peder, who is not known for his advocacy of the dance. Peder stands reluctantly, Kirsti grabs him, and they're dancing.

Thea What are you people doing?! We're at war!
Kirsti Mikkel – put down that diary of yours and ask Thea to dance!
Thea You must be joking.
Kirsti (*shouting*) Can't hear you.
Thea (*shouting*) I said you must be joking!

Mikkel grabs Thea and bang, they're dancing.

Leif Inga?

Leif grabs Inga and bang, they're dancing.

Lars Bjorn?
Bjorn De-lighted!

Lars grabs Bjorn and bang, they're dancing, and it all gets pretty hot on the mountain.
And then we hear it: the drone of a small plane overhead.
Mikkel stops dancing, switches off the radio. And now it's very loud, the plane must be flying very low –

and now there's no mistaking it: this is no coincidence, the plane is buzzing the barn.

Mikkel Put out the lights!

Machine-gun fire. Everyone drops to the ground. Haakon dives for a light-switch and throws it: lights out. More machine-gun fire, the plane roaring in our ears, and then it all fades.
Anna walks into a shaft of light.

Anna I thought I could trust him, I told him about the gold, I'm so terribly sorry.

Mikkel walks into light.

Mikkel They knew who we were, and where we were.

Mari walks into light.

Mari It wasn't your fault. He had us both fooled.
Mikkel They knew we had the gold.
Anna I've never stopped reproaching myself.
Mari You made it possible for me to escape, because of you I was able to find the others.
Mikkel The Quislings put Anna in a concentration camp in the north.
Mari You saved my life.
Mikkel She spent four years there.
Anna I was doing my best for Hjalmar's sake, but I got it all wrong.
Mikkel She weighed less than eighty pounds when they let her out, near the end of the war.
Anna I gained it all back, thank God, and then some.
Mari I voted for you!
Mikkel She served two terms in parliament.
Mari Twice I voted for you!
Anna Goodbye, Mari. Mikkel. All of you. Good luck.

Anna disappears.

Mari
　Not your nation's glory
　Not your own life story
　There's a job to finish . . .

Mari disappears. Mikkel remains.

Mikkel Haakon's truck would never run again, and
　neither would Headmaster's car. Just what they
　intended. We were pinned down.

*Low lights rise in the barn: the kids get up from the
floor.*

Haakon I've got everything here, absolutely everything!
　Skis, sledges. A toboggan for the gold, if you like.
　We'll just go!

Mikkel And we did that. We flew down the mountain
　in the last of the moonlight to the hills just outside
　of town. Most of our group stayed in a cow-shed we
　found there, with the gold, while the rest of us went in
　search of the convoy and the train.

*Peder and Kirsti pick up the crate of gold, and move
off with Lars, Siri, Haakon, Inga and Thea.*
　　*Mikkel, Leif, and Bjorn take a nervous step into
Lillehammer and immediately Mari runs to them and
throws herself into Mikkel's arms.*

Mari Mikkel, they took Anna away. She told me to run
　when she gave the sign and then they were shackling
　her hands and she looked at me and I ran and I don't
　know if I did the right thing, I left her there and they
　were taking her away.

Mikkel Mari, where is the convoy? Where is the train?
　We need to put the gold on the train.

Mari It's already gone.

Leif What?

Mari The Stationmaster told me. The train left already, it's gone, and the Nazis are after it. We've come all this way for nothing.

WHAT DO YOU DO? (REPRISE)

Leif
How does it go when there's no one you know
Who can help, who can hope, who can care?
How does it feel when you're ground under heel
And the one thing you're lacking is air?

Leif, Mikkel, Bjorn *and* **Mari**
How does it play at the end of the day
When you've run out of places to run?
What's your next move? Don't you wish you could
    prove
That the thing at your head's not a gun?

Mikkel
I wish that I'd never begun . . .

Leif We'll have to get the gold to the sea on our own, then.

Bjorn 'Course we will, Leif.

Mikkel On sledges? Over all those mountains? Do you have any idea of the distance you're talking about?

Bjorn This is the first time I was ever out of Oslo except for, you know, a little hiking.

Mikkel Bjorn! Trust me! I suppose we could hide the gold, or bury it, and hope the Germans never find it.

Leif That gold is my responsibility, damn it.

Mari It isn't, actually. The Stationmaster told me. Said there was a boy in Oslo stole a half-laden crate of gold, lit off with a couple of others in a beat-up old van, the Stationmaster said you've put the entire operation in jeopardy.

Bjorn Leif . . .You said they asked you, you said it was official . . .

Leif Shut up, will you?

Bjorn How could you?

Mikkel (*to us*) When we got back to the others in the hills above town, well – no one was very happy.

And suddenly, continuously, we're in the hills by the cow-shed and the others – Thea, Siri, Haakon, Lars, Peder and Kirsti – approach, Peder and Haakon carrying the crate of gold. A circle of accusation surrounds Leif.

Thea How could you?

Mari How could you?

Peder How could you?

Leif It wasn't stealing, it was helping!

Mari It was no business of yours, but you just went ahead and did it! And now they've taken Anna away, and we're all in danger and it's all because of you!

Inga Leif . . .

Leif I wanted to help!

Inga Leif . . .

Leif I ruined everything, I know! Everything I touch I ruin! I wanted to do something for my country, for you, for everybody, but everything I touch I ruin!

Inga Anyway, Leif, we need to get on with it, don't you think?

Bjorn Listen . . .

Inga Leif?

Bjorn Listen.

And we hear the drone of the small plane again.

I think we should get back to the cow-shed.

The others run off, except for Mikkel, Lars and Bjorn.

Mikkel The gunner hit Lars first.

We hear a burst of machine-gun fire. (Lars continues to stand, normally, as does Bjorn, in what follows.)

Lars I didn't feel a thing, I just wondered why there was snow in my right eye and then I realised I wasn't standing up any more.

Mikkel Bjorn was the only one who saw it. He ran back and was dragging Lars to the cow-shed when he was hit.

Bjorn (*conversational*) I'm glad I got to know you, Lars. It's good to get out of Oslo now and then.

Lars It was the last thing he said, he just stopped, he just died.

Leif comes back on.

Leif Everything I touch.

Bjorn pulls Leif to him and holds him while Leif silently mourns his friend. The others enter sombrely.

Mikkel The farmer who belonged to the farm that the cow-shed belonged to agreed to take Bjorn's body into the Lillehammer hospital, and Lars as well.

Lars The doctors pretended it wasn't machine-gun rounds they were pulling out of me, they put on the chart that it was a farm accident. I was able to join the Resistance six months later. Goodbye, Mikkel. Thanks for keeping that book of yours. We were young, we did good.

Lars walks off. Bjorn releases Leif, looks at them all for a moment and then walks off.

Ensemble
Not your nation's glory
Not your own life story
There's a job to finish . . .

Mikkel What do we do now? We can't stay here, they'll be back, they'll kill us all.

Haakon I say we carry on with the sledge and the skis.

Mikkel We can't ski the length of the Gudbrandsdal Valley!

Thea Even if we could, by the time we got to Andalsnes the ship that's taking the gold to England would be long gone.

Haakon No, we just missed one train – if we can get through the pass and down into the valley, we can catch another. I know all the trains and all the engineers and all the signalmen in the whole wide world, practically, and there's just about nobody who doesn't know me!

Mikkel What about it?

Leif I say yes.

Kirsti Yes.

Peder Yes.

Siri Mikkel, I can't do it, I'm sorry, I thought I could but I can't, if there was something I could do I'd do it, I wish I were the sort of person who could, but I have to find my family, I'm so ashamed, I'm not built for this.

Thea goes to her, holds her.

Mikkel There is something you can do, Siri – you can get word to our parents – let them know that we're alive.

Thea You can't go alone.

Mari I'll go with you. I need to tell Anna's people what happened, and Lars's.

Leif (*writing on a scrap of paper, giving it to Siri*) This is Bjorn's mother in Oslo. She's alone now.

Siri and Mari go.

Thea Let's get ready.

They all head off. Peder has one end of the crate of gold, and Haakon stoops to pick up the other.

Peder That's all right, Haakon, Kirsti's going to help me carry it.

Haakon Hurry, then – it's not safe here.

Haakon moves off. Kirsti takes the other end of the crate.

Peder Kirsti, wait . . .

Kirsti Are you serious? We've got to get under cover!

Peder I just wanted to –

Kirsti We cannot talk here, Peder, not at your pace! Come – into the cow-shed if you must talk.

Peder But that's not where I want to –

Kirsti Peder!

And they carry the crate and do whatever they do theatrically to suggest that they have moved into the cow-shed.

Whew! I must say there is something honest about the odour of a cow.

Peder What odour?

Kirsti Never mind. What is it? We need to get this strapped onto the sledge.

Peder Um . . .

Kirsti Yes? Peder? Please?

IF AND WHEN

Peder
　　If and when we get through this
　　I'd like to think we'd meet again
　　And talk about the bad times and the good –
　　I hope we would –

If and when we made a date
A month from now, or two or ten
I'd like to think we'd still be much the same –
And glad we came –
I'd be tongue-tied, you'd be calm
You'd smile at me, say how've you been?
You'd talk of time gone by, but all the while –
I'd watch your smile –
If I were to find the words
To tell you what your friendship means
I'd like to dare to hope what you might say –
That's just my way.

Kirsti
Days will come when I look back
And list the best that's ever been
I'd like to think the best would be your eyes –
They'd get the prize –

Peder *and* **Kirsti**
If and when I were to say
I cared for you, I loved you then
I'd like to hope when all of this is through –
You'd love me, too – that's if and when . . .

They kiss. Mikkel and Thea run on.

Thea There you are!
Mikkel This isn't . . . this isn't a walking party, you
know!
Thea Go, go, go!

*Peder and Kirsti lift the crate and run off. Mikkel and
Thea turn to us, Mikkel holding his diary. As they
speak, we hear the whoosh of skis and sled blades
cutting through snow.*

Mikkel (*reading from his diary*) 'We mainly travelled by
night, but it was mid-April now, and we found ourselves
in a race against the midnight sun.'

Thea (*reading over his shoulder*) 'Every day the days grew longer, and the every night there was less darkness to hide us.'

Mikkel 'We made it to Ringebu in the valley below . . .'

Thea (*as a rural Stationmaster*) The trains don't stop here no more, don't you know there's a war?

Mikkel 'We dragged the gold up and through another mountain pass, hoping for the next valley, the next station . . .'

Haakon and Inga walk on, and Peder and Kirsti. Those two are carrying the crate of gold, but that's the only gesture to re-enactment here: this is all very presentational. Inga takes the diary from Mikkel.

Inga (*reading*) 'We were wet and cold. Food was short. One night there were wolves in the darkness – very close, they stopped our hearts.'

We hear wolves.

'Leif hadn't said much of anything since Bjorn died, but now he blazed up in fury. I think he would have taken on a whole pack of them with his little Swiss knife.'

Leif skis on and stops. Mikkel takes the diary from Inga, closes it.

Mikkel But suddenly there was no need to fear the wolves.

Haakon What's that?

Mikkel The wolves were the first to hear it, and they ran.

Kirsti What is it?

Thea Oh my God. Avalanche.

Mikkel It was the sound a mountain makes when it falls.

We hear a low, massive, rumbling roar that goes on and on and on. The kids drop to their knees, they

cover their heads, they wait for the end. And then it
all stops. And it's very quiet.

(*whisper*) First you're amazed to be alive. Then you
realise you don't dare move. The next one might be
really big.

Haakon How do we get down from here?

Kirsti Hush!

Mikkel When we finally dared to talk, we debated.
There were only two possible paths down the
mountain. But which one was safe? Was either?

Leif Listen, I'll just pick one and go, what's the diff?

Inga No.

Leif If I get lucky, you follow me – if I don't, you don't.

Inga No, Leif.

Leif You want to sit here and starve?

Inga You didn't kill him, it wasn't your fault, you didn't
kill Bjorn!

Leif (*giving Mikkel his Swiss army knife*) Keep my knife
for me, will you?

Mikkel Leif . . .

SIX OF ONE

Leif
What's the diff if I choose to do that or do this?
Do I go to the lecture or give it a miss?
Do I rise with the robin or stay there in bed?
Do I go into law, do I break it instead?
When the count is counted
When the day is done
When the tally's tallied
At the setting sun
Make a tabulation
Of the lost and won . . .
Half a dozen of the other

And it's six of one!
What's the diff if I live to a hundred and four?
Hey you get what you get, you don't need any more!
What I need is a laugh and a friend and some fun
Who's to say that I lost if I say that I won!

The Others

When the count is counted
When the day is done
When the tally's tallied
At the setting sun
Make a tabulation
Of the lost and won . . .
Half a dozen of the other
And it's six of one!

Leif

What's the diff if I travel by this road or that?
All the world is a circle, the earth isn't flat!
So I'll get where I'm going, I'm not such a clown
When you're up on a mountain the roads all lead
    down . . .

Leif shoves off on his skis. They wait. And finally we hear the rumble of an avalanche and then silence.

Mikkel (*shoving his diary at Thea*) You take this, I'm sick of it.

Thea We're almost there.

Mikkel Where? *Where* are we? *Almost*?

Thea Even that amount of gold, in that small crate, would have bought the Nazis more death. What we did was good, Mikkel, it was courageous. We didn't spend our lives together. But I have spent my life with your courage in my heart.

Mikkel Fine, good, whatever you say.

Mikkel walks off. The others follow Mikkel, leaving Thea alone.

Thea Right, then. We made our way into the next valley, and there at the village station was a goods train.

Haakon crosses, running.

Haakon Uncle Haakon! Uncle Haakon! It's me, Haakon, your nephew, Old Haakon's grandson!

And he's off.

Thea Connections. Uncle Haakon packed us in with some farm equipment under some tarps. We travelled for days. We scooped snow from a hole in the side of the car for drinking water. It was very cold.

Inga enters, carrying a suitcase.

Inga We made it almost all the way to the one unoccupied port in all of Norway. We divided the gold among a few old suitcases we found in the car. Haakon's uncle let us off just short of town and we went on by foot. We hadn't eaten in three days.

A chill, hazy, blue light fills the horizon. Inga turns to look at the horizon. Peder and Kirsti enter, Peder carrying a suitcase.

Peder You've got the valley, that's where we'll live, and the mountain. We drive the cattle from the valley to the mountain in spring and the other way round in autumn.

Peder and Kirsti stop, looking at the hazy blue light of the horizon. Haakon stumbles on, struggling a little with his suitcase. He stops and stares at the horizon. Mikkel enters, carrying a suitcase. He joins Thea, short of the others.

Mikkel Look at them. Half-starved, half-frozen. And for what? They're kids, they're just kids. We should have quit long ago. We never should have started.

Thea Mikkel . . .

Mikkel If we could get one piece of luck, if just one thing could go right for us, one goddamned thing!

Peder There's been fighting here.

Kirsti The whole quay is charred.

Inga It feels deserted.

Haakon I wonder when the ship will get here.

A Young Man, played by Hjalmar, joins them, looking out to sea.

Young Man The last ship left days ago, there won't be any more.

Mikkel What?

Young Man No more traffic in this port, not unless it's those damned Germans.

Mikkel It's gone?

Young Man There was a terrible battle, I hope they got out safe. Some say there was gold on that ship. Some say it was all the gold in Norway.

Haakon We're too late.

Young Man I should think so, now that the Allies aren't coming.

Mikkel runs to the Young Man, grabs him.

Mikkel What did you say?

Young Man It's true, the Allies have called off their invasion, the British, the French, they're not coming. What's in the bags?

Mikkel I don't believe you.

Young Man It was on the radio. They're abandoning Norway to the Nazis, so maybe you should just get used to it.

Mikkel Who are you?

Young Man You are truly in a pickle, not so?

Inga I know you. I know you. I know him, Mikkel, look out!

Young Man (*producing a pistol*) Open those bags.

*The Young Man lunges for the Mikkel's suitcase,
Mikkel hits the Young Man in the belly, the Young
Man doubles over.*

Young Man Oh, shit.

*Mikkel pulls his hand back and the little Swiss army
knife and his fist are covered in blood. The Young
Man drops to his knees, still grasping at Mikkel's
suitcase.*

Oh damn.

*Mikkel's suitcase falls open, and an intense golden
glow rises and bathes the stage. The Young Man dies.*

Mikkel (*finally*) I want to go home.

Thea goes to him, holds him.

Thea (*finally*)
Here the fjord divides the mountain
Here it journeys to the sea . . .
Here's the birthplace and the fountain –
Norway's children, strong and free
This, the birthplace and the fountain –
Norway's children, ever free.

*And then the pulse of the music intensifies and the
kids sense someone approaching.*

Inga, Kirsti, Peder *and* **Haakon**
When the count is counted
When the day is done
When the tally's tallied
At the setting sun . . .

*And Leif enters, carrying skis and ski-poles, followed
by a young fisherman, played by Anders.*

Leif Hi, I made it.

Inga runs to him, holds him.

This is Nils.

Nils Ja.

Leif He found me in the snow. He's got a boat he says can cross the North Sea.

Nils Ja, I do.

Mikkel (*to us*) And he did. Some of us went with him, and the gold. Including Haakon, who got to meet the exiled King of Norway – King Haakon. Some of us stayed behind and worked with the Resistance. There were nearly five more years of war – (*indicating his diary*) – this was just the beginning.

JUST OUR LUCK (REPRISE)

Ensemble
Our sense of timing never failed us
We missed the train – we lost the truck
The ship we wanted sailed without us
And here we are – I call that luck.

But when this story's finally ended
Whatever ending that may be
This broken world will be defended
Because of you, because of me.

And when this story finds its ending
We'll be beginning – you and me
When all this broken world is mending
Thank God for luck, 'cause there we'll be!

ILLYRIA

Bryony Lavery

Characters

Maria Vargas, journalist
Magda, translator
Marie-Therese, servant
Two Drivers
Theresa, servant
Mary, servant
Lapin, bureaucrat
Conrad, secretary
Fabian, soldier
Violent, soldier
Obseno, soldier
Feste, soldier
Andreas, soldier
Madame, a mistress
Flavia, a maid
Shoemaker —Me
Man

Marie Colvin - MV

Absolute bareness. Little as possible for props.
Maximum ingenuity.

Can be played by any number, any gender:
a psyche of wonderful colour only.

Music. Maybe some suggestion of dancing.

It goes dark.

A ragbag of people somewhere,
poorly but imaginatively dressed.

A pile of cases, boxes containing what is needed.

The place names and character names
can be changed for appropriate settings
of the company's choice: Bosnia, Vietnam,
Iraq, Ireland, Chechnya. Also, the date . . .

A young, smarter woman, shoeless,
shoes in hand, begins the story . . .

ONE
IMAGINE

(nte2

Maria
Imagine
in your awesome
capacious
and completely wonderful
minds
that it's early dawn
it's dark as a tomb
but you touch a switch . . .
light

Light.

you touch another . . .
heat

Heat.

you're going on a journey

*She puts on her shoes
as . . .
    someone brings her a
small flight bag, palm-top,
camera perhaps . . .*

you touch a switch . . .
hot food . . .
you have some hot
chocolate

*Someone comes with hot
chocolate . . . the smell of
it pervades . . .*

perhaps some hot toast
with butter . . .

*Someone comes with
delicious toast, butter . . .
again the smell of it
pervades . . .*

and you're about to take
a bite . . .
when . . .

*She suddenly vomits . . .
hugely . . .
    People attend . . .*

Maria
Shit!

Then vomits again.

Shit!

Someone wipes her face.

It's time to go
passport
tickets
money

*They arrive for her. It is
most efficient. Ordered.
Meanwhile, she dresses
for travel . . . puts her
documents, camera, etc
in safe places . . .*

you're going to another
country

*Someone makes jet noise,
using a ghetto-blaster . . .
decks . . . whatever . . .*

*He picks up her
luggage . . . she walks
into special light.*

Someone (*from the
listeners*)
What country, friend, is
this ?
Maria
This is Illyria, Lady.

Jet noise magnifies . . .

TWO
ILLYRIA

Maria
Illyria.
Not your country.

*Decks play appropriate
sounds.
    A young woman greets
her with a handshake.*

Magda
Magda.
Maria
Maria.
Magda
Illyrian.
Maria
British (*or place of origin*).
Magda
Interpreter.

Maria
Perfect!

They laugh.

Magda
One child. Girl.
Husband.
Welcome.
Maria
Thank you.
Magda
We go this way.

*Magda collects Maria's
bags.*

Maria
Imagine.

Magda
Illyria.
Once famous beautiful
green green woods.
Maria
Yes.
Magda
Once music (*She sings.*)
Once beautiful dancing
(*She dances.*)

*They both smile . . . laugh
. . . beautiful music plays.*

now
famous for War
you come for our War . . . ?
Maria
Yes.
Magda
Sorry.

They both shrug.
  *It's a pity. They are
driven. People create the
landscape they pass
through . . . they have
only themselves and junk
to do this . . .*

Unit 4

Maria
You're being driven into a
city
that was once home to
say, four hundred
thousand people

now home to War
Imagine
Magda
devastation . . .

She points it out. Helpful.

Maria
beyond imagining . . .
shells and bombs have
collapsed
the apartment blocks into
grey concrete
Magda
grey concrete sandwiches
Maria
you're being taken . . .
our official car . . .
bucks and tips
between the heaps of
rubble
the deep craters . . .
Magda
bombs
Maria
for mile upon mile there is
no building left intact . . .
Magda
different, eh?
from your country?
Maria
Yes.
How old's your girl?
Magda
Baby.

Shows Maria photograph.

Both
Aaah!
Lovely!
Maria
You leave the remains of
the city
then through the green
green woods
we drive
Magda
long way
beautiful, ah?
Maria
you watch her wind
down the window
Magda
air!
country!
woods!
Maria
and a crack
like a branch breaking
and

*Magda slumps onto
Maria's lap.*

Maria
it's
taken her life
most of her head
is gone . . .

*Maria cradles Magda's
body as . . .*

we drive on.

Picture
arriving at your
destination
Drivers
Out! Out!

*The drivers separate
Maria from Magda . . .*

Maria
No! Please! Wait! No!

*They dump her, her bags,
out of the car. They
vanish.*

Maria
Where am I?

THREE
RUMOUR HAS A COAT OF TONGUES

*Off, we hear three female
voices raised in fierce
debate.*

Marie-Therese
  It's true!
Theresa
  It's not true!
Marie-Therese
  It is!
Theresa
  It can't be!
Maria
  It is not a language you
  speak . . .

*They enter. Marie-Therese,
Theresa and Mary.
Considerable women . . .
they will be doing all the
work here . . . they have
scrubbing brushes, water,
soap . . . vestiges of
modern cleaning
equipment.*

Mary
  Ya dung beetle with your
  little piles
  of snot and shit you made
  it up . . .

Marie-Therese
  I made nothing up!
  It is the shining truth!

*They start unpacking
equipment, aprons on,
rubber gloves, sleeves
up as . . .*

Theresa
  It is not the shining truth!
Marie-Therese
  I swear by all the saints
  in heaven
  all the angels on their
  clouds
  and on the graves of my
  beloved father
  and mother . . .
Theresa
  all the saints in heaven
  and all the
  angels on their clouds
  and your
  beloved mother and
  father in their
  graves are as big liars as
  you are then . . .
  rolling little piles of dirt
  together
  and sticking them

together with
your snot and shit . . .
dung beetle!

They look at Maria.

Maria
Journalist (*Mime.*)
Foreign (*Mime.*)

She's not worth any effort.
Big display of disdain.
  She's pond-life.
  Back to reality . . .
  Marie-Therese is the
best story-teller in the
world, who drives Theresa
crazy, Mary, who listens
. . . they begin to build
the house . . . a shell only,
half a wall, a staircase
leading nowhere . . .
cupboards as –
  Marie-Therese gets into
her narrative stride.

Maria
They ignore me.
Marie-Therese
Anyway
they took her at dead of
night
from her own bed!
they pushed her old
mother
viciously in her old breast!

Mary
Ay yi yi . . .
Marie-Therese
and her father they
clubbed
like this! and this!
with the hard butts of
their rifles!
Theresa
Oh . . .

Theresa always tries
to resist her stories, is
always drawn in against
her will . . .

Marie-Therese
In the back of the truck
on the way to prison
they took turns
the soldiers
in fondling her!
Mary
God in Heaven . . . Holy
Mother!
Marie-Therese
Every night . . . in the
prison . . . she's
lying bound and gagged
and with a
hood covering her face . . .
one guard
came and . . .

She demonstrates what
he did.

Mary
The same one?
Marie-Therese
The same one.
Theresa
How could she tell it was
the same one?
Marie-Therese
By his smell!
Every day . . .
they would take her
down to the basement
lie her on a bloodstained
bed . . .
electrocute her with
probes . . .
here . . .
(*gums*)
here
(*nipples*)
and here . . .
(*vagina*)
Other Two
Ayeeh!
Marie-Therese
One day
they take her down to the
basement
lie her on a bloodstained
bed
take off her hood
on the next bed
is her fiancé!
Mary
God in heaven Holy
Mother!

*The shell of the house
is now there . . . now
the three women clean,
polish, scrub and spray
as . . .*

Marie-Therese
the torturer comes in
with a
little tabby kitten . . .
Other Two
Aaaah!
Marie-Therese
and a bag of sacking tied
at the top
he puts the kitten on her
breast
it purrs
he opens the bag
takes out a poisonous
snake!
Other Two
Ay!
Marie-Therese
He puts the kitten in an
oil can
this big with an open end
this open end he puts
here
(*vagina*)
at the other end of the oil
can
is a smaller hole
he puts the snake in the
hole
closes the hole

then he starts to heat up
the oil can
both animals are terrified
trapped
pursued by the heat
the snake moves towards
the kitten . . .
the kitten . . . where can
the kitten go?
it is wild with fear
it scratches it claws
the kitten crawls into
her . . . (*vagina*)
the snake follows
she screams as she feels
inside her . . .

Theresa
Oh!

Mary
Holy Mother!

Marie-Therese
She faints dead away.

Her fiancé, forced to
watch
all this time
screams and screams and
screams
he is clubbed unconscious

carried away
she never sees him again!

Mary
God in Heaven!

Theresa
Holy Mother!
The poor poor man!

Mary
It's true?

Marie-Therese
As true as I stand here.
It happened in Castilia
where my mother's aunt
lives.
It's all over town.
Everyone keeps quiet.
There!

*The space is ready. It really
is clean, sparkling . . .*

Maria
It's a building
still standing
an old house
in a clearing
in the green green woods
once pleasing of shape
once beautiful of design
it is guarded by soldiers.

FOUR
A SAFE HOUSE

Three young men,
Violent, Obseno, Fabian,
enter as soldiers.

Maria
What house is this?

They freeze.

Marie-Therese
Journalist.
Foreign.

Three men do another
pantomime of disdain.

Obseno
This is a Safe House,
Lady.
Maria
A what?

Maria, Marie-Therese,
Theresa, Mary stand still,
submissive, as soldiers
check place out . . .
Decks do appropriate
sound . . . Light panel
similar.

Violent (*public*)
It's a house just a house
a regular normal house

it's regular normal but
but but but

They fan out, guarding,
but . . .

Fabian (*private*)
. . . but the kitchen

He's there, the kitchen of
his darkest nightmare . . .

stain here on the floor
no amount of scrubbing
can remove
it's the shape of a body
but the head is some way
off
the ice box holds many
packs
of unidentifiable joints of
meat
labelled simply 'Hostage 99'
labelled clearly 'Hostage 99'

They try to keep it
together. Brave but but
but . . .

Violent (*public*)
it's a ruin just a ruin
a regular normal ruin
check it out it's regular

normal
a ruin but but but . . .
Obseno (*private*)
but the bathroom

*He's there . . . worst
nightmare . . .*

a mark in every basin
as if the tap flows blood
and the plumbing clinks
and clanks
reminiscent of a code
when you flush the
handle sticks
then there's such a stench
it's foul and sweet like
pork gone off
and no cleanser can
remove it
no cleanser can remove it.

Keep it together . . .

Violent (*public*)
it's bricks it's stone it's
shit
regular normal shit
check it out it's normal
shit
but but but . . .
Fabian
. . . the staircase

He's there. Hell.

Obseno (*private*)
when you climb in the
direction 'up'

you feel you're going down
and despite the sun
through windows
you think it's cold and
dark
and halfway up a hand of
wind
clutches at your sleeve
you turn, there's no one
there
you turn, there's no one
there
Fabian (*public*)
it's air it's open air
regular normal air
check it out there's open
air
but but but . . .
Violent
. . . the bedrooms
when you open any
wardrobe
all the clothes feel warm
among the pairs of shoes
are pairs of feet
coat hangers clink like
skeletons on a gibbet
and when we fall asleep
we sleep on dead men's
hands
we sleep in dead men's
hands
we are tossed there in our
sleep
so we never fall asleep
we never fall asleep . . .

*He really loses it. Fabian
and Obseno get him
against a wall. Shove
him, tough him up . . .*

Obseno
 Check it out . . . awake!
 Check it out . . . alert!
Fabian
 so we never fall asleep
 so we never fall asleep!
Violent (*toughed up*)
 we never fall asleep . . .

*The house is clear of
anything but dread. They
take up guard positions.*

Maria
 in this house
 no switch for
 light
 no switch for
 warmth
 but someone keeps this
 house
 running . . .

FIVE
MIDDLE MANAGEMENT ARRIVES

*The sound of a helicopter
hanging over the house . . .*

Mary
 Madame!
Marie-Therese
 Already?
Theresa
 Quick!

*They repack their cleaning
equipment tout suite . . .*

Marie-Therese
 I'm worn out.

*She might have done no
more than put on her*

*gloves while exhausting
herself with story-telling.*

Theresa
 I'm sure!
Mary
 Quick . . . quick!
Theresa
 We're ants.
 Build a city of snotballs
 wash the snotballs
 scrub the snotballs
 lay eggs
 reproduce
 and all for what?
 Some Fat Queen Ant!

*They are standing ready
when Lapin, middle
management in a suit,
arrives.*

Marie-Therese
It's Lapin!
Theresa
Speaking of snotballs . . .
Mary
Shhhh!

*Lapin terrifies them. They
hate her.*

Lapin
Madame is on her way.
She will be very tired.
All this dodging from one
hole to the next.
So fatiguing!
This is her room?

*They nod. They talk to
Lapin as little as possible.*

Everything shipshape?

I hope so . . .

*She walks around, checks
every detail. It's a job and
it's a game . . .*

fine
good
perfect

They relax a bit . . .

polished

neat

delightful . . .

They relax more . . .

apart from the smell.

Gotcha . . .

there is a rank odour of
peasant sweat
that I do not think
Madame will care for at
all . . .

*She waits while the three
find some battered cans
of fresh-air spray, spray it
around . . . the smell
pervades.*

fine
good
but let's stop it at the
source.
Mmm?????

*Marie-Therese takes a
used deodorant out . . .
they take turns.*

Good.
One more time for you I
think . . .

Mary . . .

Mmmm
Better

Go and bring Madame to her
new room while you're still fresh!

They go, muttering . . .

Marie-Therese
One day
I'll have polished the floor
so shiny so slippery
when Lapin steps on it
she'll slide
like a billiard ball
cannon off that wall
onto the banister
off the banister onto the wall
wall banister
banister wall
foot of the stairs
where she'll lie
every bone snapped like a pretzel
screaming for help
I'll continue polishing . . .

Theresa can top this . . .

Theresa
One day
I'll be bleaching the sheets
in the big boiler
Lapin'll bend over to
inspect the whiteness of
the sheets
she'll tip right over

helped by the sharp whack
I'll give to her shins
with the stick I use for
tamping down the sheets
I'll tamp her down till
she's as clean and white
as my sheets
then I'll hang them and her
out on the line
where they will flap
and she will moan
and I'll pray for a good
drying wind . . .

Can Mary top this . . . ?

Mary
One day
One day
I'll be . . .

Lapin behind her . . .

Lapin
Be what?
Anything but servers?
Anything but scrubbers?
Anything but complainers
snivellers
moaners
Mmm?
Mmmm?
Mmmmmm?
Anything but whingeing
whining
Women????
Get!!!!

209

They get . . .
    Lapin puts on white
gloves as . . .

they had a party
in the kitchen courtyard
they made pies
a lot of wine
asked all the soldiers
all the guards
even the double agent
everybody knows is a
double agent
not me
I put on my blue
just in case
sat in my room
no invitation
no come down have a
good time,
Lapin
well, I don't want
affection
respect!
I'm a woman with a
position
not a lot can say that
everyone got drunk
did things in the wine
cellar
not me

I dozed off
creased my blue.
No one'll get anything on
me.

She sees Maria . . .

Who are you?
Maria
Journalist. (*Mime.*)
Foreign. (*Mime.*)
I've come to meet
Madame. (*Mime.*)
Lapin
Madame will pee her
exquisite silk
designer underwear with
pleasure.

Accompanying mime
conveys only Madame's
polite pleasure. Soldiers
smirk.

Maria
Good.
Thank you.
Can I get an interpreter?
The last one . . . Magda . . .
she was . . . she died . . .

Her words are lost in
noise.

SIX
MADAME'S JOURNEY

Decks create . . .

Maria
A dusty armoured
limousine
motorcycle outriders
an air of frenzy
scorches into the
courtyard
gravel sprays like sniper
fire . . .

*Everyone to attention . . .
Two more soldiers,
Andreas and Feste . . .
twanging like piano wires
with tension . . .*

Andreas
Fuck!
Feste
Fuck!
Andreas
Check! Fuck!
Feste
Yes! Yes! Fuck!
Andreas
Okay.
Cool.
Get the Bitch in!
Get the Bitch In!

Feste
Keep your hair
. . . on your head!

Fuck!

*Madame arrives, carried
carefully by the three
women in their white
gloves. Supervised by . . .
Madame is beautiful,
very young, and
cocooned in layers of
expensive cloths,
pashminas, silken, rather
like a huge bug.
Secretary Conrad has
accompanied her.*

Conrad
We had to have the
bullet-proof
shields up all the way!
Flavia
Careful!
Lapin
Carcful . . . Careful!!!!
Feste
Yes, miss. Careful!
Conrad
Lie down on the floor

going
through towns!
Flavia
Gently!
Lapin
Gently . . . Gently!!!!
Andreas
Gentle . . . Gentle!
Conrad
They shot at the tyres . . .
we've
been driving on flat tyres
for
the last twenty
kilometres!
Lapin
Take off her . . . take it
off!!!!

*The three women gently
unwind the bug from its
cocoon, revealing an
exquisite, beautifully
dressed, beautifully
painted toy of a woman.*

All
Ooooooh!
Marie-Therese
Oh!
Theresa
Beauty!
Mary
Tired!
Conrad
Hot!

Flavia
See to her!
Lapin
See to her . . . See to
Her!!!!

*They administer to her
as . . .*

Flavia
our moth!
are her wings crushed?
are her colours dulled?
can she still land upon
a leaf?
sip nectar from
a flower?
Our moth!
Maria
Imagine.
You are in the wrong
place.
You have been brought to
the wrong place.
This is not who you've
come to see.
You've been brought,
by some terrible error
to
The most powerful
woman
in Illyria.

*Madame stands
impassively.*
    They comb her hair.
    Arrange her.

Stand back.
Look at her.
Wait.
Finally, in a small,
babyish, carrying voice . . .

Madame
Mirror.
Flavia
Mirror.

They bring her a mirror.
She looks in it.
No expression.

Madame
My lips

Marie-Therese paints her
lips.

Mirror.
Flavia
Mirror.

They bring the mirror
again, she looks in it.

Madame
Yes.

Madame is ready . . .

Everybody stared at the
car!
all along the road
which The Generalissimo
had
cleared for me!
so we could go fast!

the people
just stood and stared at
the car
just to catch a glimpse of
me!
I sat up very straight
so they could see me
so my back is very
tired . . .
All
Ooooh . . .

They rush to sort this
out.

Madame
they like to see me
I'm much prettier than
The Wife!
Maria
You have papers to meet
The Wife!
Madame
When she travels he
doesn't
even order the car
polished
that's how little he cares
for her!!!!

At one turning the car
slowed down
and there was a young
man
with dark eyes looking in
as near as I am to you,
Lapin . . .

213

Lapin bows.

Lapin
Madame.
Madame
and he met my eyes
and he leaned forward as
if he
was going to kiss the
bullet-proof
window
and then he spat!

One of the outriders
caught him
I'm going to have him
hurt
for that!
Marie-Therese
Spat?
Theresa
At her?
Mary
Why?
Conrad
Tide's turning?
Lapin
What's going on????

*When Madame looks
again, all is silence and
respect.*

Madame
I wish The Generalissimo
was here.
Marie-Therese
Oh . . .

Theresa
There, there . . .
Mary
So in love!
Madame
I want to know when he's
coming.
Flavia
Madame wants to know
when he's coming.

*Lapin telephones.
Andreas and Feste
have a cigarette.*

19

Andreas
Fuck! Fucking fuck!
Feste
Look at the hands!
Fucking hands!
Andreas
Nearly wet-trouser job!
Feste
Nearly fucking brown-
trouser job!
Andreas
Jesus Christ!

*Both burst out laughing.
Stop as Maria is near
them.*

Feste (*quietly*)
Good bum.
Andreas (*same*)
Great tits.

Has to be quite silent and hidden as –

Maria
You wish you were a man.

Marie-Therese
If the crowd's against her . . .

Theresa
spitting

Mary
if she's not popular . . .

Violent
spitting?

Obseno
shooting out tyres?

Andreas
activity?

Madame
I must sit down.

Flavia
Madame must sit down.

Mary fetches a chair for her. It arrives in place as Madame lowers herself.

Conrad
No salutes

Lapin
no salutes

Feste
no salutes . . . no salutes!

Madame
I'm hot.

Theresa fans her . . .

Conrad
No cheers

Lapin
no cheers

Fabian
no cheers . . . no cheers!

Madame
I want to rest until My Beloved arrives.

Flavia
Madame wants to rest until her Beloved arrives.

The three women create a sumptuous bed for her.

All
Our moth!
are her wings crushed?
are her colours dulled?
has someone lit a candle?
has she flown too near the flame?
Our moth?

Madame
I want to be asleep now!

Flavia
Madame wishes to be asleep now!

Marie-Therese
Shhh . . .

Theresa
hush now . . .

Mary
there there . . .

Lapin brings a pill box.

215

Marie-Therese
  Aaagh!
Theresa
  poison?
Mary
  so soon?
Conrad
  are you sure?
Lapin (*contemptuous*)
  sleeping pill!
  just one.

  Madame takes a pill.

Madame
  It's not working
  they never work
  these pills you give me
  I'm always awake!

She is asleep.
    They put her to bed.
Arrange her.

All
  Our moth!
  are her wings crushed?
  are her colours dulled?
  is the summer over?
  is there frost on every
  leaf?
  Our moth!
Lapin
  Leave.

  Three women leave . . .

  (*to Flavia*) Leave. Leave!

  Leaves.

SEVEN
BEST LOVE

Conrad
  I missed you.
Lapin
  No, you didn't. The
  telephone's dead.
  The telex isn't working.

  Crosses to window . . .

Lapin
  Guards still guarding . . .
  they're our guards . . .
  that's Fabian . . . who at

the servants' party
was sick in the . . . or so
I heard . . .
Conrad
  I love you.
Lapin
  No, you don't.

  He starts to touch her.

Conrad
  Listen . . . the only thing
  there is to life

is waking up fucking
working eating
going to bed fucking and
sleeping . . .
let's do one of those now
then.
I know! . . . fucking!

Lapin
The only thing to do
therefore is to
wake up in the best place
get the
best fucking work in the
best place
eat the best food go to
bed in the
best bed lie down in the
best place . . .

Conrad
You're right.
Let's practise.

Lapin
No babies.

Conrad
Deal.

Lapin
Protection?
show me.

He shows her a condom.

Conrad
So romantic . . . what
happened to
green green woods
music
dancing . . .?

Lapin
Be quiet.

*She leads him to a
secluded spot.
    Violent and Obseno
take up positions where
they can watch.*

Violent (*whispered*)
Live Sex Show.

Obseno (*same*)
Entertainment for the
Boys!

*Everyone aware of the
sex going on . . .
    Meanwhile, a mime
exchange?*

Fabian
Quick man. Working
woman.
No time to . . .

*Mime for 'hang about',
'do foreplay'.*

Maria
I have been brought to
the wrong place.
I was to talk to The
Generalissimo's Wife.
Not . . .
Do you understand?

Fabian
British?

Maria
Journalist.

217

Fabian
Sweetheart?
Maria
Husband. Sort of.

*Sex scene and onlookers
hot up. Mirth as . . .*

Violent
Go on!
Give it to her!
Obseno
Hard!
Do It!
Fabian
Wartime. Fast time.

Maria vomits . . .

Fabian
Bad food?
Maria
Pregnant.
Baby.

Lapin returns.

Lapin (*to Fabian*)
Clean that up
now.
Now!
Maria
Thank you.
Lapin (*to Maria*)
I want to wake
up in her place have her
work
and her food and go to
bed in

her bed and fuck how she
fucks
and sleep where she
sleeps

*Conrad returns to
applause from soldiers . . .*

get one high up as possible
keep the others off.
Maria
I understand.
Lapin
American?
Journalist?
I doubt it.
Maria
Anyone speak English . . .?
Translate . . .?
Conrad
I do.
Many talents.

*Telephone rings . . . telex
. . . communications
operative . . .*

Lapin (*to telephone*)
Yes?
Yes.
Yes.
No.
Yes.
Yes.

Phone down.

The Generalissimo is on
his way!

Klaxons, alarms . . .
soldiers to attention . . .
three women rush in . . .

Marie-Therese
It's true!
Theresa
It's not true!
Marie-Therese
It is!
Theresa
It's not!
Lapin
The Generalissimo is on
his way!
Women
Shit!

Huge activity from
everybody.

Feste
Never stops! Fuck!
Andreas
He's there!
He's here!
Move!
Violent
What's that?
Check that!
Check *that*!
Feste
Move it!
Move it!
Obseno
Palaver!
Fucking palaver!

Andreas
Fucking *fast*!
Fabian
Doing it!
Doing it!
Feste
Move it!
Move it!!!
Obseno
Yes!
Yes!
Yes!!!!

As . . .
    Martial, victorious
music played, bunting . . .
flags hung . . . security
checked . . . uniforms . . .
as . . .
    Large portrait of The
Generalissimo is hung.

Lapin
Wake her up,
Get her ready.
Flavia
Wake her up
Get her ready.
Lapin
Here we go
puppet show
the puppet with the hole
for the puppet with a
stick.

She watches impassively
as the women wake up

219

Madame, strip her, wash her, perfume her, dress her in conspicuously unwearable beautiful sexual garb.

Maria
Can I talk to her?
Conrad
Wait.
Enjoy our favourite occupation.
Waiting.

They watch the women working.

Women's work.

Not you. Journalist.

Writing. Thinking. Clever.

These. Carthorses.
Marie-Therese
Anyway
this man would lie in wait
for women in their own houses!
Mary
Oooh!
Marie-Therese
In that town they used to leave their
doors open but when this started happening . . .

The story wafts into Madame's ears as . . .

Mary
Aye!
Marie-Therese
even so, he'd find a way in . . . under a
shutter . . . thin knife . . . in the latch . . . and
he'd be waiting . . . hiding!
Theresa
Oh . . . now . . .
Marie-Therese
and then he'd come . . . knife in hand
and hold it to their throat!
Theresa
God in Heaven!
Mary
Holy Mother!
Marie-Therese
He'd turn them over . . . off with their . . .
and stick it in . . . the back!
Mary
In the back?
Marie-Therese
In the back
then he'd turn them over and
make them suck his . . .

Other Two
Aye!
Marie-Therese
then he'd leave
taking all the money from
their purse
one of them got up after
it all
went out on the street
it was pitch-black
she saw someone coming
towards
her
she called for help
he came close to her
it was him!
Theresa
Oh!
Mary
No!
Marie-Therese
and he came in and did it
again!
Both
Again?
Marie-Therese
Again!
Theresa
God in Heaven!
Mary
Holy Mother!
It's true as I stand here.
It happened in Forniccia
where my
sister's best friend lives.
It's all over town.

They haven't caught him
yet.
There!

Madame is dressed.

Madame
Mirror.
Flavia
Mirror.
Madame
Yes.
I look beautiful.
Rest
Yes, Madame.
Madame
I look perfect.
Rest
Yes, Madame.
Madame
The Leader
my Beloved
will be hungry when he
arrives
from protecting the
country.
Maria
She wears
Versace Ferrigamo
Tiffany Manolo Blahnik.
Conrad
She wears
Money Money
Money Money . . .

*The three bring a table,
arrange it with fruit, wine,*

flowers, etc. . . . a feast
for the Generalissimo.
Madame surveys it.

Madame
Yes.
Go.
Flavia
Go.

The women go.

Madame
Any message for me?
Lapin
He is on his way.
Madame
Anything else?
Lapin
He cannot wait to reach
your side
and hold your exquisite
body
in his strong arms.
Madame
He loves me so much.
Lapin
Madame.

Madame sits quite still,
while Lapin reviews the
meal . . . eats a grape . . .
smells a flower . . . tries
the rustle of a cigar etc,
bouquet of the wine . . .

Madame
Not poisoned?

Lapin
No, Madame.
Madame
Haaah!
Lapin
Bored, Madame?
Madame
No.
I'm far too much in love.
Lapin
Madame.
Madame
Lapin . . . ?
Lapin
Madame?
Madame
I keep thinking about . . .
holes.
Maria
You keep thinking
about . . .
holes . . .
Lapin
Holes?
Madame
Holes.

Pause.

Lapin
Would you like me to
read the
Generalisssimo's love
letters to you?

Madame shakes her head.

Would you like to write
a love letter to The
Generalissimo?

Shakes head.

a manicure?

a pedicure?

a massage?

Madame shakes her head.

Lapin
A foreign journalist bitch
is
here to make up lies
about you . . .

Both look at Maria.
Polite mimes all round.

Madame
I think I'd like to see my
shoes.

Lapin
but The Generalissimo
will be
arriving shortly . . .

Madame (*screaming*)
I'm Madame The
Generalissimo's
beautiful mistress and
you do
what I want!

Lapin goes to the
telephone.

Lapin
Madame would like to
see her shoes.

Flavia
Madame would like to
see her shoes.

Lapin
Madame would like to
see her shoes.

EIGHT
SHOES

They are brought on . . .
soldiers bring large cases.
Three Women take out
pair after pair of beautiful,
useless shoes and lay them
out in rows of pairs as –

Marie-Therese
It's true

Theresa
It's not true!

Marie-Therese
It is!

Mary
It can't be!

Madame listens . . .

Marie-Therese
Anyway
he came home
and he had been drinking
all day long!
Theresa
Oh!
Marie-Therese
and his mind was gone
with the wine
but his body was as
powerful as a
bull's!
she was sitting in the
chair
and the children were all
asleep in their beds!
Mary
Ah!
Marie-Therese
He slapped her this way
across her face
and that way across the
face!
Theresa
God in Heaven!
Mary
Holy Mother!
Marie-Therese
and then he took his cigar
from his mouth and
burned her

here
here
and here
Theresa
brute
Mary
the pig
Marie-Therese
and then he took the
bread knife
off the table
and he slit her nostrils
and the blood ran down
her cheeks
like tears
and he laughed!
Theresa
He laughed?
Marie-Therese
He laughed!
and the sound of his mad
laughter
awoke the children
and he turned with the
breadknife
in his bloody hand and
started towards the stairs!
Theresa
God in Heaven!
Mary
Holy Mother!
Marie-Therese
She clung to his trousers
desperately trying to stop
him
but he went on and on

up and up
to the bed where the
children lay
Theresa
and then . . .
Mary
there they were . . .
Marie-Therese
there they were
crying piteous tears
and he gutted them
from the oldest
to the littlest baby
one after the other
and then he let the knife
fall
and that poor mother
turned
that knife upon her own
miserable broken heart!
Theresa
God in heaven!
Mary
Holy Mother!
It's true?
Marie-Therese
As true as I stand here
It happened in Manzinnia
where my second cousin's
old
schoolteacher lives.
He was a member of the
government.
Everybody keeps quiet.
There!

*There is a row of shoes as
far as the eye can see . . .
curving . . . snaking
across the stage . . .*

Madame
Let her come and see my
shoes.
Let her see how much the
Generalissimo loves me!
Flavia
Let her come and see
Madame's shoes.
Conrad
Madame invites you to
see
her beautiful shoes . . .
Maria
Madame.
Maria Vargas . . . I'm a . . .
Madame
These are from New York.
Conrad (*translating*)
These are from New
York.
Madame
These are from Italy.
Conrad
These are from Italy.
Madame
They are made of wild
deer hide.
Conrad
They are made of wild
deer hide.

225

Maria
I'd like to ask Madame
about her
feelings about the state of
constant
war in her country . . .

Conrad
Foreign journalist
wonders how may
pairs of shoes you have . . .

Madame
I don't know.
Let me think.
Let me look.

Conrad
Madame does not talk
about politics.
She prefers shoes.

Maria
They are very beautiful.
But does she not want a
state of peace . . .
where everyone has shoes
. . . a safe place for her
shoes?
what does she think of
conditions
where everybody is living
in fe –

Conrad
Foreign journalist
wonders
how you keep all
these shoes in such good
condition . . .

Madame
I only wear them.
I do not do . . . polishing!
the foreign journalist is
not
very interesting!
I want to wear these.

Flavia
Madame wants to wear
these.

*The three women run
forward with chair, shoe-
horn, willing hands . . .*

Conrad
Madame is tired with your
questions.

Maria
Perhaps we could talk
later.

Conrad
Perhaps.

Maria
Perhaps with another
translator.
Translating is so fatiguing.

Conrad
Perhaps.
What a shame you do not
have
our language.

*Maria stares at him.
Then . . .*

Maria
Everybody pretends to

226

know
what's going on.
Nobody knows what's
going on.
There's everything to do.
There's nothing to do.
Nothing's dangerous.
Everything's dangerous.
Your only story so far
is that death next to you
in the car . . .

Everyone's just
waiting
for a pull
from a
taut string
a long long way off . . .

Telephone rings . . .
communications . . .
everyone jerks on that
long taut string . . .

NINE
THE GENERALISSIMO HAS BEEN DELAYED

Lapin (*telephone*)
Yes?
Yes.
No.
Yes. (*out*)

The Generalissimo has
been delayed.

Nothing.

Why?
Delayed.
Why?
A change of plan.
Why?
Maria
The atmosphere changes
in a heartbeat

Lapin and Conrad check
the window . . . everybody
running around, headless
chickens.

Lapin
the guards are still there!
the guards are still there!
Conrad
Can you see their faces?
Can you see their
uniforms?
Lapin
I can't see!
I don't recognise them!
They're not in uniform!
Conrad
Not a delay!

227

Lapin
  A reverse!
  A reverse!
Feste
  Fuck!
  Knew it!
  All the way here!
Andreas
  Fucking peasant villages
  faces giving it 'Wait, just
  wait!'
  Fuck!

*They start to take down
the bunting, flags . . . the
large portrait of The
Generalissimo is ripped
to shreds as . . .*

Marie-Therese
  It happened
  last time
  just like this
  the people cut at the
  wires
  men with gardening
  shears
  and women with kitchen
  knives
  the wires curled back
  they rushed through and
  up
  the wide sweeping steps
  of the house itself
  the fat cats were sitting
  inside . . .

Andreas
  Fuck.
  Fuck!
Feste
  Lost It!
  Fucking Lost It!!!!

*They start taking off
badges, tags . . .
distinguishing signs as . . .*

Marie-Therese
  their powerful foreign
  friends
  were powerless to do
  anything.
Conrad (*to Maria*)
  You must be very
  careful.
  You must be very quiet.
  You must record nothing.
Marie-Therese
  the fat cats
  wet from their own wee
  soiled from their own shit
  watch the visitors
  the garden shears and the
  kitchen knives
  raise
  plunge
  again and again
  the fat-cat blood ran
  down down the staircase
  and over the wide
  sweeping stairs
  and turned the gardens
  red

228

Decks, movement, imagin-
ation creates this . . .

and
suddenly
everything belonged
to everyone again . . .

Suddenly . . . soldiers,
women . . . alert . . .
observe the shoes . . .
the house . . .

Theresa
God in Heaven!
Mary
Holy Mother!
It's true?
Marie-Therese
As true as I stand here.
Things as they are
people as they are
what else could happen?

I must go through all the
bedrooms
get all the trinkets gold
silver gems
coins notes

I need a dress with
concealed pockets!
Theresa
I must go through the
kitchen cupboards
get all the knives forks
spoons the
spirits all the good wine

I need a big case with
a false bottom!
Mary
I must get up on the
roof . . .
strip all the lead guttering
slates
gargoyles

I need a cart!

They pillage.
Violent, Fabian,
Obseno start taking
shoes.

Lapin
The papers!
The files!
Records data! case
histories!
Get them!

Conrad and Lapin start
collecting papers.

Maria
You collect your
possessions
camera passport money

She does but . . .

your visa your visa
your papers which
protect you!

Hands shaking, she tries
to find them . . .

229

Madame
Car!
Guards!
Immediately!

Flavia
No, Madame. No. (*She backs away, exits.*)

Everyone suddenly focuses on Madame. Feste, Andreas approach her . . .

Feste
Everything
belongs to everyone!

Andreas
Fuck!
Yes!
Fuck!

They seize her.

Maria
You have come from a country
where this doesn't happen
you switch on the light
light
you switch on the
warmth
warmth
it is war.

Violent, Obseno, Fabian come towards her.

Maria
Do you show courage
understanding
female solidarity?
humanity?

Feste and Andreas take Madame off somewhere to rape her . . .
    Andreas, Violent, Obseno drift towards Maria . . .

Maria
to men . . . very definite,
very fierce . . .

Maria
Journalist!
British!
Protected!
Official!

Pregnant!

Mother!!!!

Violent, Obseno, Fabian back off . . . go to watch Feste and Andreas . . .

Maria
You don't know which works.
You're just thankful it does.
Something somehow saves your sweating
thank God! privileged skin!

And what happens
happens to someone else.

Madame (*off*)
Noooo!!!!!

*As . . . men observe
while . . .*

Violent
came on a terrorist once
four of us
cornered him in a lift
wasn't working
soon as we put a gun to
his head
here
belly
here

Madame (*off*)
Please!!!!

Violent
pees himself
then
smell of shit
pathetic!
Shot him, the dog!

Obseno
Two of us
night
under a hedge
fucking platoon walks
right into us!

Madame (*off*)
Oooooh!

Obseno
We start giving it pow
pow pow
before they've time to
realise . . .

I mean, we total half
rest fucking off like
rabbits!
Just luck
but
Shite!

Fabian
Best Times, though!
Fucking Adventure!

Madame, off, screams.

Danger's what you pay,
right?

Violent
Comradeship, though!

Obseno
The Shags!

Fabian
The Highs!

Violent
Don't get that fucking
peace time!
Gonna remember this our
whole fucking lives!

*They all cheer something
off . . . rush to join . . .*

Conrad (*to Maria*)
Cigarette?
Ah . . . *pregnant!*

He lights a cigarette as . . .

They're peasants

Conrad
no education hardly . . .
no civilisation . . .

me education
me civilisation

and young

practically . . . *boys!*

and

times like these

shit happens

right?

He saunters off.
    Men run out, high as
kites . . . one or two with
items of Madame's . . .
    They dance off.
    Maria stands, picks up
a shoe . . .

Maria
one shoe
looks like
a glass slipper.

She looks at it as Madame
enters . . . horribly
shocked, diminished . . .

Madame
Oh!

Everyone has gone!

It's not allowed!

My clothes are dirty!

Someone's disarranged
them!

When The Generalissimo
comes . . .
he will . . .

someone should put the
lights on
its very dark in here
Maria
and she looks
towards the darkest
corner of
that terrible house

She looks towards the
darkest corner of the
house . . .

and sees
does she see?
is it real?

is it the light through the
trees . . .?

an old man (*woman*)
in a leather apron
he's (*she's*) stitching

There sits an old man
in a leather apron . . .
making something. He
talks to Madame . . .

Shoemaker
what a lot of shoes
well made
expensive
lovely leather

232

Dreamlike

lovely stitchwork
the craftsmanship! *get stick*

are they all yours?
Madame
Yes.

*Maria holds out the
glass slipper . . . Madame
takes it.*

Shoemaker
Think of the work that's
gone
into all that! *everything*

Eh?

*Madame finds the other
glass slipper.*

Get much wear out of
them? *notice*

Go far in them?

You know
a shoe's just something
to cover the human foot
for warmth
for comfort
no big deal
made from leather
which comes from
animal
which comes from
earth
which itself comes from a
great bang
at the beginning of time

so you see
we shoemakers know a
thing or two about
elementary construction!

More work making a shoe
than a baby!
Lot less fun!
call me God! *madam*

can I take a look at your
shoes?

*He/she takes her glass
slippers.*

Make 'em?
Buy 'em?
Earn 'em?

Don't suit you.
Not comfy.
Getting your bones all
out of whack!

*He gets hold of her, quite
gently.*

What I'd say to you, little
shoe
with my needle in your
heart
my nails in your foot
my hammer tapping you
on
your decorative skull is . . .
I think you need to
change your shoes . . .

233

Madame
Who are you?

Shoemaker smiles.

Where did you come from?

Smiles.

Go!
Go! Go! Go!

Smiles.

. . . please! . . .

Lapin!
Conrad!
guards!
women!

Women enter. Flavia has joined them.

Marie-Therese
It's true!
Theresa
It's not true!
Marie-Therese
It is!
ah!
Theresa
Oh!
Mary
So!
Marie-Therese
Just Madame!
Flavia
Just Madame!

Theresa
Wanting her clothes
changed, I suppose!
Marie-Therese
Yes.

They ignore her. Try on shoes.

Anyway
he left her alone
in this beautiful room
in this great big house
in the very old green
green woods!
Theresa
oh!
Marie-Therese
You can never trust men
like
that when they've done
all their
tricks you can't see them
for dust!
Mary
Aye!
Madame
Please . . .
Four
Shush shush shush
Marie-Therese
and she went barking
howling mad!
Three
Ouf!

234

Marie-Therese
she began to see people
in the corner of the room!
Theresa
God in Heaven!
Mary
Holy Mother!
Marie-Therese
She'd see
as if it were really there
an old man/woman in a
leather apron
stitching a piece of
leather!
Three
Ayee!
Madame
but that's . . .
Three
Yes, Madame there there
there!
Marie-Therese
and she said that
this shoemaker got up
and spoke to her . . .
Theresa
What did it say?
Mary
It's voice
Marie-Therese
in a small clear
old man's voice
Theresa
Ouf!
Marie-Therese
it spoke

obscenity
unnatural ways
the magic arts!
Theresa
God in Heaven!
Mary
Holy Mother!
Marie-Therese
It told her to forget all
the things she felt were
true
all the things she held
dear
all she believed
she was not to believe
and in order that this
be carried out
the ghostly shoemaker
sat always in the room
with her
and the poor mad girl
believed for ever after
that the ghostly
shoemaker
was always with her!
Theresa
God in Heaven!
Mary
Holy Mother!
It's true?
Marie-Therese
As true as I stand here.
It happened in this very
vicinity.
Everyone knows about it.
Everyone keeps quiet

about it.
There!

*They each have a very
nice, if highly unsuitable
pair of shoes on. Madame
walks forward and points
to the shoemaker.*

Madame
Aaaayyyyyeeee!!

*The Shoemaker smiles
and puts a finger to his/her
lips.*
    *Madame falls in a dead
faint.*

Marie-Therese
Fainted dead away
Theresa
What's brought this on?
Mary
What's all this about?
Flavia
I looked after her like a
Queen!
Marie-Therese
We looked after her like a
Queen!
Mary
Never a foot wrong.
Marie-Therese
Holy Mother!

What day is it?
Theresa
When was the last time

she
and The Generalissimo . . .?
Mary
When did she last bleed?
Marie-Therese
should we make her pure
again
for The Generalissimo?
Theresa
should we make her clean
again
for The Generalissimo?
Mary
should we make her
empty again
for The Generalissimo?
Theresa
that's our job
cleaning
Flavia
Yes.
Yes.
Yes!!!!

They go to kill her as . . .

Four
death is small
it happens only once
how small it is . . .

a rose fades
drops from its vase
onto the cloth
All
a fish jumps

236

clear of the stream
catches a fly

a bird dives
into the wood
claws in a mouse

a star dies
light years away
more darkness there

death is small
it happens only once
how small it is . . .

They struggle and try
to harm her physically.
They cannot . . .

Marie-Therese
It's true
Theresa
The shining truth
Marie-Therese
anyway
when it came to it
there in that rotten empty
house
the women
with every motive for
revenge
could not raise their
hands
to kill . . .
Theresa
God in Heaven!

Mary
Holy Mother!
It's true?
Marie-Therese
As true as I'm standing
here.
It happened to my
grandmother.
It happened to my mother.
It happens to me.
I cannot do it!

Lapin enters with Conrad.

Lapin
Ah Good!
Destroy the evidence!
End the Thing!
Killed her already!!!
Marie-Therese
No we . . .
Theresa
Haven't as yet . . .
Mary
She's still . . .
Lapin
Breathing!
Kill her!
Kill her!
This . . . little . . . dolly
here . . .
is the last very last piece
left of this old jigsaw!!
Break her into bits!
Do it!

237

Marie-Therese
It's true!
Theresa
It is!
The shining truth!
Marie-Therese
Last miserable piece.
Mary
But we can't!
Lapin
Women!!!!!

Conrad! Be a Man for us!

Kill her!
Conrad
I can't!

I can't!

Some men can't!
Lapin
Men!!

*Lapin seizes a knife,
approaches Madame.
Madame wakes and
stares at Lapin.*

Madame
Holes, Lapin.
I keep thinking of holes.
I keep thinking I am holes
Holes for people to put
. . . things in . . . their
fingers . . .
their . . . excuse me . . .
cocks . . .

put their babies in . . .
take them out . . .
put food in me . . .
wine . . . fine
wine . . . but . . . another
hole!
and these . . . ears . . .
the most open
of holes . . . no rest for
them ever ever . . .
his words by day his
gasps his grunts
by night by night his
snores!

*She looks at the three
women, and Maria.*

And all the stories!
Oh the stories!
I am quite . . . pregnant
with stories!

These are the worst holes
of all,
Lapin!
What is the knife for,
Lapin?
Lapin
It's for . . .
It's to . . . (*She can't do it.*)
Bureaucrats!!
Madame
Oh!
It's to . . . it's to kill me . . .
isn't it?
Oh, of course . . .

238

I'm sorry . . . I'm such a
stupid . . .
another hole
yes
yes
go ahead.
Do it.

No one moves.

It's only fair.
No one moves

please.

No one moves.

I don't think I love The
Generalissimo any more.

Madame breaks down.

TEN
DIFFERENCE

43

Maria
You're visa'd passported
tagged.
Files exist electronic
computerised
numbered cross-
referenced you.
From a country where
you're
on file, numbered,
docketed, credit-rated
rubber-stamped.
You can't be lost.

*Someone comes forward
as officials . . . take her.*

You're picked up
escorted
flown out
to your home
where
touch a switch

light
touch a switch
warmth

Travel sounds, jet . . .

and

Someone brings . . .

hot chocolate . . .

The smell pervades . . .
    *Madame starts to
undress herself. Gets
herself ready for bed . . .
T-shirt . . . trackie
bottoms . . . bedsocks . . .*

Marie-Therese
Anyway
she did what any broken-
hearted
woman would do
she took to her bed

Madame gets into bed.

and for a while she lay
empty
tired
alone . . .

*Madame lies curled up . . .
then –*

Madame
I need something to read.

*Three women start
bringing her books . . .
first one . . . then pile
upon pile as –*

Marie-Therese (*reading*)
This is a cracking story!
Dreadful goings on!
but . . . (*Looks to end of
book.*)
The heroine survives!

*Lapin, with her knife,
takes an apple, sits on the
bed, cuts a slice of apple,
gives a piece of it to
Madame*

Marie-Therese
she read
Jean Jacques Rousseau
Lamartine
Thoreau Saint-Just
Auguste Blanqui
Barbes, Raspail
and she read

*Lapin gets a book, gets
into bed with Madame.
They both read. Three
women bring books . . .*

Mazzini Marx Engels
Bakunin Alexander
Kerensky . . .
Lapin
Any by women?
Marie-Therese
Alexandra Kollontai
George Eliot
Mary Shelley Gloria
Steinem
Susan Sontag Alice
Walker
Zora Neale Thurston . . .

*The soldiers return to the
periphery, they read
books too . . .*

Theresa (*reading*)
This is brilliant!
tale of suffering
horror
but . . .

Sneaks look at the end.

human being
wins through!
Mary (*reading*)
. . . hey! . . . war!
this is about love love
love . . .

Conrad (*reading*)
. . . this is about
inventions
. . . travel . . .
discovery . . .

*All tuck themselves up in
bed . . .*

Marie-Therese
and she read
and reading
she fell in love
with
a beautiful idea
a kind strong passionate
idea
a gentle loving passionate
idea
in the books were words
as
wild and whirling as a
kiss
ideologies as exciting as
an embrace . . .
Madame (*reading*)
Peace.

*They all start reading
from her book.*

All (*reading*)
Peace.
Madame (*reading*)
. . . building . . .

*They are hard to
understand.*

making . . .
creating . . .
Lapin
this is better than sex!
Conrad
this is nearly as good as
sex!
Theresa
this is nowhere near as
good as sex . . .
but . . . a varied life!
Marie-Therese
philosophies that fluttered
concepts that clung
emotions which pierced
her very heart!
Madame (*reading . . .
complicated things*)
revenge!
creativity!
accomplishment!
love!
pity!
forgiveness!
Marie-Therese
she read until the first
grey light of dawn.

*Beautiful lights of dawn
colour the stage . . .*

ELEVEN
DAWN

Madame
Hungry!
Lapin
So thirsty!

*They all get The General-
issimo's feast. One by
one, the soldiers return.*

Madame
Revenge.

*She hits one across his
face. Then another, then
a third, then . . .*

Pity.

Forgiveness.

*She stops hitting. . . . gives
Andreas a piece of bread.*

Andreas
The Generalissimo lay in
a pool
of blood.
Marie-Therese
It's true!
Feste
Fuck!
Fabian
His brains plastered

the interior of his
not-quite-bullet-proof car
Theresa
This meat is . . . yummm!
Violent
Dead at the hand of one
of his
not-quite-devoted
adjutants
Madame (*to soldiers*)
Hungry?
Thirsty?
Obseno
if they waited for him
they would wait for ever
Feste
Yes!
Fuck!
Yes!

*Madame serves them
food, drink . . .*

Mary
Is there just a spot more
of the . . . mmm!
Marie-Therese
They enjoyed what he
would
have enjoyed
if he had not been

permanently delayed.
Lapin
  This cheese is just ripe
  enough!
Conrad
  Just!
Madame
  They toasted him

as if he had just
become a proud father.

*They lift up their glasses
and drink . . .*

Madame
  to . . . Peace!
All
  to Peace!

TWELVE
THE GENERALISSIMA ARRIVES

*Shoemaker comes forward
with a pair of stout,
sensible shoes . . . holds
them out to Madame.*

Shoemaker
  I've made you some new
  shoes.
Maria
  You leave Illyria.
  File your story.
  The horror. The
  devastation.
  You blow up like a
  Michelin Woman.
  You have a baby.
  He's the most
  beautiful
  perfect
  baby in the world!
  Born into light warmth
  safety.

Toast.
Hot chocolate.
He's a month old.
It's January.
As Madame put on her
new
sensible shoes
You put on yours.

With a pram . . .

You're on a walk.
You walking, Christmas
coat,
pushing him, spanking
new pram,
courtesy Grandma.
You leave the dog-
walkers behind.
The joggers.
You're in a wood.

The sweet smell of rotting
leaves.

*One of the listeners gets
up as . . .*

Then
through the wood
This Man
His shoulders up
something . . . off about
him
no shirt black pullover
he's not wearing a coat
walked past us
too close
not looking
never looks up . . .

in all your years of
foreign reporting . . .
feeling the pop of a bullet
beside your ear
here . . .
lying under a tree trunk
in snow there . . .
looking up at the iron
belly of a
gunship there . . .

nothing
compares to the terror
you feel
thinking
someone is going to hurt
your baby . . .

She stares at the man . . .

and

you look at him!

They stare at one another.

he knows you will kill

and he goes . . .

*He sits down among the
listeners.*

You feel uncomfortable
even
mentioning them in the
same breath . . .

war
you
but until that wet day in
the woods
you had not even begun
to understand the pain of
war . . .

Madame
I have been idle

lazy
slow

I have been waiting for
The Generalissimo

and
he's not coming.

I think I'll get dressed now.

How do I look?

Music.
    *The Illyrians take up
position.
    Maria looks at them.
    They look at her.
    Music begins to build.*

Maria
  In that country
famous for
its war
its green green woods
its music

its dancing
that new morning
Madame looked ready.

Music swells.
    *All the Illyrians come
forward and dance . . .
a good, strong, stamping,
kicking, twirling dance . . .
    Maria watches with
her pram, pushing it
backwards and forwards
in time with the music.
    Lights fade.
    The End.*

LADY CHILL, LADY WAD, LADY LURVE, LADY GOD

Kay Adshead

For Jodie, Sadie, Raphael and Rachel

'I hate three things: girls, women and bitches'

Eminem Pills (Freestyle) Angry Blonde

'They see something you write, they say this ain't rap –
rap is what you *do*. I could rap the phone book.'

Dr Dre, TV interview
Black Entertainment channel

'The big bad boys had their time,
now it's make way for the big bad girls!'

Li'l Kim, TV interview
Black Entertainment channel

Production Notes

Lady Chill, Lady Wad, Lady Lurve, Lady God is inspired by an interview with four young girls from somewhere around Birmingham who called themselves 'The Ladies' and went 'looking for respect'. But it borrows much more in tone and content from the infamous Girl Gangs of America: the 'Eight-Ball Chicks' of San Antonio and 'The Play Girls' of Los Angeles. Since this is set against the background of a British provincial town (your town) there is a tongue-in-cheek quality to the play.

It isn't intended as a piece of social realism. Stylistically it is closest to a cartoon or comic book, and visually the production could be influenced by this. While it needs to be played with Attitude and Theatricality, like a musical, it should always be truly felt. Real and complex relationships, and lively characterisations are the springboard of the play.

There are short sections that are written to be rapped, how much else of the verse is rapped/rapdanced is up to the individual production, but it should influence all the playing. Some young people faced with verse try and 'relax' it to make it sound more naturalistic. From day one, the verse needs to be tackled head on!

I was in a local youth drama group. I always enjoyed it most when we were told to go away and come up with our own stuff. The sound/music/rap beat of this play is to be invented by the company and can be complicated (composed electronic sound score with live percussion and voices) or simple (street rapping, young people being creative with their voices and not much else). In the play the character of Stylo plays sax: this is to be mimed (it is funky blues sax).

The play is written to be performed as a promenade (or in the round). The Hood should appear with and out of the audience. The company, apart from the Four Ladies, should rarely leave the acting space. In the Inferno, the audience are extras, dancing at the nightclub; in Our Lady of All Souls graveyard, they are sitting amongst the graves. I have written the Hood for a huge cast, but with a smaller cast lines can be redistributed as appropriate. It might be fun if Pinky was played by a girl and Whiskers was to be played by a boy.

I have been specific with stage settings, but all scene and costume changes have to happen within the action – there should be *no gaps between scenes*, so simplify and pare down to what is essential to the story.

I have devised simple video to be used interactively and concurrently with the text. While this would be wonderful, it is optional. Primarily this is a piece fired by an energetic and muscular approach to the word.

It is aimed at eleven- to nineteen-year-olds. The main female characters are thirteeen, fifteen, seventeen and nineteen. I have used the minimum amount of swearing. Any strong language can be changed.

In a couple of the longer raps I have put in brackets to suggest possible cuts.

The Flame Angels should be very simple: masks on tall poles.

Lady Chill, Lady Wad, Lady Lurve, Lady God needs to be rehearsed slow – and played fast.

Characters

The Hood
full supporting company

The Four Ladies
Lady Chill or Carly
Lady Wad or Emma
Lady Lurve or Julie
Lady God or Faith

Miss Nice Face
Smelly Nelly
Tel
Keanu
Piety

Mrs Joy Foo Yung
Stylo

Bad News
Pinky
Matches

The Pussy Posse
Missy Cat
Li'l Fluff
Whiskers

The Craven Crew
Honk
Omo
Bird
Sticky

Mrs Helpful
Julie's Mum
Julie's Dad
Emma's Dad
Emma's Mum
RYD
RYM
Rich Dick

The Chinese Shadow

*In darkness, a slow
menacing rap beat. Lights
up – blood-red.*

Voice 1
  You're looking at the
  Hood

  *They appear one by one,
  out of the audience.*

Voice 2
  We're telling a tale so –
Voice 3
  Turn off your Nokia
  3330
Voice 4
  Slip off those new Gucci
  shoes dude
Voice 6
  Gents, unzip your zipper
  a tad
Voice 7
  Chicks, lick off that
  lipstick
Voice 8
  Petrol bomb red
Voice 9
  Hey, the price'll blow you
  away

Voice 10
  One kiss and you're dead

  *The rest of the Hood
  stand, individual
  characters plus company
  members. Optionally
  one of them has a video
  camera or a camera is
  passed around. At selected
  moments images are pro-
  jected onto a screen simultaneous with the action.
  They are in silhouette.
  Maybe they click fingers,
  bang bits of wood, tap feet.*

All (*spoken in strict time*)
  Now listen here
  and listen good

  'cos this is a tale
  of our neighbourhood
Voice 11 (*freestyle*)
  The shit crack of a town
  between
All
  Windy's
Voice 12
  The inflatables factory

Voice 13
  which expanded
Voice 14
  because
  our lives are
Voice 15
  Ultra sensitive
Voice 16
  Extra lubricated
Voice 17
  Or Super Spiky
All
  The Suck it and Pick it
Voice 18
  Where the scab heads
  sit and snort pie and
  mash
Voice 19
  And the bangers really
  bang
All
  The Chinese Chippy
Voice 20
  With its broken
  brick wall
All
  Dog poo park
Voice 21
  The Washeteria with its
  six pairs of knickers a
  week
  lost for ever to the final
  fast spin
Voice 22
  All the way to

All
  Our Lady of All Souls
Voice 23
  Where the big bell
  for last chuckin' out tolls
All (*in strict time*)
  Now listen here
  and listen good

  'cos this is a tale
  of our neighbourhood

  And four ladies

  four little ladies

*The company part to
reveal the Four Ladies.
Rhythmic beat stops.
Full on musical accom-
paniment, percussion,
kazoos, sax. The ladies
should be flown in or rise
up from trap doors or be
wheeled on. Failing all
these, run in – whatever!
An explosion.*

The Hood
Lady Chill
Lady Wad
Lady Lurve
Lady God

*The Four Ladies are
dressed similarly in
current gang gear
(discuss). Though with*

*telling differences. They
should look 'costumed',
larger than life. Their
walk, their every move,
lighting a cigarette, etc.,
is heightened, stylised,
almost a dance.*

The Hood
Lady Chill

*Video close-up projected
on screen of Lady Chill.
The Hood form a tableau
round the Ladies. In the
red light occasionally and
at appropriate moments
they 'break' into dance.*

    *Lady Chill takes centre
position (perhaps she is
even lifted).*

    *Lady Chill poses: she is
the most athletic, striking
and meanest. She is also
the Leader.*

The Hood
So cool!

She burns!

*They all make a sizzling
noise.*

Voice 4
**She didn't have her
tongue pierced, man
she had it sliced!**

**So she could cuss
twice as good!**
Voice 6
**And
she's no feet
only fins!**
All (*sinister whisper*)
**Lady Chill
a queer fish
a cold dish**

*Video close-up cuts. The
Hood re-establish beat,
underneath voices may
improvise, scat or soul
sing. Overall the voices
rap freestyle.*

Voice 1
**She was left
on the steps
of the old
fish market**

**on the coldest
night
hereabouts
in a hundred years.**

**Icicles
hanging from the
wrought-iron gates;
gates
famous
for their depiction
of mermen slaying
the giant**

sea serpent.

Left
naked
wrapped
in a copy
of the Racing Times.
Voice 4
So we know
there was a bet on
that frosty night
Voice 8
Though the odds were
long
All (*spoken in strict time*)
Found at the crack-of
by a kindly fishmonger
she was taken for dead
to the City's Stiffs'
Hangar
Voice 6
To the mort

A beat.

just a mite

A beat.

on the slab

A beat.

Voice 2 (*freestyle*)
Where,
Alice,
the mortuary attendant
on her last shift before
retirement

Voice 3
detected
a breath
somewhere
in there

and not without
a certain foreboding
Voice 4
unwrapped

a cold, old soul.
All (*in strict time*)
Lady Chill
she's real mean
an Ice Queen
a Fish Fiend
Voice 5
she swims like a shark
All
Lady Chill
she strikes fear
whenever she's near
whoever she's near

She strikes fear.

*Video close up of Lady
Wad. Sudden change of
music and light; change
of tempo, saxophone,
slow, sexy r and b or soul.*

*Lady Wad steps into a
spotlight. The Hood wolf
whistle, fall at her feet as
slaves. Some smell the
perfumed air. Lady Wad
is, slim and elegant, she*

*appears more expensively
groomed and accessorised
then the others. She carries
a large bag at all times.*

*The speaking rhythm is
slower and sexier.*

Voice 1
Mmm mm
Is she the business!
Voice 2
She's the Queen
of Street Investment
Voice 3
This Lady buys and sells
Voice 4
Where she get that sweet
smile?
Voice 5
off the back of a lorry
Voice 6
Those big blue eyes?
Voice 7
under the counter
on the sly
Voice 8
Don't tell her boss
Voice 9
And those cute vowels?
Voice 10
Oh, her Daddy
paid for those
Voice 11
but she made sure
he got cost

Voice 12
What's that smell?
Voice 13
Ambishun
Voice 14
of the corporate kind
Voice 15
Multi-nationals on her
mind.
one of her own.
Voice 5
Cash is the Fash
for Lady Wad

*Video close-up of Lady
Wad on screen cuts.*

The Hood
Lady Chill
Lady Lurve

*Urgent screech of brakes.
Four or five of the Hood
now become policemen
donning hats.*

Plods (*with authority*)
Alright,
Break it up
The Hood
Now listen Here
and listen Good
Plod 1
A few
respectable people
still
live here

*The Ladies are picked up
and secreted away by the
other members of the
Hood.*

Plod 2
They don't want
scum like you
pissing on
their
flora digitalis
you dirty little sod
Yob
Here
Mr Plod
sir
strong lager
fertilises good

How else
do you think
Mrs Net Curtains'
red-hot pokers
got that big?

Many lecherous jeers.

Hood (*all*)
Lady Lurve

*Video close-up of Lady
Lurve on screen. She takes
centre, she is smaller,
rounder, rougher. Change
of tempo, tone.*

Hood (*whispered, quick
and covert*)
wants the earth

to move twice nightly

She wants her lurve
hot
we're talking
scorchin'

She wants it hard
and dark
with a gold tooth

*The police frisk the
Hood, much jeering.*

Voice 6
No biting, constable
Voice 7
No nibbling
No dribbling, sergeant, sir
Voice 8
You're getting yourself
excited
Voice 7
She wants
lurve's sweet
teeth marks
all over

*Most of the Hood are
marched off by the
police; only a small band
are left around the
Ladies. Video close-up of
Lady Lurve cuts.*

The Hood (*they whisper*)
Lady Lurve
Lady Wad
Lady Chill

Sudden silence.

The Hood
Four little ladies . . .

Lady God takes centre stage she has 'Lady God' tattooed to her forehead and a teardrop under one eye. Her mother, Piety, appears – a cool, striking beauty no more than twenty-nine. Behind her, and carrying a banner, are the followers of the Seven Day Evangelical Mission (a fundamentalist Christian sect). They all wear black, with caps or headscarves, and carry Bibles. They face Lady God.

The Hood
(*chanting softly*)
Lady God

Video close-up of Lady God.

Baby God
Crazy God
Lady God

Video close-up cuts.
    Carries on underneath following.

Piety
Hello Faith

Lady God says nothing.

Picty
You'll be home for tea, I hope

Lady God still says nothing. Chanting gets louder.

Faith . . .!

Faith . . .!!

SCENE TWO

The Mission banner has turned and says 'Golden Nights'. The Four Ladies are sitting on the broken brick wall of the local Chinese chippy. From inside, the jangle of local radio; occasionally we hear snippets of a syrupy voice, helping the local lonelies. They eat chips ravenously from newspaper. Apart from Lady Wad, who sits eating a Marks and

Spencer salad. A little way
apart, Pinky is attempting
wheelies on his mountain
bike. Bad News, another
youngster, is eating and
reading the paper. A pre-
pubescent girl, Matches,
very dirty and scruffy, sits
close to the Ladies,
listening. At a window we
see a figure in silhouette
expertly practising
Shaikwondo.

Lady Lurve (referring to
  figure in window)
  He's fit
Matches
  Gi's a chip

Wad does so.
  Matches puts it in her
mouth like a cigarette.
She takes out a box of
matches and is about to
strike one.

All
  No!
Lady Wad
  Why?
Matches
  Because
  setting fire
  to things
  is wrong

All
  Why?
Matches
  Because
  they burn down
Lady Lurve (mouth full)
  I couldn't
  see
  Brad Pitt
  last week,
  you little shit
  'cos you'd burnt
  the Odeon down
Pinky (doing wheelies)
  Want a fight
  Ladies, eh?
Matches
  I love Mondays
Pinky
  I'm your man
Matches
  I love 'em!
  I love 'em!
  I love 'em!
Pinky
  Underneath
  this T-shirt
  jacked from
  Poundstretchers

  is one hundred per cent
  toned muscle

  I'm pumped

  Tell you what

I'll take all four of you
on at once.
Lady Chill (*eating,*
underneath her breath,
good humoured)
Freak
Pinky (*to Wad*)
Any other service
you might require
Lady Wad
Cheek
Pinky
I'm bigger
than I look
down there.
Lady Lurve
Down where?
Pinky
You ask
Sheila
from Cost-Cutters
Lady Lurve
You haven't
got one, Pinky

The dog got yours
when they ran out of
cocktail sausages
your Mam says,
on that trip

for weakies, squeakies
and wackos

to stinky Rhyl (*local*
scummy seaside town)

All the girls laugh.

Matches
I love cocktail sausages
I love 'em
I love 'em

Pause.

What is a cocktail sausage?
Pinky
No,
we've all got little ones
in our family
on that side
even my Aunty Sharon

The girls laugh.

Even my Gran

The girls groan.

Bad News (*reading and*
eating)
Oh, man
this is putting me off
my Number 61
Lady Lurve
Can't they
reconstruct it?
You know
take a bit
of elbow
and sort of
graft it on
Pinky
Yes, yes
they could do that
I suppose
but

261

I'm going to need my
elbows . . .
aren't I?
seeing as how
I'm going into the
secondhand car business

*Momentary shared
puzzlement.*

Pinky
(*looking down trousers*)
Anyway. It works. I think.
Lady Wad
I managed
to get you a piece
of the World Trade
Centre
Bad News

*She takes out rock in
packaging. They all
groan.*

It's a holy relic
Treasure it
Lady Chill
Sick!
Lady Lurve (*looking*)
World Trade Centre
my tits
that's a bit
of the Bingo Hall
back of Fitz Street
See

She points.

D.D. . . .
'Doris woz here'
Lady Wad
Excuse me

She wafts it away.

It's got an
authenticity
certificate
from NYPD
Bad News (*still reading*)
Thanks

She hands it to him.

Lady Wad
That'll be a naughty forty

They all look astonished.

I had serious overheads
Lady Lurve
She bought a chisel

He gives over notes.

Look at the buns
on that one
Lady Chill
(*finished eating chips*)
I'd have to see
his eyes
Lady Lurve
He's got Frying Tonight
eyes,
I bet.
Two of them
Lady Wad
(*counting money*)

I must say
the loose
confident
cut
of his costume
does promise
a lean
almost sculpted
tautness
nether

Lady Lurve
Like I said
he's got great buns

Lady God
(*also finished eating, in
a soft sweet voice*)
It's not just fighting
Is it?
either
I mean
every move
gesture
means something
deep or ancient.
Something spiritual.
It's like a secret language
really
beautiful
like a dance.

Lady Chill
Bit of a poofter,
then?

Silence.

Lurve *and* **Wad**
Yeah

*Dismissing the figure,
they look away.*

Lady Chill
Who is he anyway?

Lady Lurve (*shrugs*)
He's new
Mrs Foo Yung's nephew?

Bad News
Oh man
listen to this
this is scary

Hideous worms, right
microscopic parasites
find an opportunistic
nick or graze
burrow into the skin
and eat the victims
from the inside out.
who experience
excruciating pain
hair loss
high fever
bulging eyes and
dementia.

Lady Lurve
Glad I finished my chips

Bad News
It's called
screw worm

Lady Lurve
I've had it

Lady Chill
No
you screw worms
that's different

263

*Bad News carries on
reading. Smelly Nelly,
a scruffy old lady with
a stick, appears. Bored,
and chips gone, Lurve
gets up. She has attitude.*

Lady Lurve (*mocking*)
Well if it isn't
Smelly Nelly
Matches
Smelly knows
all the ghosts
ghosts are Nelly's friends

I love ghosts
I love 'em
I love 'em
I love 'em
Smelly Nelly
I've been
up the Suck-It
and Pick-It
with Miss Nightingale
I said,
what you having Florrie?

She said
shandy top
and a
cheese and piccalilli

*Lurve has picked her
pocket and takes out a
packet of Senior Service.
Smelly gets agitated.*

Smelly Nelly
Give 'em back
Lady Lurve
You owe me, Smelly
you bummed that many

*A little play fight over the
cigs breaks out with Lady
Lurve teasing, offering
them, pulling away.*

Lady Lurve
Here
Smelly Nelly
You cow
You little sow
Lady Lurve
Behind you

*Everyone watches, egging
on. Lady Wad pointedly
stands and kicks away
Smelly's stick, she falls
heavily, losing her glasses.
    Silence.
    The girls roar with
laughter. At just that
moment, The Pussy Posse
arrive, a rival gang, three
glamour pusses, Missy
Cat and her two Kits, all
done up in purple, ducks'
down and sparkles. They
walk through on their
way somewhere. The
Four Ladies leave Smelly*

on the ground looking for
specs.

Lady Lurve
If it isn't the Pussy Posse!
Lady Chill
You're up completely the
wrong alley
Lady Wad
I thought we'd put
pepper down
Lady Lurve
I thought we'd put
broken glass
Lady Chill
Anyone for vivisection?
Missy Cat
No need for disaffection
Ladies
Li'l Fluff
No one's looking
for knuckle
Whiskers
Not tonight
anyway
Lady Chill
You're not allowed here
this is our
brick wall

If you wanted
temporary rights of way
you should have
texted me
Li'l Fluff
It's . . .

She gestures to the
shadow in the windows.
They all sigh and look up.

Lady Lurve
Have you met him then?
Missy Cat
Alas no but
this Saturday
he will have
the not inconsiderable
honour
of representing
our esteemed and
honoured
neighbourhood
in the national
Shaikwondo finals
held in our
crumbling . . .
Li'l Fluff
not untypical of its type
Missy Cat
venerable
Town Hall

For the event

our
valued services
have been employed
Whiskers
We're cheering
Lady Chill
You're what?
Lady God
Honestly

Lady Lurve
Not that crappy
pom-pom-waving shite!
Lady Chill
Have you no woman's
pride?
Lady Lurve
Showing your tits
showing your ass
all that
lip gloss
Lady Wad
I thought that tat
had gone out
with . . .
Lady Lurve
The Spice Girls
Matches
I love The Spice Girls
I love 'em
I do
I do
especially the green one
Missy Cat
We need to access
Mrs Joy Foo Yung's
back room
for a team talk

Colours?
Li'l Fluff
Primary
Whiskers
Pastel
Missy Cat
Script?

Li'l Fluff
Content
Whiskers
Style
Missy Cat
Hair?
Li'l Fluff
Cane Row
Whiskers
Or Fanny Cut
Lady Lurve
To gel
or not to gel?
Lady Wad (*to Li'l Fluff*)
I can do you for
spray-on radiance
pout enhancer
shiny post-coitus eyes
mister
blackhead remover
facial hair waxer
cold sore decruster

*Whiskers scratches her
crutch.*

Intimate itch powder
Whiskers
Done

They exchange.

Missy Cat
We're prepared
to offer you a Toll
for safe passage
Lady Wad
Cool

266

Missy Cat
Ten
Lady Wad
Twenty
Missy Cat
Seventeen-fifty
Lady Wad
Eighteen
Missy Cat
We have closure
Whiskers
And four free tickets
for the Shaikwondo
International Festival
Lady Chill
Stick them
Lady Lurve
Up your cat flap

*They hand over the
money, counting it into
Wad's hand. The Ladies
all stand aside, allowing
The Pussy Posse to mince
past to Mrs Joy Foo
Yung's.*

Smelly Nelly (*seething
with hurt and rage*)
You hurt me,
when I fell down
I grazed my hands
Bad News
You want to watch out
for screw worm
Mrs

Smelly Nelly (*to Lady
Wad*)
You're bad

She turns.

all of you
And you (*to Wad*)

you're the worst.
The ghosts,
will come and get you
I'll set them on to you
I will

And then you'll be sorry

*For a moment there is an
uneasy silence, then Chill
starts jeering wildly,
whooping and screaming.
The other three Ladies
follow aping the old
woman's walk.*
*Suddenly, like a bat
out of hell, Mrs Joy Foo
Yung blasts out of her
shop.*

Mrs Foo Yung
It's not enough eh?
You have cheek
to charge people
to tread my walkway,
my walkway
I rent off the council

But now
I see you

knock down Smelly
knock her to the floor
to put boots in

Well, this is too much.
Hear me?
Too bad!
This make
Joy Foo Yung
too angry!

(*to Wad*) I know your
parents
they're good people
hardworking
respectable,
clever
What you do
if I knock on door
and tell them
Eh?

Go
pronto
or I call the Plods

A terrible silence.
   *The Hood appear, as
if out of the woodwork,
on the very edge of the
acting area, listening,
holding their breath.
They create a soft,
menacing rap beat.*
   *Chill approaches
Mrs Joy Foo Yung, The
three Ladies follow.*

Lady Chill (*freestyle rap*)
Shut it,
Egg Foo Dung

You disrespect me,
or my Ladies,
you cus us
you end up
pork
chop suey
on a fork
Hear me?

And that pretty boy
nephew of yours
whoever he is,

will find his fancy
footwork
fearsome hard
floating face down
in Karachi Street Canal

And you bell
the Filth
you find yourself
listening
to the big bell
toll

Up
Our Lady
of
All Souls.
Toll
for you
Mrs Foo Yung (*whispered,
shocked*)

What's this?
Threats?
Why
you're just a bit
of a girl
Lady God
Don't hurt, Mrs Foo
Yung, Chill!
Mrs Foo Yung
What's the world
coming to?

Chill moves forward
facing Mrs Foo Yung.
As the Hood moves
back, on the screen we
see Lady Chill in close up.

Lady God (*camera swings*
to Lady God)
Don't hurt her
Mrs Foo Yung (*camera*
swings to Mrs Foo Yung)

You know
my story
Lady Chill
I know
about
the old gang fights
I know babies
got killed maybe
I know it
and I say
you disrespect
The Ladies

Camera swings back to
Lady Chill.

You is dead!

Rap beat stops. Horrible
silence. Mrs Joy Foo
Yung is terrified, Chill
means business. Camera
cuts.

SCENE THREE

A slow low light from a
different part of the
performance space, up
on the Craven Crew, the
neighbourhood Boy Gang.
Honk (quietly spoken),
Omo (grinning, spotless),
Sticky (randy), Bird
(jumpy). They are seriously

unpleasant. The Hood give
an edgy beat, they also
make nervous (joky) jungle
noises. The Craven Crew
(soft, menacing).

Honk
So you think you're
making over pitch, bitch,

All
You're just a mosquito
bite that makes the
Crew's ass itch
Bird
We're watching, we're
waiting, no lady shit
hesitation
Sticky
You keep posing and
playing you're gonna try
the Cravens' – patience
Omo
The Crew let you think
you brew in this city stew
Sticky
But you dance over the
deciding line and you're
going seriously down

Omo
We won't take the piss,
we'd hate to blunt good
blades on you miss
All
But you'll have to face
the Craven Crew fist kiss
So you think you're
talking tough
And you think you're
making out real rough
you think you're taking
over pitch
you're just a mosquito bite
that makes the Crew's ass
itch
you're just a mosquito bite
Honk
that makes the Crew's ass
itch

SCENE FOUR

Tuesday teatime
Banner turns round and
reads 'Stylo's Silver
Dreams – Video Hire Shop
& Cyber Café'.
Lights dim
At the window (as if in
a top room) in a green
spot. Stylo plays sax,
urgent, funky, charged. He
is a Teddy Boy who could
be anything from eighteen

to eighty (though the latter
is more likely) – DA hair,
grey silver zoot suit, red
shirt, bootlace tie, suede
brothel creepers, and dark
sunglasses.
Wad, God, Pinky, Bad
News, and Matches enter
talking, and then pause as
if on the steps.
Behind, minimal
changes to suggest a small

dark shop, possibly once
dealing in cinema mags
and memorabilia, now into
video hire. Modern
posters, showing today's
films have peeled away
showing layers of old
movies from Bonnie and
Clyde, *through Cagney, to*
the first Jesse James
western.
     The Ladies feel at home
here.

Lady Wad (*from steps,*
  scene changes behind)
  I want nothing with
  Drew Barrymore
Bad News (*reading*)
  Oh, no
  not Drew
  Drew was the first
Lady Wad
  I want nothing
  with Cameron Diaz
  or whales
Bad News
  She's not gone yet
  but she's on the list

  It says here
  all the Hollywood babes
  have been abducted
  by aliens
Matches
  I was abducted
  by aliens

Bad News
  And replaced
  with identikit
  robots
Matches
  They bought me an ice
  cream
  and took me to my Uncle
  Roy's
Bad News
  This has been verified
  by Carla Petensky
  a well-respected
  Hollywood stylist
Matches
  They were
  nice, the aliens.
Bad News
  Who said
  she's walked in
  four times
  without knocking
  on persons
  (female, famous)
  who shall remain
  nameless
  only to find them

  head on the table
  synthetic skin
  unzipped
  to reveal
  sophisticated
  computer systems.
  Apparently
  it's part of

an ingenious
alien plot
working towards
domination
of the planet

Using the babe robots
to manipulate
the media

they have affairs
with senators
who rise
meteorically
become presidents
and through the
influence of
the robo babes
bring about
the end of
civilisation
as we know it

Pause.

Lady Wad
Wicked

*Stylo makes his appear-
ance behind the counter.
His face is badly scarred.
He is blind*

Stylo (*his voice is low,
rasping, heavily accented*)
What can I do you for,
ladies?

Lady God (*very bright-
eyed, overexcited and
obviously on something*)
We've come in
for our usual
Stylo

Dreams to rent
gingham mums
who love their kids –
press pause

The sad
ugly plug
who grows up
good
and saves the world –

rewind

Dressing up
dads
with smiles
who tell
their friends
to keep
their hands
to themselves –
eject!
eject!
eject!

*She laughs.
A pause.*

Stylo (*sharp*)
What's the matter with
you?

God says nothing.

Stylo
What's the matter
with the shy one?
Pinky
She's cooking tonight
that's for sure

*Stylo goes mad, reaches
out for Pinky, whom he
seizes by the collar,
pulling him off his feet.*

Stylo
Who deals to her?
Tell me
Do they come in here?

*Pinky is trembling,
frightened.*

Lady God
Dreams to buy
Stylo
flat, round or lozenge
white, pink, baby blue
printed with E's
doves
eyes
butterflies
Pinky (*spluttering*)
Everyone knows
her dad
was a
crack head

*Stylo lets Pinky go, who
falls to his knees.*

Lady God
Standing up
bad dreams
in fields
after being

fixed up

when they
pull your
trousers
down

and you
watch
the red sky

the hurt sky
split open

and scream

*Long silence. Stylo is
trembling, broken.
    Lady Lurve enters, she
is panting, breathless,
laughing.*

Lady Lurve
I gave them the slip
they think I'm upstairs
having a shit
Stylo
(*desperate, to the rest*)
Who deals to her?
One of you must know!
Who?
Lady Lurve
Give us the latest

273

steamy
will you, Stylo
under the counter
HC

I don't want acting
I want panting
rude angles
I want spunk
on the lens

*A smiling, nice, young
man walks in.*

Stylo
Evening
RYD
Flubber
Stylo
please

The girls snigger.

Lady Lurve
Sorry?
RYD
Flubber
A treat
for the kids
Lady Lurve
You don't want that
darlin'
take my advice
send the kids to the park
with curry Discos
and a pint
of
Vomit Delight

And you and me'll
make Flubber
on your shag pile
after watching
Stylo's HC
and if
six-foot blondes
with legs
to their earlobes
and 'normous knockers
does nothing for you
you can always
pretend
they're me

She pinches his bum.

Eh darling . . . Eh? . . .
Eh?
How about it? How
about it?

*All but Stylo laugh, the
man leaves, embarrassed.*

I love 'em
RYDs
Matches
Respectable
Young
Dads

*A nice young woman
walks into the shop.*

Stylo
Evening
Matches
But she hates RYMs

Stylo
How's Fred?
Lady Lurve
Dead?
RYM (*unnerved as the
Ladies crowd round her*)
No, he's doing quite
nicely, thank you
Lady Wad
Now the swellings gone
down

The Ladies laugh.

RYM (*nervous*)
Yes
Stylo
Ladies . . . please
Ladies
Lady Wad
(*fingering RYM's necklace*)
I love your diamond drop
Lady Lurve
What you drop
for that love?

They laugh.

Stylo (*attempting to warn*)
Ladies . . .
Lady Wad
Can't say
I'm quite so keen
on your free
With teabags
T-shirt
Lady Lurve (*threatening*)
You need a bigger bra

Lady Wad
And the leggings are
nasty
RYM
I'm sorry Stylo, I . . . I

*She beats a retreat
running into Lady Chill.*

Lady Chill
Bitches
Stick 'em up

*There is much noise and
welcoming. They each
make a sign a bit similar
to a Freemason's salute. It
consists of the thumb and
forefinger making an L
followed by four fingers,
which is a four-pointed
crown. They chant and
hand-signal.*

Ladies
Pride
Power
Protection
Partnership
Chill
Wad
Lurve
God
Matches
I love it
I love hand signals
I love 'em

She tries out lots of hand
signals, rude ones, traffic
ones.

Lady God (*very excited*)
Something dark
something mean
something to make
little Matches
here scream
tonight
Stylo
Chill

fancies
mass murder

she's
out
for
revenge
she
feels like
a chase
through the woods
at night
with a chopper
she feels like
a bloody
but glorious
end
Lady Chill
What's she on about?
Lady Lurve
She's stashed
Lady God
They'll be

ghosts
. . .
Or
angels

Lights dip. Ladies split.
From a different part
of the acting space. A slow
light comes up on the
Crew.
From all sides they
approach Stylo making
low noises, clucks, squeaks,
kissing noises and whistles.
Stylo is alone, cashing up.
He freezes, turning in all
directions, disoriented.
The Hood creep
forward to listen.

Honk
Another uneventful week
Stylo?
Omo
No smashed panes?
Sticky
No snapped locks?
Bird
No lost stock?
Omo
No lost teeth?
Sticky
No snapped legs?
All
No smashed brains?

Trembling with anger,
Stylo hands over an
envelope full of money.

Honk
I wouldn't insult you
by counting
Omo
You need to smarten
yourself up Stylo

They smooth his hair, pull
fluff off his jacket,
straighten his tie.

Sticky
Seeing as how
you're a ladies' man now

Derisive laughter.

Honk
We look forward
to another
uneventful week
Omo
and another
Sticky
and another
Honk
Put the chain on
when we're gone,
Stylo, old man
Bird
There's a lot of bad

people
about

They laugh and go. Pause.
From a backroom
Lady Wad emerges,
cautious and surprised.

Lady Wad
How much?
How much do you pay
them?

No answer.

Fifty?
One hundred?
Two hundred?

No answer.

Weekly?
You pay that weekly?

Video camera close-up.
Stylo smashes his fist in
anger.
Wad smiles slowly and
whistles appreciatively.

You've got to hand it
to them
that's not bad
for five minutes' work

Video camera cuts.

SCENE FIVE

Wednesday morning early. Julie's (Lady Lurve's) front room. The impression of a sixties council house with inflatable sofa, two large inflatable chairs and one small one in luminous colours. Her dad and mum are rowing. Her dad in brown overalls is perched in an inflatable chair trying to brush his shoes. Her mother is a neat, anxious woman. Keanu – Julie's eighteen-month-old baby (played by company member) has been wedged uncomfortably in the smaller inflatable chair. Julie is attempting to feed him with baby gunk from a spoon and to read the Sun *at the same time. Inevitably she sometimes misses; this is messy for Julie and stressful for Keanu. The TV is on. We don't see it. Occasionally we may hear snippets. Surrounding Keanu all about are other inflatables gleaned from Windy's. Inflatable rubber rings from the seaside, large inflatable whale, funny bananas, inflatable tulip in a vase, inflatable lips . . . even an inflatable alien. Julie has just (reluctantly) got out of bed. She is bare-legged and wearing a grimy T-shirt. Her face is greasy with last night's make-up and her hair is knotted.*

Julie's Mum
I'll leave you
one day

Julie's Dad
Put a sock

Julie's Mum
Night after
Week after
Year after

Julie's Dad
The record's stuck

Julie's Mum
Looking at five walls
climbing them
with six kids
and a half-dead dog

The last three mouthfuls have missed Keanu completely.

Keanu
Ooh. Badda mama!
Julie
Stop whingeing
Keanu!
Julie's Mum
Feeling the years
close in like a coffin

*Keanu takes a bit of food
and throws it at his
mother.*

Julie
You buggerette
Julie's Mum
Spreading
your cheap sheepskin
over the park
Keanu
You buggerette
mama
Julie's Mum
I'll be
on the other side
of that door,
this town,
this planet,
before
you can say . . .
Julie
serial
neighbour-shagging
shite

*Julie's dad suddenly
jumps up, grabs Julie*

*by the T-shirt with real
viciousness; Keanu starts
to cry.*

Keanu
Badda grandpa
Julie's Mum
Leave her!
Julie's Dad (*to Julie*)
Keep it zipped
missy mouth,
or I might
have to fill it in
with my fist
Julie
Yeah
well you'll
find it hard
sad old man
tossing off
to
spankings
round the world
with one
gnawed off hand

*A clean-cut open-faced
young man enters.*

Tel
The door was open

Julie's dad lets her go.

Julie's Mum (*attempting to
cover*)
Come in
Terry, love

279

*Keanu sees Terry and
beams. He lifts his arms
and, still rammed in the
inflatable chair, he wobbles
over, arms outstretched.*

Keanu
Nice dada
Tel
Hello, son
How are you, mate?

They hug warmly.

Julie's Dad (*to Julie's
mum, ignoring Tel*)
Tea on the table
by five
there's a friendly . . . .
Oh.

He grins.

And press my pants
must look smart
for the lads

*He goes. An ignored
Keanu waves.*

Keanu
Bye bye

*Miserable silence. Julie's
Mum sits distracted –
video camera shows Mum
in close-up through –*

Julie's Mum
Julie asked

for her old job
back at Windy's
Tel
Tel
Oh?
Julie
But
following the incident
when I stuck drawing
pins
in batch 917 CBDXY
for a laugh
resulting in twelve
thousand
packets of six condoms
to be urgently
returned to the
manufacturer

I'm banned.
Julie's Mum
They gave
your grandpa
a clock
Tel
Who'd watch Kenny . . .
Keanu

*Pause. They look at
Julie's Mum.*

Julie (*offhand*)
You've got a love bite
on your neck, Tel
Tel (*good-humoured*)
No I haven't

Julie
but nice try.

Tel takes the bowl of food and spoon and takes over breakfast. He plays aeroplanes. Each spoonful hits the spot. Keanu is suddenly giggly, relaxed, playful.

Julie (*peevish*)
You're not supposed to do that
gives 'em
anorexia

Tel ignores this. Julie is still glued to the paper.

Julie
What's on the agenda?
Tel
Well,
Park first
Keanu
Bada Pigeons
Julie
(*defensive*)
Yeah
Well, watch
he doesn't
get that Hong Kong flu.
Last time
you brought
him home
his hands
were blue

Tel
Of course . . . Oh. I've brought him some new gloves

He takes mittens out, and puts them on Keanu.

Keanu
Nice and warm
Dada

He hugs him. Julie pretends not to notice.

Tel
What about you,
Julie?
What will you do,
today?
Julie
Hang out
with the Ladies
I suppose,
at lunch.
Tel
The Ladies?
Julie
You have a problem
with that?
Tel
They're
a rough bunch
Julie
Says who?
Tel (*he lowers his voice*)
The whole town's
talking,

say you steal
take drugs
say you . . .
Julie
the usual then . . .

Pause.

He might
not be yours
you know
that
don't you?
Tel (*hurt*)
Yes
Julie
He could
be half
this
town's
Tel
I don't care
I love him
Julie (*TV cuts*)
Well, why don't you have
him then?
Tel
I'm sorry?
Julie
Take him!
Take him
for good.
Keep him!
Julie's Mum (*soft, distant*)
Oh, Julie, Julie
Tel
Take

Kenny . . .
Keanu
away from you
but . . .
Julie
I'm his mum
I know
but . . .
well . . .
he doesn't

really like me
Tel
Julie
Julie
I mean
we've never
really hit it off
Tel
Don't be hard on yourself
you were fourteen
Julie's Mum
Too young
Too young, Tel
Tel
I was old enough
to know better

To Julie's Mum.

I was lucky
you
didn't call
the Plods
Janet
Julie's Mum
You're a good person Tel

Tel
I should have
used something
Julie
No excuse
I suppose
considering
we did it
in the grounds
of the largest
manufacturers
of barrier
contraceptives
in Europe

They both laugh.

Julie's Mum
It's nice
you both
get on.
It's nice.

*They move away. Video
camera cuts.*

Tel (*softly*)
Do you mean it?
About
keeping him
Julie
Yes . . .
yes I do
Tel
But you'd see him,
would you?

I mean
he needs
a mum
Julie
Yes
Tel
Often?
Julie
Give me a couple of
months
to sort myself out
I mean
find somewhere to live
p'raps
get a job
Tel
You're clever
Julie
Julie
Crap!
Tel
Our Kath
says you
were the cleverest
in the class

You could have got
exams
you could have gone
to university

*Hood creep forward.
They make background
rhythm.*
    A very fast sour rap.

GIRLS LIKE ME

Chorus.

Lady Lurve
  Girls like me don't do
  university
  Girls like me get stuffed,
  up the duff, up the spout
  In the wrong club,
  knocked up, out for the
  count
  The last shout, before
  dropping out, the last
  shout

  Girls like me
  have unusualee small
  birthweight babies
Tel (*pointing*)
  Well, that's not true
  of our Keanu
Lady Lurve
  Due to
  Poor housing, smoking
  and inappropriate
  cravings,
  Sex, white rum,
  prescription tabs,

  Nike Air Max and
  sherbet dib-dabs

  Oh – and licking creosote
  off Mrs Hubbard's
  wheelie bin cupboards
  'Don't do that, honey,

creosote costs lotsa
money'

Chorus.

(Girls like me, sign on,
space out, jiggle their jugs
about
in a silver cage, on a sleazy
stage, on a steamy Sat
night
Don't feed the punters
'cos the big ones bite.
GRRR
See what's writ, the little
one's spit (*She spits.*)
Wearing a sly smile, a
G-string, a fake diamond
  ring,
One hand on the
Emergencee Ejaculation
cord
Girls like me are
responsible for eighty per
cent of
  all known fraud.)

(Hold onto your credit
card, baby
that'd buy me a trip to
Spendsville maybe
'cos we're up for a spree,
naughty girls like me.)

Girls like me get wed
eventualee in something
old,

crusty kex,
something new, this
season's flu, you can
sneeze
but don't spew up on the
pew
the dress borrowed from
Carol-Ann from No 2
who borrowed it from
Jan who borrowed it
from Stan.
You heard. And the lips
are blue
but we scrub up real nice,
when we show, girls like
me

And in the photos,
courtesy of Ken's Cosy
Camera Cabin,
famous for being at all
the best stabbings,
with hard hair, high heels,
and dumb empty eyes
we are unrecognisable in
years to come

Chorus.

Girls like me get shopped
to the DSS Bless
Go down, lose their kids
'Cos the old man's doing
serious time for the fine
sports shop job
Get run out of town,
before being found arse

up,
face down
In a stinking alley, where
the end's sharp and sticky
Only to turn up, more's
the pity, the next day on
the
front page
smiling sweetly
In our best dresses, no
more lies, finally touching
hearts
with those big brown
eyes.
A little too late.
Girls like me.

Video close-up of Keanu.

Tel
You don't have
to be
that person
Julie
you can be
anything
you want

*Julie laughs. Keanu doesn't
like it, he starts to cry.*

Julie
Yeah
I can, Tel.
It took
a long time
but you finally
got

285

the
plot
Tel
(*comforting Keanu sadly*)
Shall I get his stuff now?
Julie
Might as well
Tel
Come on Kenny

Who is whimpering

You tell me
what we've got
to pack

*They make to leave. Julie
stands looking after them.
Video close-up cuts.*

Keanu (*turns holding his
dad's hand*)
Laugha Mamma
Sadda Mamma

SCENE SIX

*Lady God's bedroom.
Approaching midnight.
Candlelight only.
It is something of a
shrine to alternative visions,
a young fantasist's room.
There are pictures borrowed
from Narnia and Terry
Pratchett's Discworld,
Merlin-type wizards,
maidens, pre-Raphaelite
angels, with crystals hanging, slabs of shiny rock,
interspersed with posters
of pop stars, aliens and pets.*

*Lady God holds a large
old chocolate tin, battered,
but still grand-looking in
gold and purple with a
purple satin ribbon.*

*She unties the bow,
takes off the lid.*

Lady God
My memory box

*Sound made by the
Hood, wind, a man's
voice singing a lullaby,
whispers, rain, a clatter
of pots and pans,
whimpers. Sweetly sung
or intoned, in whole or
in part.*

Angels sent me
that's what he said
see
here are the feathers

*She takes out five white
feathers.*

from their left
wingtip

She strokes her cheek
with them.
    She takes out a strand
of hair.

A lock of baby hair
my angel hair
he called it

She turns it round.

He twined it
with his own.

His broken watch

She takes out a very fragile
Christmas ornament
wrapped in gold tissue.
    Whispers:

A glass angel
for the Christmas tree.

It dropped
and chipped

red blood
spotting
the linoleum,
he sucked
my cut finger,

next day
a miracle!

She smiles.

But I knew
he'd stuck
the angel's tiny hand
with glue.

She takes out.

A bus ticket
to the Zoo

And a special
photo too
him and me
and very far away

the angels see.

She takes out:

And the five-pound note
he gave me for
emergencies

His thumb print
in coal;

he laid a fire
that night

we watched it blaze
the flame angels
frightened me

Lights shift, song stops.
The Hood creep forward.
They create a rhythmic
beat. Underneath they
musically improvise,
soul or scat-sing over all,
God raps, freestyle.

Lady God (*rapped*)
When I was about five
they came for me
out from the
empty grate
the cinders
and the ash

their wings
neatly folded
like butterflies
resting on a rose.

I told
them

I'd
prefer
to
stay

where I was

thank you

in the
small
dirty house

with the cockroaches
and the flying ants.

They argued,

the fieriest

warned
the others
of

the consequences
if they
let me stay

and
they
talked
about
mother

'The Mother'

which was
a
waste of time
because
I
knew

she'd gone away
at the
end of
my first year
on earth,

deciding
she
didn't
like us,

me
and
him.

They
came
back again

many times

always blazing,
usually
on a
Sunday afternoon

making
him turn off
the afternoon
western
and
hide stuff,

their flame
wings

whipping up
a wind,

making
the
chipped cups
shiver
on
the
draining board.

And once
far away
on a jagged beach
somewhere

I saw
a trillion
angels
red hot
blind
but
beckoning

on the
other side
of the horizon.

I see them
now
all the time

I see them
as I roll up my sleeves
tie the bootlace

And try
to remember
to breathe

Lights lift slightly.
The four Ladies are
gathered around four
large candles. Lady Chill
is heating a large bobbin
needle in the flame. They
are drinking flavoured
vodka (by the pint). Lady
God has just died her
hair and has a towel
wrapped round her head.
She is holding an ice-bag
to her nose. There is
an ice-box at their feet.
Although they are in gang
gear, alone together and
out of the public eye,
they are not very different
from any other four young
girls having a social night.
Lady Lurve is separate,
quiet, morose, drinking

heavily, on her way to
oblivion.

In the background,
from another downstairs
room, we hear many
voices, a gathering at
prayer.

Occasionally this stops
and there is silence, then
the tinkling of many
small bells before it
resumes.

Lady Wad enthuses,
they listen, so do the
Hood, who establish a
beat.

Lady Wad (*fast rap*)
I want to call shots
I want to sack grubby
suits
for leering at my tits
over their laptops
I want to be strict with
silly slappers
who snigger at my vision
I want to hog page three
of the FT
I want my Big Idea to be
revered
I want bank managers to
whisper
awesome and orgasm cash
all over my preliminary
planning
I want sucksess

because power and
money's
better than sex
I want to go from bitch
to Top Dog to Big Boss
to Profit Goddess of the
Western World

Lady Lurve
Is that all, girl?

Uneasy pause.

I don't get you,
with all your big ideas
why hang with us,
this gang?

You're a posh kid
from the right side

Mummy and Daddy
are intellectuals
they 'socialise'
Why slum it here?

Pause.

Lady Wad
Because it's more fun
than slumming it
at Mummy's book club

All but Lurve laugh.

Lady Lurve
Oh, that's all right then
Em,
as long as you're having
fun

Lady Chill (*warning*)
Julie
Lady Lurve
Can I join
the book club?
I'm banned from the
library
for jacking
Das Kapital
Lady God
What do you want
Julie?

Julie shrugs.

Lady Lurve
Know
what
I
don't want,
to spend a dead-end life
in a one-horse,
putting a trillion teas
on a table,

for a
fanny poking
shit

with
breath fresheners
in his
back pocket
and
a crocodile
smile,

shiny shoes
and
itchy feet.

A life
of lipstick lies
Lady Wad
Oh, talking of lipsticks

*She opens bag and takes
a fistful of lipsticks.*

Bobby Brown
the real thing
for you
to take the sting
half-price
Lady Lurve
Where do you get that
crap?
Lady Wad (*eye to eye*)
I steal it
Lady God
You know
what I really want,
it sounds
an impossible thing

Dad used to say,
you should try
to leave the planet
a better place than
when you arrived

*There has been a few
minutes' silence from the
prayers. The bell tinkles,
the prayers start again.*

Lady Wad
(*referring to the prayer*)
I don't know how you
put up with it?
Lady Chill
It's giving me the willies
Lady God
Wednesday is for
'Gathering Prayer'
Lady Lurve
Leave that dye
on any longer
and it'll
be
buying a wig day
Lady God
Oh dear

*She disappears into the
bathroom.*
    Pause.

Lady Chill (*to Lurve*)
What's up
with you?
Lady Wad (*it bursts out*)
Tel's kidnapped Keanu
Lady Chill
What?
Lady Wad
The whole town's
talking
Lady Chill
Why didn't you say, girl?
What are we here for?
Tell me?

Pride!
Protection!
Power!
Partnership!

We're the Ladies
You're in trouble!
We're in trouble!

Get your coat
we go to his door
give it a kicking!
give him a licking!

And bring baby Keanu
home
to Mama
now!

Lurve laughs.

Lady Lurve
I gave him away, Chill
Tel didn't take him
I gave him up

A long uneasy pause.

Did you hear me?

Just like
your mum
gave you up
at the shrine
of the giant
sea serpent

I've given him up
Lady Wad
I see

Lady Lurve
You have a problem
with that?

*Pause, no one speaks. She
laughs, she's very drunk.*

I didn't love him
alright?
I couldn't
love him
And he
didn't like me
I couldn't . . .
love him
Lady Wad
It's cool
Lady Lurve
Chill? Is it cool
with you?

Chill says nothing.

Is it?

Lurve laughs.

Chill's not
cool
with that

*Lady God comes in. She
has a green quiff. She
looks delighted.*

Lady God
Like it?
Lady Lurve (*sour*)
Fabulous

matches your skin
Lady God (*takes ice-pack
off, touches her nose*)
I can't feel anything
Lady Wad
You're sure
your mum's
not going to scream
at this?
Lady God
I stayed out
all night once
she didn't utter a word
Lady Chill
When did you meet her?
Lady God
Six months ago
when Dad died
Lady Wad (*referring to the
bobbing needle in the
flame*)
Right the needle's sterile
Lady Chill (*distracted*)
Yeah . . . Right

*Light goes down on
them, light up on Piety
and the Hood as Seven
Day Evangelists. They are
all in black, women wear
headscarves.*

Piety
And God said
let there be light

SCENE SEVEN

*Thursday morning. Just
past midnight.*

  Piety's living room.

  *Scene starts with Seven
Dayers moving from sitting
position (even though no
chairs) as if after a pro-
tracted session. They shake
hands, smile, hug. There is
a burr of civilised chatter.*

  *Suddenly a scream, a
babble of voices, cursing,
feet careering down steps.*

  *Faith (Lady God) enters,
blood is pouring from her
nose. Her T-shirt is sodden
and red. The towel she is
holding is also covered in
blood. She is wild-eyed
and screaming. The Ladies
follow. Assisting her is
Wad, Lurve and Chill
follow, sullen, sheepish.*

Lady Chill
  I told
  her
  it would
  hurt
Piety
  Oh
  my poor
  Faith

Lady Lurve
  It's her own fault
  Chill's an expert nose
  piercer
Piety (*to Lurve*)
  All that blood
  from one tiny hole

  Be brave
  my darling girl

  Attending to Lady God.

  (*to Ladies*) How lovely to
  meet you all at last
Lady Lurve
  Pardon?

  They are all surprised.

Piety (*animated*)
  I've seen you
  I wanted to say hello
  but I was shy.

  There
  all done

  *The Seven Dayers are
  departing. Piety says
  goodbye to them shaking
  hands, introducing.*

Piety
  Have you met my
  daughter Faith?

Piety seems radiant, happy.
    Suddenly Faith pulls
away, sharply violently.
The Hood creep forward
providing background
beat. God raps freestyle.

Lady God (*rap*)
    That's enough!

Tense silence. To Piety:

Do you hear me?

that's the end

I don't want
to meet
your weird friends

I told you
they make my
skin crawl
and my soul bleed

If they
want to do
good deeds

tell them all
to jump

in
the canal.

I don't believe in God

Not your
sick

old
worn
out
God,

who sits in the sky
wringing his hands
getting mad
settling scores
making wars

A prick
with a
big stick
spitting and screaming
at the fleeing angels

Video camera close-up on
Piety.

Piety (*softly*)
    God
    loves you
    Faith
Lady God
    And you,
    do you
    love me?

Agonised silence.

I said
do you love me?

Short video close-up on
Lady God – which cuts.
    Lights dip.

Chill and Lurve sit side by side. There is a strained atmosphere. The Hood creep around them. They provide a tense background pulse, maybe a musical note. Suddenly it stops.

Lady Lurve (*still pissed*)
You never said
what *you* wanted

Pause.

Lady Chill (*sour*)
I didn't
did I?

Lady Wad walks slowly. She looks shaken.

Lady Lurve
What?

Wad says nothing.

Lady Lurve
What?
Lady Wad
She's . . .
Lady Lurve
Yes
Lady Wad
She's . . .

you know
injecting herself,
now, in there,
fixing up
whatever you call it

Lurve starts to laugh.

Lady Wad (*to Chill*)
Did you know?

Pause.

Did you know?
Lady Chill (*completely expressionless*)
Yes

A slow light comes up on Lady God. She is white-faced, sweating, eyes dilated. It is frightening.

Lady Lurve
Has she got any stuff?
Lady Wad
What?!
Lady Lurve
Ask her?

Pause.

Lady Chill (*softly*)
Ask her?

SCENE EIGHT

*Lights up. Banner says 'Not
at all Friendly Neighbourhood Building Society.'*

*Emma (Lady Wad) is
centre stage. She sits
behind a representation of
a building society perspex
counter and wall. She is
dressed in 'smart' uniform.
A nasty nylon blazer and
frilly collar. Her hair is tied
back. She looks scrubbed,
respectable.*

*From her desk is a long
queue (full company – the
Hood, including Smelly).*

Emma
No, no
you can't
do that – Next!

Honeyed Electronic Voice
Go to Cashier No 6
please

Smelly Nelly
Sorry?

Emma
You can't get thirty
pounds out
when you've only got ten
pounds in

*She hands book back,
shouting.*

Emma
Next!

Honeyed Electronic Voice
Go to Cashier No 6
please

*Person behind Nelly
pushes forward, Nelly
pushes back.*

Smelly Nelly
Hang on
I don't understand

She peers at the book.

I haven't got my specs

Emma
Next!

Smelly Nelly
Don't 'next' me
you cheeky little sod
Give me my life savings
or I'll call the Plods

Emma
You've only got a tenner
in
you daft bat

There's new rules now

Smelly Nelly
Daft bat?
New rules?

Emma
There's a queue

297

I haven't time
to argue

I'm forced
to implement
new security measures

She presses a button.

**Loud Gravelly Electronic
Voice**
Leave the premises
I repeat
Leave the premises

You have insufficient
funds

You
are a poor
time-wasting
insignificant
little saver

Withdrawal not authorised
Withdrawal not authorised

Miss Helpful
What's going on here
Miss Wanting?

*Emma whispers furiously
in her ear:*

Emma
Look!

She shows her the book.

Miss Helpful
What's happened is

you've shown us
the wrong book

*Smelly gets another book
from her pocket. Miss
Helpful takes the book
and shows it to Emma.
It obviously shows a
phenomenal amount.
Emma is gob-smacked.*

With her late husband
Jack, Mrs Staines
pioneered a popular chain
of amusement arcades

That's the right account,
Nelly.
You withdrew rather
heavily
on your weekly money,
remember,
to buy a camcorder
to record . . .

Smelly Nelly
The ghosts

Miss Helpful
Yes . . .
were they . . .

Smelly Nelly
successful?
Very
got a lovely close-up
of Boadicea

*A middle-aged couple
enter. Smiling and*

respectable, they never-
theless have the air of old
hippies.

Emma's Mum
Hello, sweetheart
We've finished for the
day.
So we thought
we'd take you out

for a slap-up.
What do you say?
Our treat.
Emma (*looking out into*
street, horrified)
I've told you.
I meet
my friends
for lunch
Emma's Dad
Well, that's okay
we'll treat them too
Emma
They're
not your type

He spies Nelly.

Emma's Dad
No! No!
It can't be
Nelly Staines
Old Aunty Nell
Smelly
Eh?
Emma's Dad
It's me. Annie's boy!

Smelly
Never!

Annie's boy
had his arse
hanging out
of his pants

Emma's Dad turns around
shows his arse hanging
out.

Dad
It's me, Nelly
(*introducing*)
My wife Jean
you've met my daughter,
Em

Emma opens and closes
her mouth.

Dad
Nelly
was an old friend
of your grandma's
when she was alive
they were wicked girls
together
so I'm told

Smelly laughs warmly.

Look

let's catch up
over lunch

Join us.

Emma
 Dad
Dad
 My treat!

Lights down on scene,
pin spotlight on Emma
(*Lady Wad*).

STUFF SOCRATES

Lady Wad (*freestyle*)
 Sitting in a Café Naf
 making dough bullets out
 of bread
 Mummy pretends Nelly's
 stink's not doing in her
 head
 She practises smiling,
 patronising every Monday,
 Wednesday
 and Friday
 In the Help the Stinkies
 Shop
 Where, voluntarily, she
 gets first crack at the hand
 knits
 and all the best crap
 Daddy's in philosiphee
 He mouths off in the
 local below bog standard
 Poly
 Trying to take the sting
 out of this Nietzschian
 nightmare existence
 Whatever the frig that is!

Chorus.

Stuff Descartes, Thales
Hulme and Socrates
I work not to think too
hard
For me the future of the
planet's corporate
I'm looking for investors
To Mummy and Daddy,
I might be coming from
Mars.

(Mummy's making a fan
out of her paper napkin
Nelly orders moules
marinière
and a sly steak done
medium rare
Mummy gags at the tag
Daddy spits out Marx,
Wittgenstein and Locke
Nelly just spits chilled
sauvignon blanc down
her dirty frock
And he's getting wet
about his cobblestone
boyhood.
The knobhead. Heard it a
million times.)

Chorus.

I pocket three hundred
bendy straws
tied with a ribbon, given
with a scented sachet of
torpedo sweeties

they make a neat freebie
With my Bacardi and
liquorice allsorts
Breezers,
popular with the under
nines
You buy 5.95 for 6 – I
buy . . .?
that's for me to know and
you to . . .
I'm thick, not dyslexic,
thick as pigshit
so they sent me to a
Steiner
to be good with my

hands, make bird tables,
and act in plays about
gangs

Instead I set up a mobile
tuck shop
from my sports bag
lugging the profits up
town
to bulk buy pirated tapes
to sell at a skull and
crossbones mark up
and an honest guv
markdown

Chorus.

SCENE NINE

Thursday night, ten-ish.
At the top window as if
in his shop overlooking the
park, Stylo, in silhouette,
plays blues sax. At another
window further away the
Shaikwondo expert
practises.
Scene change. Park bogs.
Two doors with stick
emblems of man and
woman covered in the tags
of the Four Ladies. As well
as ancient graffiti, etchings,

dating back decades. Lights
suggest trees, bushes,
enclosure.
Chill, Lurve run on.
They are red-faced,
panting, out of breath.
They are in gang gear and
holding aerosol paint spray
cans. Following on his bike
is Pinky, with him is Bad
News, wearing a gas mask,
and Matches. Sax stops,
Stylo remains as a
silhouette.

Lady Chill (*giggling,*
whispering)
Oh man
that was scary
Matches (*very excited*)
I love scary
I love it
I love it
Lady Chill
I did that
garage door
next to Fat Jak's
paper shop
Bad News (*putting gas*
mask up)
Fat Jak's
dead.
Well
he will be
next week!
Lady Chill
A perfect tag
four feet high
from a shot
six foot away
beautiful
all in one
sweep

When this plod
taking a piss
steps out of the alley
zipper unzipped

I'm holding
the can

he's holding
his pride and joy

So
you know what
I did?
Lady Lurve
You sprayed his dick

They roar with laughter.

Lady Chill
Let's see him
explain that
to his desk sergeant
Lady Lurve
We all know
there's a plod
on the beat tonight
with a green knob

More laughter except . . .

Pinky
I don't think
that's very funny

He winces.

Was it
touch-up
car paint?

Chill nods.

Pinky (*serious*)
He'll have to
dip
it in
turps

More hilarious laughter.

all
night

*Wad appears, she too has
a spray gun. She appears
subdued.*

Bad News
The suit didn't fit Wad
Lady Chill
Where's . . .?

She looks around.

Lady Wad
She needed . . .
stuff
Lady Chill
She's
been
at the blow

all day

Long uneasy pause.

Pinky (*quietly*)
One of the
Craven Street
Crew
deals for her,
Sticky
they've got . . . a thing
Lady Chill
What!!
Lady Lurve
The Pussy Posse
run

with the Crew
Sticky belongs to Missy
Lady Chill
You'd better fetch her
She'll need watching
bring her back here

If
Missy Cat
finds out
Lady God's been
messing
with her man

She'll scratch
her bowels out
Matches (*very excited*)
Follow me
I haven't burnt the park
down
Follow me

*Chill watches. As they
leave, a figure with a
torch approaches from
behind, at first unseen by
Chill.*

Miss Nice Face
Carly?

*Chill swings round,
drawing her knife. She
sees a young, athletic
woman.*

Miss Nice Face
(*she is panting, breathless*)
Put that away

Chill hesitates.

Miss Nice Face
Please

Chill does so.

Miss Nice Face
Well, you lost
the policeman
Lady Chill
with the green dick
Miss Nice Face
Yes,
so
you're obviously
still fit

Pause. They look at each other.

Lady Chill (*suddenly*)
Look
I can't stand
around here
all night
Miss Nice Face
We need
to talk

How are you?
Lady Chill (*pauses, slowly smiles*)
Breezy
Miss Nice Face
They've closed down
the children's home!

Video camera close-up on Lady Chill. Lady Chill stands very still.

Miss Nice Face
Just last month
they're knocking it down

You can go and see
the bulldozers

It was a terrible place
Carly
Lady Chill
(*sourly, very softly*)
Was it?
Miss Nice Face
Yes
and it did
terrible things
to you

Very softly.

I'll never forget that
morning
finding you.
Lady Chill
That was okay
all you had to do
was wait and see.
you got to be
an older kid
yourself
one day
Miss Nice Face
It was hell

304

and it was hell
for me
watching
them do stuff
torture you
torture children

day in
day out

I . . . I . . .
didn't
couldn't
do enough . . . I'm sorry

Lady Chill
(*video close-up finishes.
Suddenly aggressive*)
Shut it . . . Shut it
right
I got out
I got away
I survived

I do my own
thing now
have friends

I take charge,

I've got plans
big plans.

I'll have a future

Pause.

Miss Nice Face
Do you swim
still?

*Pause.
Chill laughs.*

Lady Chill
No

Miss Nice Face
Why?

Lady Chill
I gave up
that shit

I . . .
stay away
from water

I . . .
don't like it

Miss Nice Face
Oh Carly
that's nonsense
you are the best
the very best
young swimmer
I have ever seen

She gets out card.

I coach now
at national level
I help pick the team,

Let me help you
Carly
that's why I've come

*Lurve enters, she is
panting, breathless.*

Lady Lurve
You've got to come

305

turns out
those Cats
aren't Pussies
after all,
Missy Cat's
got wind
God's
screwing her
man
in the bushes,

and they've
swapped pom-poms
for blades
Lady Chill
Blades?
Lady Chill
We'd better
find her
before they do

They make to go. Chill
stops, turns and smiles.

You arrive
from your Nice Life
dealing favours
dripping smiles
sticky with guilt
thinking

you'll click fingers
and I'll dive.

No one
fires no starting gun.

No one
yells from the tiles.

No one
takes down my time.

I'll never swim
I'll never dive again.

Lights dip on main scene,
lights down on
Shaikwondo expert, up
on Stylo. At the window.
Now open to the night.
He wears pyjamas;
without sunglasses his
eyes are blind and
staring. His face terribly
scarred. His voice low
and thick with a heavy
local accent.

Stylo
People say,
why are you blind?
Because I was a bad man
and I did bad things.

Pride
Power
Protection
Partnership

This was the fifties
so protection
was our line,
our life,
a living,
for our kind.

We owned
the streets.

Our patches
were marked up
in red biro
over the dog-eared
maps.

A small business
paid
to be kept safe
from
the next street's
lads,

but
a week's arrears
from the Protectorate –
we'd put the windows in
smash the locks

a month,
take out
their business advisor,
the youngest son,
for a lesson
in economic sense,
insuring
he might
never walk again.

One night,
I can still see,

It's branded
on the inside
of my skull,

It seared my soul,

a Chinese family
two proud sons,

a nice little chippy,
think they're Triads

send out word
they won't pay
another shilling
no way!

unless we meet
on the canal bank
to settle
like gentlemen.

while they tumbled
I was sent
to torch the joint,
which I did
with petrol rags
and my best silver lighter,
without questions,

only to hear
the screams
of the three tiny girls,

a little too late.

Lights go down on Stylo.
Up on park, the doors
have gone. We are in a
bushy enclosed area.
Faith (Lady God) is
screaming, panting,
crying. She is holding her
trousers, which are
undone. Her clothes are
dishevelled. Sticky is
zipping himself up,
sweaty, disorientated.

Sticky
  Man
  you're a crazy
  Lady.
Lady God
  You hurt me.
Sticky (*without malice*)
  Sure I hurt you
  that's why I'm here
  to hurt you

*She screams again. He
jumps, puts his hand to
her mouth, but it's too late.
  The Pussy Posse
appear. Missy Cat is
alone, white-faced,
stony-eyed, Li'l Fluff and
Whiskers behind.*

Missy Cat (*soft,
  threatening*)
  Lady Tart
  Lady Bitch
  Lady Trash
  Lady Witch
Sticky (*nonplussed*)
  Look Puss
  You mustn't
  make too much
  of this,
  take it
  too much
  to heart.

  I gave her stuff,
  she had no cash

I could have taken
plastic
but instead
being a red-blooded male
I took
tail.

It was
purely
transaction.

A business deal,
an into-knickers
experience
in exchange
for a quick fix.
Whiskers/Li'l Fluff
  Happens all the time.
Missy Cat (*to Sticky*)
  And you!
  she's trash
  how could you?

*From the darkness, a soft
threatening voice.*

Honk
  Yes, Sticky
  how could you?

*Slowly, very slowly, a red
light comes up on the
Craven Crew. Honk, the
leader, Omo, Bird: they
all have blades.
  From nowhere, the
Hood creep and crawl
forward, frightened but*

wanting to see and hear.
They establish a tense
beat.

MAD BOYS

Whispering creeping closer.

The Hood
  Mad Boys
  on the tail trail
Omo
  I don't know,
  if you like
  skinny slags
The Hood
  Looking to deal
  day and night
  sniffin' it out
Bird
  And Stick
  likes
  skinny slags
The Hood
  From the
  other side of Crack town,
  there's no going down
  with the glue crew,
  it's bang bang
  you're dead
  lucky,
  though it's messy
  though it's bloody
  coming
  from the crew

Voice 1 (*whispered*)
  I knew a sweet girl
  turned down 'a date'
  next day . . .
Voice 2
  Found her papillon pup
  nailed
  to the front gate
Voice 3
  My cuz
  cut them up one night
  in his customised Toyote,
  took him off the road
Voice 4
  down a ditch
Voice 5
  his face needed
  two hundred and nine
  stitches
  when they finished
  teaching him

  their highway code.

Beat stops.

Honk
  The point
  is
  Sticky,
  the stuff
  you dealt
  belongs.
Bird
  belonged

Honk
  to us
  right
Omo
  the whole Crew!
Honk
  And if you
  got tail
  for it

  then

  To Lady God:

Honk/Omo/Bird
  we all
  want
  a bit
Honk
  like now.
Missy Cat
  Teach her
  to screw
  my guy.

They all make a move on
the terrified Lady God.
The Posse hold her down.
The Crew stand over her.
Lady God manages a
scream. Honk puts a
hand over her mouth.
The violence is ugly and
the threat real. The Hood
back off and away. They
make a background beat.

WHORES AND SNITCHES

Honk (*fast rap*)
  I hate squealy slags
  skinny hags with dirty
  teeth and needle tracks

  thin hair, dead stare

Omo
  I hate fat bitches
  screaming witches with
  bad skin and saggy titties

  ankle chains, daggy
  names
Bird
  Berry Jane, Saffron Mae
  I hate sneery slappers

  don't touch fuckers with
  short skirts and boyfriend
  rappers

  'Treble rum and coke
  please'
  some hope sleaze!
Omo
  We hate four things
Bird
  girls, women, bitches
  and . . .
Honk/Omo/Bird
  Ladies
Honk
  They're all whores or
  snitches

Bird
  And of the four I think
  maybe . . .
Honk/Omo/Bird
  We hate
Honk
  'Ladies'
Honk/Omo/Bird
  Most

Beat stops.
    *Suddenly Lady Chill
appears. She grabs
Whiskers round the neck
pulling her away,
pointing a knife at her
throat.*
    *Behind her Lady Lurve
and Lady Wad.*

Lady Chill
  You touch one hair
  I cut

*Everyone looks on.
Absolute silence.*
    Then:

Lady God
  No, Chill, no!
  Don't hurt her,
  Don't hurt her
  for me

*Pause. Omo starts to
laugh crazily. Following
happens quickly.*

Omo
  Hear her?
  Fish tail
  Put that knife down now
  she might
  break a nail.

Suddenly cold.

Honk
  or . . .
  Cut!
  Go on
  I dare you
  Cut, cut!
Missy Cat (*scared*)
  Honk!

Li'l Fluff starts to cry.

Bird
  Cut!
Missy Cat
  Sticky . . . Bird . . .
Bird (*not so sure*)
  yeah, cut

*Whiskers starts to whim-
per. Chill tightens her
hold. She looks dangerous.*

Lady God
  Please, Chill
  don't hurt her

*Chill looks at Lady God.
The Crew start to move
in, softly chanting*

The Crew
  Cut! Cut!

Chill tightens her hold on
Whiskers, who gags.
    Siren of police car.
Sudden mayhem. Lurve
snatches at God and pulls
her to them. Running
feet. Chill shoves a half-
choked Whiskers at the
Crew. They all have to
split. Furious whispers.

Honk (*to Chill*)
  You wouldn't cut
  You ain't got spunk
  enough
Chill (*vicious*)
  wave it
  This way
  Honk
  one dark night

She slices the air with her
knife.

  Rat food
Honk (*angry*)
  You bring
  the skank
  formally known
  as Lady God
  back here to the park bogs
  and leave her
  same time tomorrow
. for The Crew

If not
all of
The Ladies
prepare
for serious strife,
a fight
for gang pride

at The Inferno

midnight, Saturday,
outside
on the foggy
canal bank.
Bird
  You owe Lady Tail
Omo
  If we don't get it
  from Crazy Tail
Honk
  We'll get it from
  some other
  Ladies' end

They laugh.

Lady Lurve
  Promises!
  Promises!!

Derisory laughter from
the Ladies.

Bird
  You owe
Honk
  And you'll pay

Police sirens get louder.
Running footsteps.
Everyone but Chill and
Honk splits. They hold
their ground eye-to-eye
video close-up of Chill.
A whisper:

if you bitches
don't show

that's the end
of Lady rule.
We take the streets

Close-up cuts. Lights dip.

SCENE TEN

Outskirts of the park. Lady
Chill is dragging Lady God.

Lady God
I can't . . .
I can't . . .
Lady Chill (*looking*
behind, nervously)
Catch your breath

Lady God starts to laugh
softly.

Lady Chill
What?
Lady God
I . . .
I don't know

Pause.

Lady Chill
Did you . . . ?

Lady God shakes her
head. From a pocket she

takes out a small packet.
Her fingers close around
it. She puts it back in her
pocket. Pause.

Lady God (*serious again*)
You'd have cut
Whiskers
Carly?
wouldn't you?

Pause.

Somebody's hurt you
somebody's hurt you
very badly

Suddenly Lady God hugs
Chill, holding on to her
like a tiny child. Chill is
taken aback. She freezes,
neither pulling away nor
returning the hug.

Lady God (*very softly*)
I love you

SCENE ELEVEN

*Short video close-up of
Lady Chill.
Secret enclosure. Bushes in
different part of the park.
 The Ladies squat,
panting. Video camera cuts
jerkily from face to face.*

Lady Wad (*Softly*)
 You can't pull a tumble
 at The Inferno
Lady Lurve
 Too many crazies
Lady Wad
 Too many
 dangerous maybes

 On Saturday
 the town
 will heave
 with those
 Shaikwondo creeps
Lady Chill
 On the canal bank
 they said
Lady Wad
 that water
 cold and black
 makes me afraid
Lady God
 You must
 take me
 back now

 to the park
 and leave me there.
 just as they say
Lady Chill
 Never.
 Pride.
 Power.
 Protection.
 Partnership.

*Wad takes Chill slightly
to one side and whispers.
Video camera cuts.*

Lady Wad
 You're mad

 A girl
 I knew
 two-timed
 the crew
 they took her
 to a lock up.
 kept her
 for a week
 when she got out
 she couldn't speak,
 still can't
Lady Chill
 What we lose in weight
 we gain
 in brains
Lady Lurve
 Spirit

314

Lady Chill
  Courage,
  make up
  in female cunning,
  what we lose
  in male muscle

  but better take
  your blades
Lady Wad
  No
Lady God
  I won't hurt anyone.
  Not them
  or anyone,
  whatever
  ever
Lady Wad
  Hear that
  we get sliced
  while Lady Yella Belly . . .
Lady Lurve
  Yella Belly
  I'll tell you who's yella . . .
Lady Wad
  lights
  friggin' candles!
Lady Chill (*suddenly
  furious, grabbing* Wad)
  Why are we
  in this gang?

  To sell T-shirts
  on street corners

  To party?
  To pose?

The gang
protects its own,
fights for its own,
fights to keep
the streets.

Why are we
in this gang?

*The Hood provide musical
base.*

GANG RAP

Freestyle.

Lady Lurve
  **They don't scream 'slag'
  at the Gang
  'Ugly easy shag'
  They don't point and
  whisper 'like father like
  daughter'
  'Cos I'm in the Gang**

  To the Hood:

  **They don't spit at my kid
  in the street**
Lady God
  In the Gang

  To the Hood:

  **I've somewhere safe to go
  somewhere sweet to be,
  somewhere warm to be
  me
  something bright to hope**

to see
In the Gang
Lady Chill (*to Wad*)
**Why are you
in this Gang?**

Wad hesitates.

In the Gang

To the Hood:

**I don't just rule the streets
I invent the rules
I play the tune
you jig to
I pull the strings
I call the shots
but hear me, ritzy lady
when the fast buck stops
It stops with me.**
Lady God (*starting to cry*)
Please
take me
to the park
and leave me there
I couldn't bear

If you were hurt
for me
Lady Chill
Never
we're here
for you

tonight
tomorrow
And for ever more.

Smelly Nelly (*with a lead
calling a dog*)
Stinker!
Stinker!

*She sees Wad, stops in
her tracks.*

Smelly Nelly (*intense*)
It's you
is it?

She sighs.

Well,
I've no stick
you see
tonight

It's by the fire
keeping the cat
company.

Pause.

My shoelace
is undone
you could

stamp on that

steal my bag
my keys
my purse.

There's no end
to the brave
and fearless
things
you could do
big girl?

The Ladies appear
uncomfortable, for once.
No one wants a fight.

Well,

I'm
waiting.
Lady Chill
(*attempting a laugh*)
Go home
old woman

Smelly Nelly (*cackles*)
Old
older than you think
They're coming
I feel
them
the ghosts
ready
to
bite
your heels.

SCENE TWELVE

Four Ladies stand centre
stage. During rap they peel
off clothes to reveal Gang
club gear.
   Fast rap. Hood make
musical background.

LOOKING FOR RESPECT

The Ladies
Make no mistake the
clock's not ticking back
And the Ladies won't
wait for no sick
Sorry you took the rap
crap
Lady God
We're hot and high and
humming

All
and look out 'cos the
sparks fly
When you're bummin'
And we're looking for
respect.
Lady Chill
Take your face out my
space, mate
Watch your lairy stare,
'cos you're breathin' my air
Lady Lurve
At chuckin' after pullin'
And the tenth rum and
spliff and virgin coke
When you're comin' full
on and we tell you
Get your coat
It's in out unzip and
shake it all about

Lady Wad
  Before bye-bye boy wave
  to the nice lady
  No matter if you're shit
  hot and shootin' straight
All
  We're calling shots, 'cos
  the clock's not ticking back
  And the Ladies won't
  wait for no sick
  Sorry you took the rap crap
Lady God
  We're hot and high and
  humming
All
  and look out 'cos the
  sparks fly
  When you're bummin'
  And we're lookin' for
  respect
Lady Chill
  Don't think, we won't
  punch it out
  You bitch us up and we'll
  tout for a fist fight
  And we're talkin' steel on
  every knuckle

Lady Lurve
  'Cos only we give the lip
  muscle
All
  On these streets
  On these sweet streets
  On these sweet streets
Lady Chill
  You see that piece of dirty
  sky up high we own
  Lady paving stones, we
  own the cracks
  So watch where you step,
  the clock ain't tickin' back
All
  And the Ladies won't
  wait for no sick
  Sorry you took the rap crap
Lady God
  We're hot and high and
  humming
All
  and look out 'cos the
  sparks fly
  When you're bummin'
  And we're lookin' for
  respect

SCENE THIRTEEN

*Saturday Night. Deafening
club music, strobe lights.
The Hood are dancing.*
  *A banner says 'The
Inferno'. This is the hottest*
nightclub in the 'hood.
  *The Four Ladies dance,
Chill and Lurve with
defiant abandon – God
seems preoccupied. Wad is*

staring up at well-dressed
middle-aged man who
stares back. He stands
short. Video close-up of
man – a small gesture.
Wad looks questioningly to
Chill. Video cuts.

  Music dips suddenly to
allow dialogue to be heard.

Lady Chill (*whispers*)
  Make sure

  you're back
  by twelve.

  Wad makes to go, she is
  stopped by –

  On the stroke
  we'll scarper,
  hide, for a while
  in the cellars
  underground
  while rumours
  of our flight
  sweeten the night
  for the Craven Crew
  and
  soften their resolve.
  Fatally soften.
  At a quarter past
  the hour
  like rats
  in a drainpipe
  we'll make
  for the tunnels.

At half past
waiting for an
impartial moon

to disappear
behind
a friendly cloud,
we'll come up
and out
on the canal bank
exactly where
they loiter,
careless.

Remember,
pride,
power,
protection,
partnership.
Lady God
won't fight,
three on four
we have
a chance,
but two,
we lose
the night.

Don't let
some rich dick
come between
your duty
to the Ladies,
to the future.
Lady Wad
  Look
  it's no big thing.

Lady Lurve
From the small
protuberance
in his crutch
I'd say you're right.
Lady Wad
We'll chat.
Lady Chill
Keep shtum
about the spat.
Lady Wad (*smiling,
attempting to leave*)
Stay cool,
Lady's Rule.
Lady Chill
And by midnight,
return.

*Wad leaves.
To God, encouraging:*

Chin up
I'd die
before I'd let
the Craven Crew
hurt you.
Lady God (*to Chill and
Lurve*)
I can't bear it
They're mad boys,
pumped
on hate
Lady Lurve (*softly,
attempting to calm*)
You're forgetting tactics
we'll outwit
those mad street hos.

You'll see.
You'll see.

*As Wad accepts a glass of
champagne from smiling
Rich Dick, lights suddenly
change. We see a smaller
banner proclaiming 'The
Hoods Piggin' Ugly Town
Hall – Shaikwondo
Contest'.*

Pussy Posse
Clap your hands
and stamp your feet

for tonight's
Shaikwondo heats
Missy Cat
We're here
no fear
Li'l Fluff
to cheer
on
the boys
Whiskers
We're their
cuddly toys
Li'l Fluff
Love those
rippling
muscles
Ho!
Whiskers
Press our
tummies
and we squeak

Li'l Fluff
And
I'm talking
seriously
fluffy
all over

Don't be
mean
with the
baby oil
geek
Pussy Posse
Clap your hands
while we
shimmy
shimmy
shimmy

while the boys
in the crowd

go

Gimme!
Gimme!
Gimme!
Missy Cat
I just
love it
when their
tongues
hang out
like that
Whiskers
I just
love it

when
their eyes
pop out
on stalks
like that
Li'l Fluff
I just
love it
when
little pearls
of sweat
appear
on their
top lip
like that
Pussy Posse
We torture
and we tease
you can look
but don't squeeze
please
Missy Cat
You fiddle
with my pom-poms
chum
and you're looking

at seven months'
youth detention
minimum
Pussy Poss
'Cos
judges
love us
Missy Cat
Fresh Pussy

Pussy Poss
  with our
  sweet
  helpless
  giggles

They all giggle.

  push-up tits

They push up tits.

Li'l Fluff
  All the
  best babes
  get a
  boob job
  on their
  seventeenth
  birthday
Whiskers
  And our
  batty

  scatty –

  baby blue
  flappy
  eyes
Pussy Poss
  Clap your hands
  and stamp your feet.
  the Chinese Shadow's
  in the final heat.

*The Hood in The Inferno
now become the Hood in
the Town Hall, watching
the martial arts*

competition.
  *A pool of light shows
Mrs Joy Foo Yung's
nephew in the middle of a
Shaikwondo karate
contest.*
  *The fight is stylised,
formalised, like a fierce
dance.*

Li'l Fluff
  For us!
Whiskers
  Our very own
  good guy!
Missy Cat
  Kicking out for the
  Hood!
Whiskers
  He's shaikwondoed
  his way through the six
  towns.
Missy Cat
  Like he was
  chopping wood!!
All
  Two. Four. Six. Seven . . .
  Who makes you feel
  like you've gone to . . .

A communal gasp.
  *The Chinese boy has
his partner in a dangerous
hold. Then, in one swift
strong move, he brings
him to the ground.*
  This is the final throw

*of the match. A huge
cheer. The crowd take the
Chinese boy onto their
shoulders, as if bringing
him to The Inferno.*

*Light change. Music
still low, back to the club.*

*Lurve and Chill dance
as before. God is not to
be seen here.*

*Wad is getting better
acquainted.*

Lady Wad
Dock leaves
help cellulite
I know
I've tried
Rich Dick (*touching*)
Your own smooth thighs
would advertise
Lady Wad
They freeze dry
attractively packaged
the health shops
would be
gagging for a try

A cure
for cellulite!
Potentially
the global markets
massive
Rich Dick
Impressive

Lady Wad
Women
get long hair cut
Rich Dick (*touching*)
And instantly
regret it
Lady Wad
On site
make a simple
clip-on switch
for extra versatility
Rich Dick
So, effectively,
you sell them back
their own hair
Lady Wad
Exactly

Rich Dick laughs.

Lady Wad
For my ideas
I'm looking
for investors,

*From below Lurve
whistles, points to her
watch.*

Rich Dick
Your common
little friend
calls time
Lady Wad (*uncomfortable*)
Yes . . .
Yes . . .

SCENE FOURTEEN

Inferno.
  *Lady God stands
central. Absolutely still.
The Hood dance around
her. Strange lighting.*
  *Music distorts. Lights
change. The dancing
bodies start to join, climb
up each other. They create
a monstrous Flame Angel
all in red in front of Lady
God. It is topped by a
mask, just like the pot-doll
face of the Christmas
Angel from her memory
box. She stares. From her*
*pocket she takes out the
little packet of heroin.*

Lady God
  I was frightened
  of getting lost
  and never being found

  so I wrote my name,
  see,
  on my frown

  making me
  easy to claim
  by the Angels
  when they came
  to take me

SCENE FIFTEEN

Inferno.

Rich Dick
  I too
  have
  an idea
  I wish to sell.

  My market
  up to now
  has mainly been
  friends, businessmen,
  away from home
  looking to dabble

in something
a bit different
for a night.

My little hobby
made me
a substantial profit.

I'm looking to expand
but

I need a fresh market
and young agents
savvy and streetwise

on a sale by sale
commission
who know
the club scene
Lady Wad
What?
What do you want
me to sell?

He puts his hand in his

*pocket. Very discreetly, he
places a small packet in
her palms. He smiles,
puts his fingers to his lips.*

Rich Dick
Dreams.

*Lady Wad looks at the
packet in her hand. She
is thinking.*

SCENE SIXTEEN

*The Inferno tunnels. The
sound of dripping water.
Chill paces alone.*

Lady Chill
Five minutes
past midnight
betrayed
by my own

I'll fight alone
Lady Lurve (*enters
breathless*)
Postpone
your martyrdom
for another day

What's that?
Lady Chill
A rat
or two!

Where's Wad?
Lady Lurve
I hope she follows

*Pause. They look at each
other.*

Lady Chill
And Lady God?
Lady Lurve
She can't be found

They pace.

Are you afraid?

No answer.

Are you afraid?

Footsteps, they turn.

Lady Lurve
Bad news

Bad News
  (*frightened, whispering*)
  Lady God sent me
  She's gone
Lady Chill
  Gone?
Bad News
  To the foggy
  canal bank

Given herself up
To the Cats
And the Crew,

to save you
getting cut
she says

given herself up
for you

SCENE SEVENTEEN

Foggy canal bank.
  *Pin spotlight on Lady
God up high, as if on top
of a wall overlooking the
canal. Video close-up of
her eyes throughout. She
stands, white-faced,
perspiring, trembling. She
has injected heroin and is
senselessly euphoric.*
  *The Hood stand as a
group, watching, silent.
They have their instruments,
bits of wood etc., and
through this scene there
could be a sporadic break-
out of percussive sound.*

Voice 1 (*whispers*)
  The canal
  below
Voice 2
  It's seen it all

Voice 3
  Slit throats
  Cracked bones
Voice 4
  Slashed lives
Voice 5
  It listens
  to the last scream
Voice 6
  Over and over
Voice 7
  Chopped up
  dreams
  in bin liners
  float down
  to the municipal latrine
Voice 8
  Someone kissed
  that hand
  once
Voice 9
  That small foot
  Those black lips

It sneers
at the stars
Voice 1
And now this
little girl

Light spreads. The Hood
part, we see Honk, Omo,
Sticky and Bird, The
Craven Crew.

Sticky
Crazy Tail
The Craven Crew
Dive
and you're
dead for sure
there in that
city
cesspit stew.
Sticky
Better take it now.
Omo
Brace yourself.
Bird
You bought
the buzz.
Omo
And at a
quarter cost.
Honk
You know
you owe.
Sticky
Who knows?
You might
enjoy

Omo
We plan
to pull a train.
Honk
And I'm in the tunnel first
no sloppy seconds
for this ho
Sticky
Sorry, and all that,
if it was up to me
I'd let you have it
as a freebie,
no sweat.

Light spreads. The Hood
silently part to reveal
Chill and Lurve. Chill has
a knife. Video cuts from
blade flashing in moon-
light back to God's eyes.

Lady Chill
We come
to fight
Lady God
No!
Honk
You come too late
Omo
She's
surrendered

He gestures. Omo, Sticky,
and Bird ceremoniously
carry a tin. They present
it to her. She's incapable
of opening it. They do so.

*She looks down, her eyes
a-flicker. With a shaking
hand she takes out a
single white feather.*

Honk
Badge
of the cowardly
skank

*The Crew move forward
towards Lady God. Lady
God stretches out her
arms (her eyes still in
video close-up) as if
about to fly. Video cuts.
She jumps from the
barrier, and is caught by
the Hood (as the canal).*
  *Lights change, music,
the pound of the
nightclub.*
  *Chill watches horrified,
frozen for a split second,
then, panting, breathless,
tears off her clothes and
looks down.*
  Music dips.

Honk
Don't waste breath
she's already dead
Lady Chill
No

*In slow motion now, the
Hood appear to surge,*

*Chill expertly takes up
the position to dive and
she too dives off the
ladder into the Hood.
Exactly at that moment a
breathless Wad appears.*

Lady Lurve (*furious*)
Bitch
Lady Wad
Where's Lady God?
Lady Lurve
She jumped

*The crew turn to Wad
and Lurve.*

Lady Wad
I'm sorry
I'm so . . .
Honk
You will be

Music, louder, faster.

Honk (*to Lurve and Wad*)
Now you're
really gonna need
some stitches.

*With a sudden ferocity
Sticky grabs Wad, forces
her hand behind her
back.*
  *Honk appears to
deliver a ferocious punch
to the mouth that knocks
Wad out.*

Bird
You punched
her out.
Omo
Unfortunate,
awake
and kicking
would have
been more fun.

Sticky grabs Lurve, Omo
kicks her several times in
the stomach.
Both Omo and Honk
make for the zips, just as
the figure of the Chinese
Shadow, Shaikwondo
expert, appears suddenly.
What follows, possibly
in strobe lighting, certainly
against fierce pulsating
club dance music, is a
stylised, choreographed
fight/dance in which Omo,
Sticky, Bird and Honk are
annihilated à la Jackie
Chan.
As Honk, the last, bites
the dust the Hood let out
a huge cheer. The Pussy
Posse, whose allegiance
has changed, cheer.
Lights lift music stops.
It becomes clear that the

Chinese Shadow is in
fact a . . .

Li'l Fluff
He's a . . .
Whiskers
She's a . . .
Missy Cat
It's a . . .
Entire Hood
GIRL!

The Chinese girl formally
bows, then a sudden huge
explosion. The stage is
flooded in red light.
Flames crackling fire.
Everyone stops still and
watches. Screams, cries,
shouts. Emerging from
the Hood with a box of
matches is little Matches.

Matches (*sheepish*)
You mustn't
play with matches.
You mustn't!
You mustn't!
Lady Lurve (*dazed*)
Why's that kid?
Matches
I'll tell you why.
Because
they burn
things down!

SCENE EIGHTEEN

Lights up. Red flames.
A blaze, thick smoke,
Canal bank now littered
with injured souls. Sound
tape of screams, cries and
crackling fire. The Hood
make a strange musical
sound, like an ancient
chanting. Underneath they
create a low rhythmic beat.
  A pin spotlight from
another part of the stage
picks out the face of Chill
and Wad.

The Hood (*all, intoned*)
  Down, down, down
Tel (*from out of the*
  smoke, searching)
  Julie, Julie
Smelly Nelly (*standing in*
  the smoke to Wad)
  Here Annie's little girl
  canal dip
The Hood (*all, intoned*)
  Down, down, down
Smelly Nelly
  What did I tell you
  the ghosts'll get you

The Hood look at Chill.

Voices 15 and 16
  In the slurry

she meets severed heads
full of questions
Voice 17
  An arm hoping
  for one last embrace
Voice 18
  A battalion
  of restless legs
The Hood (*all*)
  Through the iron gates
  of the old fish market,

  hurtling
  Deeper,
  Deeper

Intoning intensifies.

Lady God
  Higher,
  higher
  I see my face
  in the stars
Voice 20
  Her eyes
Voice 12
  but no tears
Voice 13
  The canal sweats
  and pushes
Lady Chill
  And there
  in the bloody
  black

I'm born
again

Intoning intensifies.

Lady God
Higher than
the moon,
higher
than Mars
from a screaming sky
Voice 19
She sees
Lady God
Flame Angels
Voice 1
Just

as he described
Lady God
to rescue me

Intoning intensifies.
Lady Chill is hauling
the lifeless sodden body
of Lady God, dragging it
out of the canal. They are
both soaked. Lady Chill
sweats and shivers,
panting, exhausted, but
exhilarated, triumphant.
Wad and Lurve crowd
around. Smelly watches.

Lady Chill
I got her

She floated
like a lily

Clasping
the white feather
in a prayer

Singing
to the stars

Lady God is lifeless.
Lady Chill expertly
tips God's head back,
opens her mouth, pinches
her nose and attempts
mouth-to-mouth
resuscitation.
She hammers her chest.
The Flame Angel created
in The Inferno appears,
and another and another.

Lady Chill
I won't let you die
Tell the ghoulish angels
to fuck off!

Lady Chill beats them
away.

The sky's
too vast
and cold
for your small
wormish spirit.
Come back
to the warm
throbbing earth

I'll beat
the life
back in you

Breathe!
Breathe!

*Intoning intensifies. A
cosmic hum, which grows
into a kind of strange
encompassing music that
comes in waves . . . The
flapping of great wing on
wing. Video close-up.*

What did I say?
Away

She flails at the air.

Fiery angels!
You come
too soon,
back beyond
that ship-wrecked moon.

*Far away the great bell of
Our Lady of All Souls
starts its chime to
midnight. Chill carries on
desperately trying to
resuscitate God. The
cosmic noise gets louder
and louder. The Flame
Angels start to fade away.
Camera swings violently
from face to face.*

Smelly
You're running
out
of time

Intoning intensifies.

Lady Wad
Her lips are blue
Smelly
Her shirt's too tight

She loosens it.

Lady Lurve
Someone
call
an ambulance
Smelly
Let
her get
air
Lady Lurve
Someone . . .
Lady Wad
Her lips

*Intoning intensifies, the
sound of wing on wing is
deafening.*

Lady Lurve
Someone . . .

*The last chime. Chill falls
back exhausted. All
sound stops. Stillness.
  Silence.*

Smelly
It's no good
this little girl
is dead.

Video camera cuts.

SCENE NINETEEN

*Church graveyard. Our
Lady of All Souls. Dawn.
Misty morning. Stylo plays
sax. Banner says 'Our
Lady of All Souls'. Full
company including Miss
Nice Face, Smelly Nelly,
Piety and Tel.*

*They are under the great
bell tower. The shadow
image of the clock face
falls over and dominates
the scene.*

*Here and there broken
crosses, images of
damaged, mutilated angels.*

*The windows used for
the Chinese Shadow and
Stylo are now arched; and
coloured lights rainbow
from them as from stained
glass.*

*Separate now, the three
Ladies.*

*Behind them Stylo, and
opposite Mrs Joy Foo Yung.*

*It's a post-disaster
scene, almost a holocaust.
As if the whole town had
climbed to the small
churchyard.*

*Stylo's sax is unbearably
sweet and sad.*

Mrs Joy Foo Yung
We were sleeping
myself and my two
sisters,
baby-dreaming,
when the ugly night
called out
sudden, red-hot
and hammering

screaming
on and on
with bulging
flame eyes
spewing
the thick
black, murderous smoke

fingering sleep soft
curls

squeezing
a slim white pretty throat

*Piety appears. She is
holding Faith's memory
box. Saxophone
continues softly.*

Piety (*soft, red-eyed and
trembling, she holds out
her arms to the Ladies*)
My dears
I've seen her
and she's

at peace
at last

I know
Faith
didn't
go to church

but she believed
in something
greater
than
herself

A little laugh.

She talked
to
angels

bless her

I know,
I heard her

She's cradled
now
in their sweet arms,

they carry her
to a forgiving Lord

(*to Chill*)
She adored you

*She hands memory box
to Chill who holds it for
a second then hurls it to
the ground.*

Lady Chill
Shit!

Saxophone stops. Raging:

She's thirteen
and
she's fucking dead

Lady Lurve (*trying to stop
her*)
Chill

Lady Chill (*hot angry
tears*)
No
I won't
shut up

She 'talked' to Angels
because
poor cow
she had no one else
to talk to

because
she was young
and sad

when her kind
crackhead dad

just
didn't wake up
one day

Yes, I failed her too.
We failed her
She gave her life for us

She laughs.

Look at us
a slut
a conwoman
and a bully

What was her life for?
What did it mean?
Hanging around filthy
streets
getting rat-arsed
screwing to score
turning old and ugly
with Fear.
Lady Lurve
Chill . . .
Piety
My daughter
was beautiful
Lady Chill
Will she be beautiful still
in a month?
A year?
Ten years?

She'll be manure
Piety (*furious, shouting*)
I have regrets

Silence.

When I gave birth

I was young
younger than you

I needed
my name
tattooed on my brow

to tell me
who I was
Lady Lurve (*softly*)
That was then
this is now

You could
have said

'I love you'

*Lights dip to dusk. Same
scene. Full company.
People are sitting in small
groups comforting each
other, reluctant to leave.
Julie and Tel. A long
awkward pause.*

Tel (*softly*)
I'd better go
Julie
Oh?
Tel
Kenny
he's with my mum,
they'll be wondering
where I am
Julie
Oh, yes

*He starts to go.
Calling after.*

How is Kenny?

*He comes back. Looks
at her.*

Tel (*sternly*)
Fretful
Julie
Oh?
Tel
Missing you
these past few days

Pause.

Julie
Missing me?
Tel
Terribly
Julie
Missing ME?
Tel
Every morning
he asks
where Mama is
and every night
he cries
himself
to sleep
Julie
Missing ME!
Tel
Yes, Julie
what did you
expect?

He makes to go.

Julie (*swallowing a sob*)
I miss him

He stops and turns.

I miss Keanu
I miss him

Can I . . . see him?
Tel (*sternly, looking at his watch*)
Now?
Julie
Yes, now
it's urgent

I . . .
I have to tell
him something!

A long pause.
    *He holds out his hand,
she takes it.*

Julie
I don't love you
Tel

Slight pause.

Tel
And I don't love you
Julie

Smelly Nelly and Emma.

Smelly Nelly (*softly*)
We were
Fair people
hammering together
Hoop-La
and Hook-the-Fish

Out of driftwood

Helter-skeltering
our way
through respectability

Things grew
I hired
and fired.
I got the caras
rolling
and arranged the pitch

Jack was the ideas man,
the first
Dragon River
in Europe
was ours

Pause.

Emma
I have ideas

Slight pause.

Smelly
Yes?

Slight pause.

Emma
I have good ideas

*Stylo and Mrs Joy Foo
Yung.*

Stylo
In the first years
I couldn't sleep
I kept hearing
their screams

in the dark,
feeling the flames
eat my flesh

Every time there was a tap
at the door
I hoped Revenge
stood there

Your Revenge
to bring sleep

Mrs Joy Foo Yung
Would Revenge
have mended
our broken hearts?

Not even
the years
did that

Stylo (*struggling*)
I'm sorry

*Tape (quite faint): the
two baby sisters laughing
and playing. The sound
gets louder and comes
from every direction.*

Smelly Nelly
What did I tell you.
The Ghosts!

*Short strange ghostly
video shows the two tiny
girls laughing.*

Mrs Joy Foo Yung
My sweet sisters,
Forgiveness and Peace

*Lady Chill and Miss Nice
Face sit together.*

Miss Nice Face
What now?

Chill says nothing.

What now?

*Slowly lights fade. Hood
create rhythmic beat and
musical background.*

Lady Chill
It's not the end
do you hear me?
All this shit!
It's not the end
of the Gang!

*Lights fade to blackout.
Light full up.*

CURTAIN CALL – RAP

The Hood
(*half, in strict time*)
Now listen here
and listen good

To this here
tale
of sisterhood

And Four Ladies

I said four little ladies
Voice 1
Lady Chill

She takes her bow.

who made it
from cold to hot
Voice 2
Who beat time
Voice 3
put hate on hold
and went for gold
Voice 4
Lady Wad

She takes her bow.

Voice 5
who
with her backer
Mrs Staines

*We see Smelly in a new
suit. She takes her bow.*

Voice 4
spent her life
making a mint
Voice 1
they bottled
northern
rainwater
Voice 2
and
flogged it
to
daft southerners
Voice 4
and in the wink
of an eye

gave it all
away

Voice 5
Crap!

Voice 4
What else
do you do
with money?

Voice 6
But that's
another
rap

Voice 1
Lady Lurve

She takes her bow.

Voice 2
who learned
to like herself

Voice 3
and love her son

Voice 4
You know
she went
to university

Voice 1
What did she study?

Voice 2
Her PhD
was something
about
homo erectus

Voice 4
that figures

Voice 3
And Lady God

*Everything stops. Silence.
Stillness.*

Lady Wad
Who had
only wanted
one thing

Lady Chill
An impossible
thing

Lady Lurve
To leave
the planet

Lady Chill
A better place
than
when
she came in

Lady God takes her bow.

The Hood (*all, they shout*)
Lady Chill
Lady Wad
Lady Lurve
Lady God

*A white feather falls from
the sky and another and
another. A shower of soft
white feathers which
becomes a carpet.
The Hood and full
company take their bows.*

NUTS

Fausto Paravidino

translated by Luca Scarlini
in collaboration with Zachery James Kinney

Characters

Buddy
Cindy
Girl
Piggy
Minus
Silly
Party
Magda
Snappy
Woodschlock
Schkreker

*At the beginning of the play, all the characters
are between the ages of fifteen and twenty.*

*Scenes One to Eleven and Scene Twenty-Three
take place in a house/apartment.
There are a large sofa and a large television.*

*Scenes Twelve to Twenty-Two take place in
a police station. There are a table and several chairs.*

*Between Scene Eleven and Scene Twelve
approximately ten years have passed.*

ONE
POLITICS OF WORK

The living room of a luxurious apartment. The elegance is suggested by an enormous sofa and an extremely large television many inches wide. There is also a telephone. Upstage there is a strong door that opens to the outside.
Cindy and Girl are seated at the table or on the sofa. Enter Buddy with two glasses of Coca-Cola.

Buddy Finally I was there with the girl I liked. And with a friend. I don't know if the girl I liked knew that I liked her. By the way she was laughing with her friend maybe she knew, although maybe they were only laughing because they couldn't help laughing. Girls never like me. The girls I've liked, I mean. Anyway, this is how the whole story began. Here are your Cokes.

Cindy So this is what you do?

Girl Every day?

Buddy Noo, only sometimes, when they ask me to stop by or when they have guests.

Cindy You don't have like a sort of schedule or something?

Buddy No, it's like we're friends . . . I mean, they treat me like one of them.

Girl They who?

Cindy The owners of the house, right?

Girl Oh, it's not yours.

Buddy Noo, no.

Cindy Do you think that a person is a servant in his own house?!

Girl What do I know? Do you think that a person is a servant in his friend's house?

343

Buddy We're not exactly friends. I mean, it's not like I eat with them. Maybe sometimes if there aren't any guests, they ask me if I want to sit with them because they're nice, I mean, they like me. If not, I eat in the kitchen. It's a little bit like work.

Girl They pay you?

Cindy They give him the scraps.

Buddy No! What do you mean, 'scraps'? No! They're kind of like my friends, I told you. Look, I don't even have to wear a waiter's uniform, I mean, I'm dressed like this, normal.

Girl Wow!

Cindy And do they let you watch the TV without having to wear a bunny suit?

TWO
RESIDENCE PERMIT

Buddy You can't stay here.

Piggy is standing in the doorway, covered in filth, and with a backpack over his shoulder.

Piggy I thought I could stay.

Buddy No way. No one can. I mean, who told you you could stay?

Piggy Cindy.

Buddy Cindy?

Piggy I didn't have anywhere to go. I asked her if I could stay at her house, and she told me no because her mom is there too, and she told me to come to your place. You're mom isn't here, right?

Buddy No, she's not . . . Cindy shouldn't have told you that, it's not her house.

Piggy She told me it's not your house either.

Buddy No, that's the point. That's why you can't stay.
If it was my house, it wouldn't be a problem . . .

Piggy If it was your house, your mom might be here.

Buddy I'm sorry, I can't let you stay here. There are
these people who asked me to watch their house . . .

Piggy Like a dog?

Buddy I'm responsible for this.

Piggy A dog would host his friend.

Buddy *I* can't.

Piggy Cindy stayed here.

Buddy Just for a drink.

Piggy Can I also have some water?

Buddy Sure, okay, I'll go get you some water, but listen,
you want to *stay* here. Cindy came by just for a drink.
It's different.

Piggy Cindy told me that she's coming back, she told
me, 'I'll see you there.'

Buddy She didn't say anything to me.

Piggy She must have forgot.

Buddy Listen, the fact is that with Cindy, it's different.

Pause.

Piggy Because she's a girl?

Buddy No, that's not it . . .

Piggy Aren't I your friend?

Buddy Listen, I'm sorry, do you want me to tell you the
difference?

Piggy Yes. Sure, I want to know why she can stay here
and not me.

Buddy You stink. You're dirty, you stink. I'm sorry to
have to tell you, because you're my friend and never
did anything bad to me. But you're dirty. There's
nothing wrong with that and we really are friends
because it doesn't matter to me if you stink or not, but
I'm responsible for this house. If you sleep and stay
here, the couch will get all dirty and the stench will

never leave. I've got to leave the house how I found it.
It's important.
Piggy You're saying that if I was clean I could stay here?
Buddy Yes. If you were clean, yes.
Piggy Can I use the bathroom?
Buddy No, you can't use the bathroom.
Piggy To wash myself off, I want to clean up so I can
stay. Can I use the bathroom?
Buddy No, I don't want you to come in the house and
I don't want you to use the bathroom.
Piggy Did you let Cindy use the bathroom?
Buddy With Cindy it's different.

Pause.

Piggy Because she's a girl?

THREE
THE MASS MEDIA CONTROL THE WORLD

*Cindy, the Girl and Piggy on the couch. They're
watching the TV. They're very serious. Buddy and Minus
are speaking amongst themselves.*

Piggy It's funny.
Cindy Not so much . . .
Piggy Doesn't it make you laugh?
Cindy Nooo. It's frustrating to laugh at this stuff here.
Piggy Oh, I didn't know. I've never seen this before.
Cindy Uh uh.

Pause.

Piggy You guys always watch it?
Cindy No. From five to seven. Then there's *The Smurfs*.
Girl We also like to go out, talk . . .
Piggy I like to go out too. (*Pause*) And also talk.

Cindy Shut up, we can't hear it!

Buddy I'm glad you came.

Minus Cindy told me she was coming here, so I asked
her who was here and she said Buddy's friends, so
then I told her that it had been a while since I had
heard from you and I didn't know what you had been
up to and so then she told me that you might be here
too, so I came with her, and in fact here you are.

Buddy She told you that I might be here?

Minus Yes, that's what she told me and in fact here you
are. What are you doing here?

Buddy What am I doing here? What are they doing
here!?

Minus I think they're watching TV.

Buddy Of course they're watching TV . . . the fact is
that . . . I have a big problem.

Minus Yes, I figured you'd get me involved in something
sad.

Buddy Yeah, I'm sorry, but I absolutely need to talk to
someone who will listen to me.

Minus Yeah, sure I'll listen to you; I always listen to you
when you have a problem.

Buddy Okay then, right, I'm in love with your sister's
friend . . .

Minus Yeah, for like ten years.

Buddy I don't know if she feels the same about me, and
I don't know if she knows that I feel like this about
her . . .

Minus You could try mentioning it to her . . .

Buddy Sure, I should, but look – it's something that
would take all my energy and effort, and right now
I don't think I can do it.

Minus Why?

Buddy I have a big problem.

Minus The same or another?

Buddy Another one. Listen . . .

347

Minus I'm listening.
Buddy I have to watch this house . . .
Cindy *The Smurfs* are starting, Minus!
Minus Oh. I'm sorry, I'm really sorry . . .
Buddy Are you listening to me?
Minus Yeah, yeah, I'm listening . . .
Buddy I'm responsible for this . . .
Minus I'm sorry. Forgive me, I'm sorry, I can't help it . . .
The Smurfs . . . I know you have a problem or two . . .
I'm your friend, I always listen to you . . . I need to
watch *The Smurfs* . . . We'll talk about it in a half-
hour, okay? In a half-hour.
Buddy But . . .
Minus Sorry.

Minus goes and sits with the others in front of the TV.

Buddy (*to himself*) . . . Alright, I have this problem,
I'm responsible for it and everyone . . . I mean, my
friends . . . just don't care. They just don't care.

FOUR — SHENGEN
FREE CIRCULATION OF PERSONS AND CUSTOMS

*Minus, the Girl, Piggy and Cindy watching the TV. Silly
is on the telephone.*

Silly Yeah, I'm at my brother's.
No, I don't think it's his house, he usually lives with
us . . .
I think it's like a kind of job, yeah.
It's really beautiful here, yeah, it's a luxurious house,
there's a fridge, a sofa, a 58-inch TV . . .
Yeah, there are already a lot of people, even my love . . .
Minus I'M NOT YOUR LOVE!!
Silly Yeah, we're having a lot of fun.

Just to stay together . . .

No, my brother isn't really grumpy, he's a little weird,
but he isn't mean.

Yeah, I'm sure he'd be happy to see some friends.

Right – the only thing – I'm not sure if there's anything
here. Bring some Cokes and some chips, if you can.
I don't know, four six-packs? Whatever you want.

Enter Buddy.

Silly Okay, see you later.

Yeah, 'bye . . . 'bye.

Buddy Where are you going?

Silly Me? Nowhere. I just got here, you haven't even
shown me the house . . .

Buddy I mean – who are you seeing later?

Silly Oh, some friends, yeah, they're coming here.

Buddy Here?

Silly I told them to bring some food and drinks.

Buddy No, no, no, this is not good, not this . . .

Silly Do you want to die of hunger and thirst?

Buddy They can't stay here . . .

Silly It's full of people!

Buddy That's the point, we're already too many . . .
I mean, I should be the only one here.

Silly All alone in this huge house?

Buddy Yeah, that's right. Exactly.

Silly I hope you realise that this is not right.

Buddy It's not exactly a question of right or wrong.

Silly You want to kick out all your best friends and your
sister, who all came here to keep you company and who
want to party here at your place – we're even bringing
our own stuff – for the satisfaction of staying here all
by yourself in a beautiful house with a 58-inch TV
that's all for you?

Buddy It's not exactly like that.

Silly And I – who throughout all – still love you, even
if you're my brother. And I try to convince the others
that you're not mean, that you're just a little anti-
social and that if we just encourage you, you'll join
the party. And while I do my best to make the others
accept you, you thank me by telling me that you want
to kick everyone out of here? At this point, I hope you
realise that you're a monster.

Cindy *Shut up!!*

Buddy Listen, this isn't my house.

Silly Okay then, so, what do you care?

Enter Party, Magda, Snappy, Woodschlock.

All Surprise!

FIVE
GLOBALISATION

Enters Magda with an empty bottle of Coke in her hand.

Magda Finished.

Party Finished?

Minus It's finished.

Cindy The Coke's finished.

Minus Arrrggghhh.

Magda We need to go buy some more.

Silly Four six-packs.

Magda Pay up.

Piggy Two bucks?

Magda Two bucks apiece.

Woodschlock No way, not me.

Silly What . . . how come? We're paying together, right?

Woodschlock I don't like Coke.

Party To be honest, neither do I.

Cindy Listen to these complaints . . .

Snappy Yeah, me neither, really . . .

Girl Hey, it's not that bad . . . everyone likes certain tastes . . .

Silly Okay. What do you want?

Woodschlock Fanta.

Party Sprite.

Silly You?

Piggy Not me, maybe water. Yeah, water.

Cindy There's the tap.

Piggy I don't like that water.

Cindy You *have* to like it.

Piggy It's got chlorine and calcium.

Silly Water, okay.

Cindy How much?

Piggy A litre-and-a-half bottle.

Silly Fanta?

Woodschlock Two cans.

Silly Sprite?

Party One.

Cindy He's getting two and you're getting one? And when you finish that one?

Party I drink less.

Silly Alright, then you need to put in different amounts.

Piggy Yeah, me too. Water costs less.

Cindy But if you so much as take a drink of someone else's Coke . . .

Piggy If anything I'll ask, and if you want to give me some . . .

Woodschlock No, that doesn't work.

Piggy And why not?

Woodschlock It's obvious that if you ask, they'll give it to you, but that's not right. They're paying for it, not you. If it's an emergency, then okay, but in light of the fact we're actually planning this – which we are – we might as well make things fair.

Piggy But if any of you want some water, I'll give it to you.

Cindy And who's going to want water . . .

Silly Shit! Shit! Shit!

Minus . . . if there's Coke?

Snappy I want some Pepsi.

Cindy Come on, they taste the same.

Snappy Alright then, let's buy Pepsi.

Cindy No.

Silly Come on, this is not going to work. One person's buying one thing, another person's buying something else . . . different amounts of money, everyone has to figure out exactly how much they will drink . . . We're going to buy Coke for everyone . . . everyone pays a little and, all together, we'll drink however much we drink.

Woodschlock But if I don't like Coke.

Cindy If you don't like Coke, then do it yourself! Don't make a shopping list for your servants. Go out and buy it yourself.

Party But you're going there anyway.

Magda Yes, if it's something for everyone so we can all hang out together, then fine. If we have to do your personal little shopping with different amounts of money from each person, I'm not going.

Piggy Okay, I'll drink Coke, fine.

Woodschlock You don't want water any more?

Piggy If it's that big a deal, I'd rather go with Cokes for everyone.

Cindy Okay, I think this is fair. Now then, we're just getting Coke. Whoever wants to put in will put in, whoever doesn't want to doesn't have to give two bucks, but that means they can't drink anything.
If you want to buy something yourself, you can buy it and you don't have to share.

Minus Okay.

Silly Are we all agreed?

Party There's not much choice, if you are going to buy it yourselves . . .

Cindy Good. Now, whoever's in, put your money on that table there.

Cindy, Silly, Minus, the Girl and Snappy put in the money. Then, slowly, one by one, so do Magda, Party, Piggy and finally Woodschlock, but:

Woodschlock I'm also putting in an extra buck for a Fanta.

SIX
RESPECT OF PROPERTY I

Snappy, Buddy and Cindy.

Snappy Sorry.

Buddy No, sorry nothing. You shouldn't have done it.

Snappy I didn't know. I said I was sorry. That's enough, right?

Cindy What do you mean, you didn't know? It's not something you should have to know.

Snappy No one ever told me.

Cindy No one has ever told you not to get on the sofa with muddy shoes?

Snappy Told me that? Told me that?

Buddy But you think I have to . . . Look what you did. Look at this mess.

Snappy So, I see it. And I said I was sorry. What do I need to do? Kill myself? Beg on my knees? Look, I'm begging on my knees.

Kneels down.

Here. Is this okay? I'm sorry, I repent.

Buddy You don't have to do that.
Snappy Alright then, enough? Are we okay?
Buddy Yeah.

Snappy stands.

Now let's clean this sofa cover.
Snappy No way, you can't ask me that.
Buddy But wait, I mean, we need to clean it.
Snappy I can't do it . . . I don't want to. I don't want to do it.
Buddy But you . . . Goddamnit *you* got it all dirty!
Snappy I said I was sorry, you said we were okay, we were even, you said it yourself.
Buddy Yeah, but now we need to clean it.
Snappy You're asking me this as a favour?
Buddy No, I mean, yes, I'm asking you this as a favour, fine.
Snappy Say 'please'.
Buddy No way . . .
Snappy Alright then, do it yourself.
Cindy He's right, you should say please.
Buddy Fine. 'Please.'
Snappy Kneel down. I knelt down.

Pause. Buddy kneels.

Buddy Please, help me clean.
Snappy Look, I would do it, but I don't want to. I'm sorry. No.
Buddy But how come . . .
Cindy You're not very with it.

SEVEN
IDEALS — RIGHT NOW

*Buddy is apart, inconsolable. The others are speaking all
together.*

Minus He's just trying to create something for himself,
for his future.

Cindy Good for him, and what about us!?

Minus I suppose we have ours.

Cindy I hope so. I'm just saying that his future is not
a good enough reason to make him mean.

Girl He's not mean to me.

Cindy To you, he's not mean . . . but that's another
story.

Silly He's mean to me.

Cindy Of course, you're his sister.

Silly That's true.

Piggy I think he's just really . . . anxious.

Snappy Just as long as he doesn't try to pass his anxiety
on to me.

Cindy In that sense, you seem pretty invincible to me.

Snappy Yeah. But don't take advantage of me.

Magda But don't you understand that he has an
enormous responsibility?! He's here to look after this
house and we should be helping him but instead we're
making it impossible for him!

Snappy Excuse me, why should we help him? What the
hell do I care about this house?

Magda But we're his friends!

Cindy Well, let's not exaggerate.

Magda He feels responsible to the owners of the house,
poor thing . . .

Snappy And what the hell do I care about the owners
of the house? I'm *his* friend; that's *their* business. It's

355

wrong to feel responsible to those who exploit you. What more can I do than tell him that . . . if he screws up, I certainly can't help him . . .?

Magda Everyone sees it his own way . . .

Snappy And I see it like this.

Magda But you never screw up?

Snappy Rarely, and I certainly don't pretend that people do what I want.

Magda He's just asking us not to bother him . . .

Cindy And he's the one bothering us. We could easily just hang out here as good friends, and instead Buddy always creates problems.

Party I think we should help him understand what he really wants.

Silly To be left alone. We already know that. Thanks, Party.

Party No, listen to me, that's not it! He wants to be left alone to . . .

Cindy Right, be a servant.

Party Exactly. However, there's no way that his life's dream is to be a servant.

Snappy Why not? To me he seems perfect for it.

Party He accepts this thing here because he wants that thing there . . .

Cindy Which is . . .?

Party *That* I do not know, but he must know it.

Cindy A servant is a servant. You don't go anywhere by being a servant.

Party Right, maybe he doesn't know this, and this is what we should do. Ask him what he wants to do and then make him understand that this is not the way to do it. That if he wants to do something, he's got to do that thing – not something else . . . like how Magda doesn't want to be an engineer and in order to not be an engineer, she studies engineering.

Snappy *This* you'd better explain to me.

Magda Yeah, I hate engineering. I've always hated it.

Cindy And that's why you study engineering?

Magda My parents want me to be an engineer, and if
I say, 'No. I hate it,' it would hurt them too much. So
I try not to upset anyone. I'm registered in engineering,
they're happy, I only need a few more exams, they're
already in their sixties, and my dad's also a diabetic . . .
say I do engineering for fifteen years at the most, then
my parents die happy and I can do whatever I want.

Snappy That seems like a great solution to me.

Party Not to me – this is what we need to explain to
Buddy – I mean, I respect Magda's plan, but I want
everything and I want it *now*.

Minus And what do you want?

Party Right, *that* I do not know . . . but I'm not
accepting any compromises.

Snappy This also seems to me a very convincing
argument.

*Break. Then Buddy is there with them. They're all
together for a serious discussion.*

Minus Buddy, we've been thinking about the matter a
lot.

Buddy I'm touched.

Silly Don't be mean, we're trying to help you.

Party Yeah, we love you and we thought that you're
acting this way with us because you feel responsible
for something that you shouldn't feel responsible for. I
mean, do you want this or something else? We don't
think that this is what you want so we're saying,
'Buddy, we want to help you, but you've got to know
what you want.' And you've got to tell us, because
otherwise we can't meet you half way. For example:
Magda knows that she doesn't want to be an engineer;
he wants to be your friend for ever; (*Minus nods*) Silly
wants . . . What was it you wanted?

Silly A 58-inch television, all for me.

Piggy I want to stay here.

Girl I want to get married.

Snappy I want to party.

Woodschlock I want to become a great fisherman.

Cindy I want to be king.

Party And I don't know, but whatever I *do* want, I want it all and I want it now. And this is the most important thing. You . . . what do you *really* want? Really.

Buddy I want you to get out of here – all of you, and right now.

Woodschlock I think he seems very clear.

EIGHT
REVOLUTION AND NEW FIGHTING TECHNIQUES

Party You and Buddy are hopeless, you accept everything the way it is – you don't even try to find a solution.

Magda Do you see a solution?

Party Well, I *try*.

Magda And where has this gotten you?

Party For now – for example – I feel like breaking everything.

Magda Oh, interesting . . . very dialectic

Party Of course, they don't listen to us.

Magda Who?

Party Everyone, right?

Magda Why? What do we have to say?

Party Uhm, I don't know.

Magda Right, not 'we', but 'you' then?

Party You can be sure I'd have lots to say!

Magda So say it!

Party But they don't listen to us.

Magda I listen to you.

Party Well, of course.

Magda Okay then, let's see what you have to say.

Pause.

Party No, no, it doesn't work like that.
Magda Well then, do you know what this means? You don't have anything to say.
Party That's not true.
Magda Okay then, convince me.
Party If you ask me so aggressively, I'm not going to tell you anything.
Magda You see?
Party I have an intense desire to break everything.
Magda Alright then, break everything. Good.
Party That's exactly what I intend to do, you know? That's exactly what I intend to do.
Magda However, remember that you're doing it only because you feel like breaking everything, not because you want to be listened to.
Party You can't say that.
Magda You said it yourself just a minute ago.
Party What?
Magda That you don't have anything to say.
Party That's not true.
Magda Okay, tell me what's so important about what you have to say that makes you want to break everything.
Party That if they don't listen to me, I'll break everything.

NINE
RESPECT OF PROPERTY 2

Girl Ohmygoodness! What a disaster . . .
Minus I can't . . . I can't . . . I can't . . .
Silly Well, without the TV, I don't think it makes sense to stay here any longer.

Snappy I don't think it made much sense before either, but at least we weren't doing *that* bad.

The television has been destroyed.

Minus Someone do something before seven o'clock! I'm going to have an epileptic fit.

Snappy Would you like a neurological specialist, or a new television?

Minus This is not something to joke about. I'm . . . now I'm really alone.

Silly Well, I'm here.

Minus It's not the same thing.

Silly Sure, I'm not 58 inches . . .

Cindy I don't want to ruin the party, but I think that the real problem will be when Buddy comes back.

Woodschlock Something's going to happen.

Party You know where he is right now?

Cindy He's probably gone off somewhere to worry about some *other* thing.

Girl He's always sad.

Cindy I'm sure he won't be able to recover when he sees this disaster. By the way, does anyone know who did it?

Snappy Not me. I'm the one who gets the sofas dirty.

Minus If I catch him, I'm going to strangle him with my bare hands.

Party We need to figure out what to say to Buddy. I think that this time he'll really take it badly.

Magda You could buy a new one.

Party Sorry?

Magda I'm saying that if you buy a new TV, this would solve a lot of problems.

Minus Great idea.

Party What are you insinuating?

Magda I'm not insinuating. I'm only trying to make you see what your tendency to break everything has done.

Party When I was saying, 'Break everything,' I was saying in general. I certainly wasn't referring to the TV.
Magda Oh, well then, what were you referring to?
Party To your nose, if you don't stop it.

Enter Buddy.

All Hi.
Buddy Hi. I've been thinking a lot about our situation . . .
Magda Don't say anything you might regret afterwards!
Buddy How come?
Party If there was something nice, you could let him say it, right?
Cindy It's not likely to be something nice, coming from him. Listen, Buddy, it's useless to delay this any longer: someone broke the television. It's in pieces. This will destroy you, but it's better that you know it right away. We don't really want to see your reaction so one of us – we don't know who – apologises. Period.
Buddy The . . . the television . . .
Silly Yeah, that thing with the little men who move inside it.
Buddy I don't . . . I don't . . . First the sofa, now . . .
Snappy Again with the sofa? I already said I was sorry.
Buddy Guys, I . . . I . . .
Girl We'll buy a new one. Okay? We'll buy a new one. One of us made a mistake, and didn't mean it, but have patience. We'll buy a new one all together. How much could it cost?
Woodschlock That doesn't seem like a good idea to me.
Girl Why?
Woodschlock To buy a new one like that, as if nothing ever happened, devalues the gesture of having destroyed it.
Girl Well, it didn't seem like a wonderful gesture to me.

Woodschlock Good or bad doesn't matter. We've talked about it a lot. It's something that exists for everyone – we can't deny it like that, taking a collection to go back to where we started. Instead, let's ask ourselves how this thing that has happened can interfere with our lives.

Minus That seems obvious.

Cindy It seems like the usual argument of one who broke the TV.

Woodschlock No, you stupid little girl. I didn't break any TV, but now that it's broken, instead of putting in fifty bucks to buy a new one, I'd prefer to see how he will live without the Smurfs at seven, how Silly will use her brain now that she can't leave it there for half the day . . .

Silly I don't understand, is he insulting me?

Woodschlock . . . how much time we will stay here arguing about this, and how Buddy will resolve this terrible crisis. These are the things that make you grow up. And so I say, why don't we all become adults?

He goes into another room.
Everyone is horrified.
From the other room, we hear the sound of more destruction and catastrophe.

Buddy Ohmygod.

TEN
LAWS OF THE MARKET

Snappy I'm hungry. I'm really hungry. Only I don't have any money, like, five – five bucks, you follow me? I go in, like, the first restaurant I find. It's expensive – all good stuff, but it's expensive. Check the menu, and I order what I can order with the money I have: one thing on the menu has, like, twelve ingredients, right,

it costs less than everything but there's a lot of stuff in
it. I look around: gigantic plates. Mine comes and it's
a tiny starter. I eat it in two bites and instead of going
away, my appetite got bigger. It was also really good.
It was then that I lost it. I looked around and there
was this guy eating something that would make your
mouth water just talking about it. I grab the waiter
and ask him for the same thing that he brought to the
guy. Really nice, the waiter, says, 'Yes, sir.' After a little
while he comes back with what I asked him for. And
I lost control. I order drinks too and eat one hundred
dollars' worth of food. As the hunger begins to pass,
anxiety starts to hit me, but I decide not to think about
it until I have my coffee and after the coffee, I get a
drink to boost my courage. At this point the waiter
brings me a little plate with the bill folded in two and
I don't open it – not even out of curiosity. The escape
route is impossible because I'm a little weighted down
and also a little tipsy. So then I start to think. I'm
sitting there for a lifetime, no one comes to disturb
me. But slowly the place begins to empty out and the
waiters start to whisper, when one comes up to me to
say . . . I beat him to it and I tell him that I would like
to speak to the cook. The waiter asks me if by chance
I wasn't satisfied and I say no, no, on the contrary.
The cook comes and I look him right in the eyes. I give
him a big smile, I stand up and say, 'This is the best
meal I've ever eaten in my entire life. Unfortunately
I don't have the money to pay for anything, but don't
take it as a sign of disrespect, on the contrary. Because
I don't have any money, I would never have eaten so
much if it hadn't been so good.' I was doing everything
that I could do. I waited.

Buddy What were you waiting for?

Snappy A fist in the face or a reaction worthy of my
speech.

Buddy Of course.

Cindy And you think there exists a reaction worthy of a speech like that?

Snappy He should have said, 'I work with my heart, as you yourself tasted with your palate, but after years of honoured service, the sensation of working only because you are part of a machine like this is always stronger. Your speech has moved me. There are those such as yourself who help lift up those such as myself. Go, your faith has saved you.' Something like that.

Silly And he said that?

Cindy Yeah, that's a great idea, so somebody let the word out and every beggar went there expecting to eat by scrounging.

Piggy Not bad!

Party Well, no, it could be that they created a kind of pact of honour with each other.

Minus Yeah, the honour of the laws of supply and demand.

Buddy Well, did he do it?

Snappy He said to me: 'If I were younger, I would have beaten and kicked you to death, but since I'm of a certain age, I leave these things to the police . . .'

Buddy Very instructive.

Piggy He called the police?

Snappy He was about to do it when I told him to wait, that my esteem towards him was such, and therefore I was offering myself as a dishwasher until I was no longer indebted.

Silly Did he take you?

Snappy He told me that if he needed a dishwasher, I was not the one, and he asked if I was ready to pay the bill or if he should do something else to solve the problem.

Piggy Did you have to explain to him again that you didn't have any money?

Snappy No, he didn't care if I had any or not. That wasn't the problem. However, I had digested some of the meal, and he was really fat so I ran towards the exit. The waiters were ready, like they expected it, and they came at me from behind. So then I ran – I ran for a long way. Seriously, a long way, with those waiters always behind me, until in the end – well, in the end I didn't see them there any more.

Minus And then?

Cindy 'And then' . . . Goodness, you are an idiot, the story's over, right?

Minus How should I know? Maybe then something else happened to him!

Snappy Well, in effect, I'd had some food, I'd had some drinks, I'd had some exercise . . . all I needed was a woman. There were some prostitutes there, but I only had five bucks, so I went to one –

Cindy Stop it!

Piggy Well, it was a beautiful story.

Buddy Very instructive.

Cindy Yeah, but he ruined it! Now no one will believe it! (*to Minus*) It's your fault. Why do you ask stupid questions? Huh? Why do you ask stupid questions?

Snappy A beautiful story is always a beautiful story.

Woodschlock But it's only a story.

ELEVEN
PLUTOCRACY

Night, everyone is asleep in sleeping bags. The outside door opens, and a ray of light from the hallway shines in when Schkreker enters.

Schkreker And who are you?

Snappy And who are you?

Schkreker turns on the light. One by one, everyone wakes up and sits up in their sleeping bags, like caterpillars.

Cindy Hi! Remember me?

Schkreker No, I don't remember, who are you?

Cindy We were together, we were engaged, I mean, you were really busy with your things but . . .

Schkreker What are you doing here?

Pause.

Cindy I . . . Buddy!

Buddy What is it? Oh, ohmygod, you're here? Hello, I mean, welcome back . . .

Schkreker What are you doing here?

Buddy I . . . your parents asked me to look after the house, I didn't know that you were here . . .

Schkreker I'm here.

Woodschlock You want to join us?

Schkreker Hello, you're here as well?

Woodschlock Yeah, yeah. I'm fine. You want to join us?

Schkreker No, I had no such intention.

Snappy Listen here, it's a nice place.

Girl You're the son of the owners of the house?

Schkreker And who are you?

Girl I'm a friend of Cindy's.

Schkreker Who's Cindy?

Cindy But it's me, don't you remember?

Party You're breaking her heart . . .

Schkreker Who spoke?

Pause

Party I did.

Schkreker What are you doing here?

Party I . . . Silly invited me.

Schkreker Silly? Silly who?

Pause.

Buddy Listen, there are a few things I should explain
to you . . .
Schkreker Yes?
Buddy An unpleasant situation has happened.
Schkreker An unpleasant situation has happened?
Buddy That's what I said.
Schkreker I heard you. Well then?

Pause.

Minus It's not exactly Buddy's fault . . .
Schkreker Who spoke?
Minus I said this situation isn't exactly Buddy's fault . . .
Schkreker It's my fault? (*Pause.*) It's my fault?
Minus I would say no . . .
Buddy I didn't know you were coming back, your
parents asked me to watch the house and little by
little, my friends . . .
Schkreker Your friends? These? – These are *your*
friends? – The ones that are in my house right now
are your friends?
Buddy Some, yes, some . . .
Schkreker You've betrayed my mom and dad's trust by
bringing your friends into their house?
Buddy No . . .
Schkreker No? – No?
Buddy No.
Schkreker I don't understand. These people are here . . .
Buddy Yes.
Schkreker Is it your house?
Buddy No.
Schkreker Is it my house?
Buddy Certainly!
Schkreker Did I invite them?
Buddy No.

Schkreker Are they my friends?
Buddy No.
Snappy Make friends. It's easy.
Cindy Once we were together, when we were little.
Schkreker Who spoke?

Pause.

Schkreker Are they your friends?
Buddy No.
Schkreker No?
Buddy No.

Pause.

Schkreker Well then, tell these strangers to get out or
I'll kick them out.
Buddy Sorry . . .
Snappy We understand.
Magda 'Bye, Buddy.
Party 'Bye . . .
Schkreker Tell them.
Buddy Get out.

*They slowly leave, one by one. The last is
Woodschlock.*

Woodschlock (*to Buddy*) Later, huh!

Exits.

Schkreker What will we tell Mom and Dad?

TWELVE
SOME TEN YEARS LATER

A police station. Bare walls, oppressive, no windows.
A table and two chairs. The shift from one room in the
police station to another can be conveyed by repositioning
the table and chairs.

The characters have no memory of themselves in the
previous scenes. The relationships have all been zeroed.

REVOLUTION AND NEW FIGHTING TECHNIQUES 2

Magda What were you thinking of doing with this?

Party is leaning against a wall. She's covered in blood.
On the table is a toothbrush.

I asked you a question. Did you hear the question?
Party Yes.
Magda Good. Then you understand. And did you
answer the question?
Party No.
Magda What were you thinking of doing with this?
Party Nothing.
Magda What?
Party Nothing.
Magda Nothing? You said nothing?
Party Yes.
Magda I ask you a question. You claim to have
understood the question, and you answer, 'Nothing.'
If you hadn't understood the question, that would
be one thing, buf if you understood the question you
cannot answer, 'Nothing.' How long do we want to
stay here? How much longer do we want to stay?
Party Not long.

Magda Well, then, don't make me angry! What did you
want to do with this? Huh?

Party Brush my teeth?

Magda Brush your teeth? Brush your teeth? I try to help
you, but you continue to go against me. What did you
want to do with this? You said you didn't want to
stay here long, but if you keep this up, we'll be talking
again tomorrow. I'll give you one more chance. What
did you want to do with this?

Party I don't know.

Magda You don't know? You don't know?

Party Please tell me?

Magda Eh, my dear, I can't tell you. I can't help you if
you don't let me. You yourself must know what you
want to do. I know what *I* want to do; I can't know
what *you* want to do. You yourself must know this.
Responsibility. If I tell you, then tomorrow I'll find
you back here again. And that will not work. What
shall we do?

Party What do you want to do?

Magda I would like to no longer have anything to do
with those like you, but unfortunately there are
always more and more. And I don't really know how
to help you.

THIRTEEN
APOLOGIES

*Snappy is all swollen. Schkreker, elegantly dressed, is
seated, a little distracted.*

Cindy (*to Snappy, indicating Schkreker*) Look what you
did to him. Look what you did to him. In your opinion,
what should we do with someone like yourself? Huh?
What should we do? Bring you back there? Start again

from the beginning? And what would that get us?
You would start again. You would do it again. At
least apologise to him. Didn't they teach you that?
You know what the difference is between those like
me, like him, and those like you? Do you know? You
don't know! The difference is that we were at least
taught to apologise. And that would not be enough.
But at least we apologise. And they didn't teach you
that? Certainly they taught you that. Because at least
we all start with the same possibilities. At the very
least. But you never learned this. Why? Why? Perhaps
one day we'll know why. But certainly not from you.
However, all the same we want to give you another
chance. There will come a day in which those such
as yourself are not given another chance, but we want
to give it to you. Apologise to him. Can't you speak?
Can't you speak any more?

Snappy Uhmpf . . . uhmpf . . .
Cindy Do you have something over your mouth?
Schkreker No, he doesn't.
Cindy Is something wrong with his mouth?
Schkreker Ask him if something is wrong with his
mouth.
Cindy Apologise, for . . .
Snappy Uhmpf . . .
Cindy Is something wrong with your mouth?
Snappy I want . . .
Cindy I want?
Schkreker There, he can speak and 'wants'.
Snappy I want to go back to the hospital.

*Cindy raises her hand to strike him, Schkreker motions
to her to stop. He stands up and walks towards him.*

Schkreker What is it you want?
Snappy I want to go back to the hospital.

Schkreker And I want an almond cake like my grandma used to make. But it can't be done.

FOURTEEN
NICE THINGS

Buddy and the Girl are making tea.

Buddy How's it going?

Girl He's very tired.

Buddy Does he want to set someone free?

Girl No, he says it's better to keep those that we have *here*; the more you keep here, the more time will pass before they come back.

Buddy True. Did they give *you* any trouble?

Girl No, I wouldn't say that. There was one who was yelling, yelling so much that I couldn't stand it any longer, truly annoying to listen to . . .

Buddy Yeah. Have you already moved into the new house?

Girl No, not yet. There's a lot of work to be done, and it's going to take a lot of money. You know – all things considered – he's a very proper gentleman . . .

Buddy Yes . . .

Girl I'm saying . . . he has a great deal of dignity . . . He doesn't want to depend on Mom and Dad, asking for money . . . even if they'll give it to him, certainly.

Buddy Certainly . . .

Girl Anyway, he hopes to be promoted, for him and for me, you know, they give him a raise, everything changes . . .

Buddy Certainly, and he seems . . . Anyway, is there a good chance of it?

Girl Well, for how he's conducting this job, there should be. The bosses – way up at the top . . . just between you and me . . . they're rather happy with how things are going here.

Buddy Well, if there's anything I can do to help you . . .

Girl You're very kind, but don't worry yourself about us. Keep working like you always have. If he doesn't say anything to you, I think that means you're doing well.

Buddy Yeah. I think so. You know – I see the others, however – and at times I think that I'm not strong enough, that I could do more . . .

Girl It's the way you are. I think that you're doing fine with what you do.

Enters Schkreker. Buddy stands to attention.

Schkreker Hello, beautiful.

Passionately kisses the Girl.

(*to Buddy*) At ease. Cell 91. A colleague is already there, he'll tell you what to do.

Buddy Yessir.

Buddy exits.

Girl How are you?

Schkreker I feel like if we don't make love now, I'm going to die of a heart attack.

Girl I love you.

Schkreker Of course.

They embrace.

FIFTEEN
OF MEN AND DOGS

Woodschlock is savagely beating Piggy.

Woodschlock You think that now you could talk. (*Hits him.*) You think that you could give up the names of some of your friends . . . (*Hits him.*) And that they would find themselves here in your place . . . (*Hits him.*) But I want to be honest with you. I don't give a damn about your 'names'. (*Hits him.*) Because it's not my job. We have very precise roles. (*Hits him.*) As I suppose you do as well. I'm not so good at obtaining information. So I'm the person who hits. Then the person who is good at obtaining information will come, and you must give it to him. If not, then I come back and hit you. (*Hits him.*) It's better that you pay attention and learn our respective shifts so as to save me time and punches. (*Hits him.*) If you were in our position – it's a possibility I can't exclude – will you be among those who ask questions or those who give out the punches? (*Hits him.*) Maybe you'll be among those who are hit again. Who knows . . .? (*Hits him.*)

Enter Buddy.

Hey, is it finished already?
Buddy I don't know, they sent me here.
Woodschlock Change shift. (*To Piggy*) See? Try to figure out which group he belongs to. Maybe next time I'm assigned to this cell I won't find you here. Let's hope so, huh? 'Bye, Buddy. Later, huh!
Buddy 'Bye.

Woodschlock exits.

Eh, he beat you pretty badly, huh? He's like that, he's not bad. I'm sure you must think that he *is* bad, but it's not true. If you knew him like we know him . . . He tells the best jokes. He's a little crazy, but in a certain sense that's the best thing about him. I mean, it's that craziness that makes him so special. I don't have it, I don't know if I would like it; but I would like to know how to deal with the others like he does. The others, I don't mean you, the others like us. But I'm giving you all these speeches that probably don't interest you at all. I mean that, in your position, you can't understand. I talk. I like to talk. Sometimes those such as yourself think that there's a hidden meaning in what I'm saying, that they need to pay attention to understand it because then they can obtain something. But it's not like that. I don't know how to say two different things in one sentence. I talk only to chat. I have to stay here to be the guard, and so I talk.

Piggy Li–ke a do–g?

Buddy Dogs don't talk.

SIXTEEN
COMIC INTERLLUDE

Party, Minus, Snappy and Silly are standing with their legs open, against a wall. They are dressed like cooks.
Cindy and Magda are pacing in front of them, Schkreker somewhat apart, watching them.

Cindy You!

Magda goes and grabs Snappy by the hair and drags him to the centre of the room.

What does a kangaroo do?

Pause. Magda hits Snappy.

A kangaroo. Be a kangaroo.

Snappy begins to jump about the room like a kangaroo.

Magda Higher. The kangaroo hops higher, don't tell me you're tired because you did the green lizard so badly.

Cindy You!

Cindy grabs Silly.

A chimpanzee.

Silly looks at her. Gets clubbed.

A chimpanzee! It's a monkey, it's not difficult!

*Silly begins to hop around and make monkey faces.
Magda grabs Minus.*

Magda Come on. The curlew! I SAID 'THE CURLEW'!!
Schkreker (*to himself*) Intellectuals . . . this one is
driving me crazy . . .
Minus I don't know how to do it . . .
Magda That's not my problem. The curlew!

Minus tries to do something.

You think that's a curlew? Do all of you think that's a
curlew?
Schkreker No. (*Goes to the door.*) There's a curlew to be
taken away!
Silly No, where are you taking him!?
Cindy You! Continue with your chimpanzee!

Woodschlock enters and takes Minus away.

Minus Silly!!

They are gone.

Cindy It seems to me to be more like a maggot than a
chimpanzee.
Schkreker But what is a curlew?
Magda It's a bird, sir.
Schkreker Well, he wasn't that far off.
Magda To me he seemed more like a tuna fish.

SEVENTEEN
WATER AND PEE

Buddy and Piggy.

Piggy Wa–wa . . .

Buddy What? Are you speaking to me? Well, of course, I'm the only one here . . .

Piggy Wa . . .

Buddy Wa?

Piggy Ter.

Buddy Ter? Ter what?

Piggy Wa . . .

Buddy Ter? Wa – ter? Water? Water what? Ah, some water, you want some water? Is that what you were trying to say?

Piggy Yes.

Buddy I can't give you some. I'm sorry, if it were up to me, I'd give you some but I can't. Yes, it's true, no one would know, I could give you some, but . . . it's not that I can do everything I like. I mean, I can't do it. Maybe you think that I'm kind and you think that you can take advantage of me. Many people do. But the fact is that even if I'm more kind than the one who was here before, however, I . . . I try to do this job well. I believe in it. Sometimes it's not easy, but . . . I can't give you water. You feel awful, you're thirsty, but I can't. There's salt water – I'm authorised to give you some of that, but I don't think you want it. No one ever wants it. That's because it makes your mouth dry, and then you're even more thirsty, you feel worse. I don't know if you've already tried it. Maybe you would like some but I don't recommend it. However, it's your choice. Do you want some salt water?

Pause.

Right, just as I thought. I understand that you think that
I'm not a good person because I don't give you some
water, but if you were in my place, you'd understand.
You know, sometimes you need to use strong methods
to protect democracy from the threat of its own
citizens. That's what they say when we're feeling a
little down. But generally, we don't feel down very
often. Up and down, like everyone.

Piggy Bath–room.

Buddy You want to go to the bathroom? The bathroom,
here?

Piggy Pee . . .

Buddy No, I can't. I can't. You would need to ask that
of my superiors – the ones who could accompany
you. I can't. You have to wait until there's a higher-
ranking official here, don't ask me. If you can't hold
it any longer, you can go on yourself . . . I'll be
reprimanded, but I can't stop you from doing it.
I really can't do any more than this. EVEN YOU COULD
TRY TO UNDERSTAND MY POSITION!!!

EIGHTEEN
COMIC INTERLUDE 2

Cindy and Magda.
    *Party, Silly and Snappy still standing against the wall
with their legs open. They're singing.*

Party *and* **Snappy**
    'Are you sleeping, are you sleeping?
    Brother John, Brother John?'
    Morning bells are ringing, morning bells are ringing –'

Cindy Why aren't you singing? Huh?

Silly (*to herself*) I didn't even get to say, 'I love you' . . .

Cindy What are you talking about?

Silly (*to herself*) They carried him away and I didn't
even get to say, 'I love you' . . .
Party (*softly to Silly*) It's better if you sing . . .
Magda What do *you* have to say?
Party Nothing.
Magda Nothing? Well then, don't say anything, right?
Cindy Come on, louder! Sing!
Party *and* **Snappy**
'Are you sleeping, are you sleeping?
Brother John, Brother John?
Morning bells are ringing, morning bells are ringing.
Ding ding dong, ding ding dong . . .'
Cindy We're not together. You must sing all together.
You need to sing too! All together, understand?
Silly (*to herself*) Together, always together, you and I . . .
Cindy You don't understand. Right, then we'll do it this
way. I am the King. You will sit on imaginary chairs,
I'll leave, and when I pass this line, you all stand up,
like how you are now. Understand? It's easy.

*She exits. Party and Snappy sit against the wall on
imaginary chairs. Silly stays standing. Magda makes
her 'sit' down. Cindy re-enters. She passes the
imaginary line; only Snappy stands.*

What are you doing now? Didn't you understand?
Party It's my period.
Cindy It happens. Once a month, it happens. At least
you're not pregnant. Aren't you glad you're not
pregnant?
Party I have to go to the bathroom.
Cindy When you say you have to go to the bathroom,
you *do* have to go to the bathroom, but when I tell you
to stand up because I am the king, you don't do it.
How can I believe you actually *know* what to do and
what not to do? STAND UP ALL THREE OF YOU!!!
Snappy I'm already standing.

Cindy And you, where do you think you're going in this world? Do you want a kiss? Do you want to be promoted?

NINETEEN
FAMILY AND RESPONSIBILITY

Minus, Woodschlock and Schkreker.

Minus Where's Silly?

Schkreker Silly? Who's Silly?

Minus She's . . . she's my wife.

Schkreker She's your wife. And why should I know where your wife is? You should know this. I know where my wife is – you should know where your wife is.

Minus She was with you . . .

Schkreker Clearly you can't control her very well. Those such as yourself, they go around, they think only of their own affairs, they cause damage, they put democracy in danger and then when someone finally begins to deal seriously with them they pretend that we should also take care of their families. You must assume responsibility and learn to look after your wife. If she truly is with us, it's clear that she was also going around, thinking only of her own affairs, causing damage, and putting democracy in danger. So then, she's probably also around here somewhere having fun with one of us or imagining that we're also looking after you. And, we're doing just that.

Minus She's pregnant.

Schkreker In this regard, I can set you at ease. It wasn't one of us. Tecnhically, there hasn't been enough time for it to happen. But from what I know of you, I also have my doubts that it was you.

TWENTY
CONCERNING NATURE

Cindy and Magda are drinking tea.

Cindy What are you thinking about?

Magda Anything is better than being an engineer.

Cindy You're an engineer?

Magda Yes.

Cindy I would have liked to be an engineer but I didn't do so well in school. This job isn't bad. However, I'm afraid that sooner or later it will end.

Magda Why should it?

Cindy Well, we're really doing our best, sooner or later, we'll win; we'll be unemployed.

Magda They won't permit it.

Cindy Who?

Magda Our leaders won't permit it. They would also be unemployed. When these enemies are dead, they'll invent new enemies even more evil, and they'll need us even more.

Cindy How do you know?

Magda The leader of those who we captured this time is a colleague, a friend of our leader.

Cindy Really?

Magda The fishermen don't want to eliminate all the trout. They fish as a hobby. If the trout all die, the fishermen breed more and when they are big enough, they begin fishing again. If there weren't any fishermen, there wouldn't be any trout either. It's nature.

Cindy So, *we* were the ones who put the carrots in the exhaust pipe of the prime minister's car and the pink cow in the embassy garden?

Magda Or somebody did it for us.

Cindy No, I don't think so, you're talking nonsense . . .
that would be too frustrating for us.

Magda Anything is better than being an engineer.

TWENTY-ONE
NICE THINGS 2

Snappy, Party and Silly are against the wall with their
legs spread. Party's clothes are stained with blood
between her legs.

TWENTY-TWO
UNPLEASANT SITUATIONS

Minus with Woodschlock and Schkreker.
Enter Buddy, accompanied by the Girl.

Schkreker What is it?

Girl My love, I'm sorry if I'm disturbing you . . . Buddy
is in a situation that's a little unpleasant.

Schkreker A situation that's a little unpleasant?

Buddy Yes, exactly, sir.

Schkreker Well, what happened?

Buddy The prisoner, the one in Cell 91, who I was
entrusted with . . .

Woodschlock Yeah, Cell 91, I was there.

Buddy I think he's dead, sir.

Schkreker Dead? What do you mean, dead?

Buddy He asked me for some water, and according to
the procedure I didn't give him any . . .

Woodschlock There was salt water.

Buddy Yes, I told him that. He refused, and then, after a
while, I think he died.

Schkreker What do you mean, died?

Buddy In that he's not speaking, he's not breathing, and his heart isn't beating.

Schkreker This is a problem, correct?

Buddy I think . . . I think so, sir.

Schkreker For every problem, I think there exists an official emergency procedure and an unofficial emergency procedure, correct?

Buddy Yes, sir.

Schkreker What is the official emergency procedure?

Buddy Report to our superior.

Schkreker Very good, and in fact here you are. And the unofficial one?

Buddy I . . . he was dead, at the time I didn't think about the procedures . . .

Schkreker The unofficial one?

Buddy I don't remember.

Woodschlock You tear a strip from the prisoner's shirt, you go down and buy a chandelier, you mount it in the prisoner's cell, and you hang the prisoner from the chandelier by his neck using the previously obtained strip of shirt. In case the procedure results in too much inquiry, you open a window and you shove the prisoner through said window, catching the attention of the passers-by and the cars of our colleagues. You file a nice report, and you write 'Suicide'.

Schkreker Did you remember that?

Buddy No, sir.

Schkreker And hearing it again, did that refresh your memory?

Buddy Yes, sir, hearing it again, yes.

Schkreker Is the unofficial emergency procedure still applicable?

Buddy I'll go right now and buy a chandelier . . .

Schkreker I asked you if the procedure is still applicable?

Buddy I think so, sir.

Schkreker I think not. There's a prisoner here who has heard everything. And it's not important whether or not he will be set free, sooner or later he must speak with his lawyer, and then the emergency procedure is at risk.

Minus I didn't hear anything.

Schkreker You would be put on trial, as would I, and this would not be useful to anyone.

Buddy Therefore?

Schkreker gives a gun to Buddy.

Schkreker Go buy two chandeliers.

Buddy I have to . . .

Schkreker If not, what will we tell Mom and Dad?

Minus I didn't hear anything.

Buddy points the pistol at Minus's head.
Long pause.
Buddy hears the voice of Party.

Party 'He wants to be your friend for ever.'

Minus Really, I don't remember anything . . .

Buddy has the gun pointed at Minus's head.

TWENTY-THREE

The apartment from the beginning with the broken TV, the sofa, and all the rest. Reset to Scene Eleven. Schkreker has already entered, the lights are on, and everyone is sitting up in their sleeping bags.

Buddy Listen, there are a few things I should explain to you . . .

Schkreker Yes?

Buddy An unpleasant situation has happened.

Schkreker An unpleasant situation has happened?

Buddy That's what I said.
Schkreker I heard you. Well then?

Pausa.

Minus It's not exacly Buddy's fault . . .
Schkreker Who spoke?
Minus I said this situation isn't exactly Buddy's fault . . .
Schkreker It's my fault? (*Pause*) It's my fault?
Minus I would say no . . .
Buddy I didn't know you were coming back, your
   parents asked me to watch the house and little by
   little, my friends . . .
Schkreker Your friends? These? – These are *your*
   friends? – The ones that are in my house right now
   are your friends?
Buddy Some yes, some . . .
Schkreker You've betrayed my mom and dad's trust by
   bringing your friends into their house?
Buddy No . . .
Schkreker No? – No?
Buddy No.
Schkreker I don't understand. These people are here . . .
Buddy Yes.
Schkreker Is it your house?
Buddy No.
Schkreker Is it my house?
Buddy Certainly!
Schkreker Did I invite them?
Buddy No.
Schkreker Are they my friends?
Buddy No.
Snappy Make friends. It's easy.
Cindy Once we were together, when we were little.
Schkreker Who spoke?

Pause.

385

Schkreker Are they your friends?
Buddy Yes.
Schkreker Yes?
Buddy Yes.

Pause.

Schkreker Well then, tell your friends to get out.
Snappy We understand.
Magda 'Bye, Buddy.
Party 'Bye . . .
Schkreker Tell them.
Minus There's no need. We understand.
Buddy No, you don't understand.
Schkreker Tell them to get out!
Buddy No.

A laugh escapes from someone.

Minus Buddy, there's no need for you to do . . .
Buddy I *do* need to do it, you have no idea how much
I need to do it.
Schkreker Listen, if you don't tell them now to get out,
I'll have to kick them out by force.
Buddy I don't think they'll go.
Schkreker Get out of here now!!!

Silence.

Buddy (*sings*)
'Are you sleeping, are you sleeping?
Brother John, Brother John . . .?'
Schkreker Are you crazy?
Buddy
'Morning bells are ringing, morning bells are ringing . . .'
Magda What's he doing?
Party I don't know. Sing.
Buddy
'Ding ding dong.'

Buddy *and* **Snappy**
'Ding ding dong!'
Schkreker And what will I tell Mom and Dad?
Buddy *and* **Snappy**
'Are you sleeping, are you sleeping . . .?'

*Slowly Minus, Party, Silly and Piggy begin to sing.
And then also Cindy, Magda, Woodschlock.*

All
'Brother John, Brother John?
Morning bells are ringing, morning bells are ringing.
Ding ding dong, ding ding dong.'

*While all continue to sing, except Schkreker, Buddy
separates himself from the group and says:*

Buddy If I had done it like that, who knows if things
would have gone differently . . . Maybe not . . .
nothing would have changed . . . I simply would have
found myself on the other side, but I like to think so,
just the same.

*He returns to sing with the others, louder and louder.
Blackout.*

OLIVE

Tamsin Oglesby

Characters

Olive

Dad

Mum

Father

Big Sis

Little Sis

Oliver

Magda

Ella

Lady F

Girl

Act One

The stage is set with oversized letters spelling out the name, 'OLIVE'. These letters will be reassembled throughout the action for different spellings, as indicated. They can also be disassembled and used to represent various scenic elements as required (a tree, a chair, a bed, a tunnel).

The actors are both the characters and the scene-makers of the play. Like the letters, they remain onstage throughout; when not in character they either return to a neutral space (e.g., a circle at the edge of the action) or adjust the letters, or become part of the 'furniture' of the scene.

The production should aim to be inventive rather than literal, so that, instead of wheeling on cupboards and tables for a kitchen scene, the actors themselves can provide the materials: two people holding a cutting board; someone whistling signifies the boiling of a kettle; a knife may be received from another actor as and when it is needed.

There are no blackouts in the play. One scene leads directly into another with changes of music, space, 'furniture' and lighting to suggest differences in time and place.

Olive, a girl of about sixteen, kneels upon a prayer mat, centre stage, and prays, her eyes open. She has a book in her lap.

Olive Dear God – I can't talk very loud, alright, because if *he* hears me I'm in deep – you know – but I want to go home now. To my family. I want to see my little sister with her sticking-up hair.

Unseen by Olive, a young girl enters – with hair that sticks up – and stands, reading a book.

I want to see my big sister who loves me more than double-chocolate-chip-with-fudge ice cream.

An older girl joins the young girl. She is finishing off a tub of ice cream.

I want to see my mum. The only one who really knows where I'm ticklish.

Mum stands by the two girls. She tickles the younger one affectionately in the ribs.

And I want to see my dad. My real dad. Who would never say I'm just a stupid little girl.

He joins the others. He puts his arms around them.
    Olive opens her eyes, looks straight ahead, and in her mind's eye, she sees them.

I can almost touch them. (*She holds out her hands but there's nothing there. She screws up her eyes again and prays.*) Oh God, please take me back.

Music. Four actors cross to pick up the mat, one at each corner, and fly it across the stage, in and out of the letters. They place it at the feet of the family and disappear again.
    Olive opens her eyes and jumps up in surprise. They embrace each other and talk all at once.

Little Sis You came back! I knew you'd come back. See – I told you she'd come back.
Mum What are you doing here? Oh, my little squirrel.
Little Sis How did you come back?
Olive I've no idea.
Mum Look at you, so thin.
Big Sis Hey, birdbrain.

Olive Hey, big bum.

Little Sis (*waving her book*) Guess what? Sally Barker ends up in hospital in the next book because she spits the gaff on Tito. And he tries to get in disguised as a doctor but they catch him out 'cos someone notices his hairy toes sticking out his shoes. You can borrow it – (*Olive puts her hand out; Little Sister holds on to it.*) when I've finished it.

Dad We've missed you, my girl.

Olive Oh, Dad. Oh, my Dad.

Little Sis And then Romy – you remember, the one she meets up the Incaberg – Romy finds this telescope, right, which, if you point it at someone's head, like that, you can read their mind, it's fantastic.

Olive's father enters, stopping everyone in their tracks. Olive holds on to her dad. Father approaches him.

Father We had an agreement.

Dad We did.

Father You said I could have her back.

Dad We did.

Father Then why is she here?

They all look at Olive. She looks down.

Dad Because she wants to be.

Father How did she get here?

They all look at Olive. She looks at her prayer mat, and back again at her family, nonplussed.

Father You bribe her.

Dad We have nothing to give her but love.

Father And this book.

He picks up the book from the prayer mat.

Mum It is hers.

Father She doesn't need it any more.

393

He hands it back to Olive's mum.

Mum What does she need?

Father A stiff hand.

Mum I don't understand. Maybe a language problem.

Father She needs order. She needs rules. She needs Haja.

Dad She already has her own God.

Father No. Her God is Haja. Is the god of her ancestors. Is in her blood. Your heathen pox religion is compost. My ancestors, they cry in their sleep to hear her pray to your God.

Dad You should have thought of that sixteen years ago.

Father What you say to me?

Dad I said, you should have thought –

Mum But what – ssh, not now – what does *she* want?

Father You people talk of want as a thing to be answered. We say it is thing to avoid. The vessel should be empty of desire.

Mum No. 'Only to those who desire to know the will of God will he make it be known.' Ganotians three, verse four.

Father 'Seek not to know the mind of God, but fear him and do not exceed the truth'. Chapter of the Tree.

Mum But 'Those who believe, and act righteously, and are steadfast in prayer; there is no fear in them, nor shall they grieve.'

Father 'Those who fear are gardens for their Lord, beneath which rivers flow.'

Mum 'For I am the Lord your God. And my name is mercy. He who lives by my word will know my name, and he who knows my name will likewise use my name and so shall mercy be shown.' Book of Nurture, chapter eight.

Father And he said unto his people, 'I have many names and many faces, but one voice. Listen and you will see. Look and you will hear.' First chapter of the Malitites.

Mum 'God is the east and the west, and wherever you turn there is God's face.'

Father 'There is only one God, / and whosoever lives in love lives in Him.'

Mum 'And whosoever lives in love lives in Him.'

Silence.

Father Damn you to hell and back, you twist your words to sound like mine. Is enough. She goes with me. You go back to your land of noddy and leave her alone. Come, Olive.

She looks at her family and they at her. No one makes a move.

Father COME!

Olive jumps and follows him off. But, unseen by him, she doubles back and grabs the book from her mother. Then catches up with him again. He leads her through and over the letters which spell out her name.

The family return to the neutral space from which they came.

SCENE TWO

The kitchen. Father, preparing supper. Olive, helping.

Father You like olives, Olive? Ha ha.

Olive I hate olives.

Father How you hate olives? They are old and wise as earth.

Olive I hate them.

He shrugs and continues cutting vegetables.

Father You like tomatoes, Olive?

Olive Yes.

Father Good. Tonight we have ratatouille. You like?
Olive What is it?
Father 'What is it?' she says. Is my favourite. I tell you.
Tomato. Onion. Plant egg. Garlic.
Olive Plant egg?
Father Egg plant.
Olive Egg? Plant?
Father Ah, what you say? Aubergine. Yes.
Olive Yuk.
Father You no like?
Olive Never had it.
Father Oh, what have they done to you?
Olive It's not a big deal. I've just never had it.
Father What am I to do? Where to begin?
Olive I'll try it, okay. I'll try it.
Father Good girl, good girl.

He pats her, his knife still in his hand.

SCENE THREE

The garden. There is music, more light, birds sing.
Father exchanges his knife for a trowel and begins to dig upstage, humming as he does so, while:
Downstage, Olive scatters fertiliser on the ground. She covers a wide area of ground, distributing it rhythmically.

Olive Blood, fish and bone. Blood, fish and bone. Bone, fish and blood. Fish, blood and bone. Yuk, fish and blood. Yuk, yuk and yuk. Yuk, yuk, yuk. Yuk, yuk, yuk. Yuk, yuk –

Father comes over.

Father What you do here? You must put in the earth not on the earth. *In.*

Olive Why blood?

Father Is no good like this. You must first dig, so. (*He demonstrates.*)

Olive *Whose* blood?

Father Then scatter scatter scatter.

Olive What fish?

Father And cover up, begin again.

Olive Whose bone?

Father What?

Olive Why am I putting all these horrible things in the mud?

Father You feed it.

Olive With pig's blood and dead . . . mackerel?

Father Like you, it needs food.

Olive It's not natural.

Father What you know about natural?

Olive What do *you* know about natural?

Father Okay, I explain. This plant in this soil take away all his goodness.

Olive Then don't put it there.

Father It grows there, idiot girl. What you want me to do? Take it out?

Olive I am not an idiot girl.

Father Yes, you are idiot. You talk about things you don't know. And you are certainly a girl.

Olive And what is wrong with being a girl?

Father Nothing.

Olive Then why say it?

Father I don't understand.

Olive And I don't understand you, because you know what? You're *foreign*.

Silence.

Father Here, give me this.

He takes the fertiliser from her and digs.

Olive Sorry. I'm sorry. (*Pause.*) When my mother died –
Father No.

Silence.

Olive Can I go and play with Tao?
Father No.

*Olive shuts her eyes but doesn't move. He continues
to dig, down on his knees.*
The light focuses on Olive. She prays.

Olive Dear God. You see what I mean? I can't seem to
say anything right. He won't let me play with the girl
next door. He says I have to grow my hair. He won't
let me out of his sight. He won't let me read the Book.
He won't let me wear your ilket. He makes me wear
this round my wrist. (*She produces a necklace from
her pocket.*) He doesn't like me singing. He says I
should obey *him*. You say I should obey *you*. The
Book says I should obey my father. My dad never
asked me to obey him, but I did, no question. It was
easy. This is impossible. Amen.

*After a moment Olive opens her eyes, turns straight to
her Father and speaks at once, with a new authority.*

I remind you of my mother. I inspire emotions in you
which you don't understand. You don't know me.
And I don't know you. We have to get to know each
other. That's what we have to do.

Silence.

Father How dare you talk to me like like like . . . this!
Olive Like what?
Father You don't tell me what I understand or no
understand. I tell *you*. Child. I am growed up. Okay?
Okay?

Her authority challenged, Olive is a child again.

Olive Okay.

Father Okay. Good. Now. Enough. Suppertime. Come
  eat.

Olive What is it?

Father Ratatouille.

Olive I hate ratatouille.

Father You like it.

Olive Not every day.

Father Yesterday we had small bird with schmollet.

Olive I want pasta. And roast chicken. And my mother's
  fish pie. And chips. And tomato ketchup. I want
  tomato ketchup!

Father Tomato ketchup with ratatouille is like toffee
  with apple. Is no good.

Olive I like no good.

Father Are you taking the puppy from me?

Olive What?

Father You are laughing at me. You go to your room.
  Go to your room and stay there until you ready to eat
  my food with me like proper growed-up person. Go.

Olive I'm not laughing at you, I'm not.

Father Go!

She does.

SCENE FOUR

Two separate rooms, one next to the other.
  *Both Olive and Father set up for prayer in their
respective spaces with their respective ceremonies. Music.*
  *Olive lays out her mat; Father puts down his prayer
stool; Olive takes off the bracelet round her wrist and
puts on her ilket; Father clasps his bracelet, and rolls his
wrist three times while muttering a blessing under his*

breath; Olive paces along the four edges of her mat to arrive at a fixed point in the middle, facing out; Father draws a circle in the air with his finger then kneels on his stool; Olive passes her hands in front of her face repeatedly, as though drawing an imaginary veil over her face; Father rests a finger on each (closed) eyelid for a while; Olive raises her face to the sky, eyes closed, and holds her arms out at her side: she prays; Father puts his hands together and forward, eyes closed: he prays.

After a while, Father stops suddenly, and listens.

He gets up. Goes to Olive's room and creeps up on her, unseen. He treads on her discarded bracelet.

She jumps up. He picks up the bracelet and firmly replaces it on her wrist, then removes the ilket from around her neck and lets it fall. She makes no resistance.

He stands back, indicating that she should continue her prayer. She resumes by passing her hands in front of her face repeatedly.

Father No.

She stops.

You know this.

He leads her in his ritual, watching her all the while. She imitates him, obediently, but without conviction.

Satisfied, he leaves and resumes his prayer next door.

Olive stares into space, vacant, for a while. Then gets up with energy and recovers her Book from a drawer. She sits down and studies it.

Father comes to the end of a prayer, stands up and goes to Olive's room again. He sees her engrossed in the Book.

Discob halamet! Give it to me you disobedience. *Nit! Nit na rushlikon.*

Olive No.

*He wrests the Book from her and throws it out of the
window.*

You can't do that!
Father I have done it.

He goes. He stands outside her door, waiting.
*Olive leaves her room via the window, and returns
with the Book.*
*Hardly has she sat down with it before Father
bursts in on her. She hides the Book.*

What you do now?
Olive Nothing.
Father You disobey me one time. I forgive. You disobey
me again. I get angry. And again. I get very angry. I
am very angry. I punish you. You stay in your room.
You don't eat. You don't go nowhere.

*There is the sound of a blade hitting wood. The
kitchen is set up and the vegetables are being cut.
Father goes to the kitchen, retrieves the knife, and
continues to cut vegetables on the 'table'.*
Olive gets out her Book and continues reading.

Olive 'Verily there is no God but he, the living spirit
amongst you. He has sent down to you the Book of
truth, that you should understand, and law, that you
should obey. Verily, those who disbelieve in the signs
of God, for them is severe torment, for God is mighty
and avenging.' (*She stops reading.*) What signs? What
signs? (*She continues reading.*) 'Verily there will be
those who twist their tongues concerning the Book.
They are imposters. They will say, "It is from God,"
but it is not from God, and they tell a lie against God,
the while they know.'

Father calls from the kitchen.

Father Come! Eat!

Olive 'For the truth is a light that flatters not him upon whom it shines. But it shines that you might see, and reveals what you must speak. For as you speak the truth so shall the truth be known.'

Father goes over to her room and catches her with the Book. He advances on her.

Father Again you betray me. You think I don't know what is best for my own flesh and bone?

Olive Yes.

Father *Hele tok. Az na yol miri holete. Kita – kita – tontimilcinok! Fa yezznoo –*

Olive You're doing it again. You're speaking that language.

Father *That* language. That language is *your* language. Is the language of your family, your grandfather's language, your grandfather's grandfather's grandfather's and all. Is your mother tongue. *Kalimanchke ti wottoka.*

Olive I never heard my mother speak. I never knew my mother. The woman I call mother speaks my language. I speak hers. You speak nonsense.

Father *Kalivalismak yol. Irik. Dooly ho marinolte wik olch fa na yol. Diyolte ne na? Diyolte? He? He?* Why do you talk to me like this? I am your father.

Olive Maybe because I don't understand you. Maybe because you want me to be like you. Or maybe because you abandoned me when I was six weeks old, gave me to a family who loved me, then came back sixteen years later and took me away. That might have something to do with it.

Father You are disobedient rude mood girl. You are ignorant how to behave. And give me – *irika fa* *keman* – give me this book of lies and heathen devil worship.

Olive walks away from her Father towards the kitchen with the Book. He follows.

Olive Don't be silly.

Father *Oh zendara mi ho.* She calls me silly. HAKA! MITZINA! FIS O GALLIE POK! You don't give me this book, I cut off your hands. No daughter of mine, / I tell you –

Olive I am not your daughter.

Father You are my daughter, damn you to buggery!

Olive I am not your daughter. I am the daughter of my mother and father, the people who love me. The people who have given me my shape. The people who told me it was alright when it wasn't alright and made it alright. They are my parents. You are an imposter.

Father I see now, they soften up your brain with rubbish and sweets and tomato ketchup and pour lies in your ears and stuff these words in your mouth. Oh evilness. You give me this book now or I cut off your hands.

Olive I won't.

Father You disobey me, I cut off your hands.

Olive I disobey you.

Father I cut off your hands.

Olive Cut off my hands.

Father I cut off your hands.

Olive Do.

Father I will cut off your hands ungrateful – stupid – bad – mad –

Olive Go on then.

Olive puts her hands out on the kitchen table in front of her, still holding the Book.

Father I WILL CUT OFF YOUR HANDS.

*They stare at each other for a moment, then Father
makes a lunge for the Book with one hand. There is a
brief struggle, then he brings the knife down hard.
Olive screams. Then silence.*

SCENE FIVE

*Music takes us into another time, another place. A forest
is created by the actors and the letters which have become
scrambled.*

*Olive makes her way through the forest. She has lost
her fingers; her hands are bandaged. She is oppressed by
flying insects, tiredness and hunger. She sneezes.*

Olive Oh this countryside. Makes me – (*She sneezes
again.*) I hate the countryside, I hate these insects,
I hate the weather, I hate nature, I hate animals, I hate
trees, I hate flowers, I hate birds, I hate EVERYTHING.
But more than everything, God, I hate you.

*She looks up at God, then turns her back and walks
away.*

SCENE SIX

*Oliver, a boy of eighteen, and Magda, his mother. He is
preparing to go out.*

Oliver Just going out.
Magda Out?
Oliver Side, you know.
Magda Outside?
Oliver Yes, Mum, I'm going outside.
Magda Oh, darling.
Oliver What?

Magda Your head.

Oliver What about my head?

Magda Here. Put this on it.

Oliver I don't need a hat.

Magda What's wrong with it? I made it for you in the winter of '91 when it snowed so hard that the snowman we thought was a snowman turned out to be Mrs Heineman, caught, on her way to the post office, don't you remember?

Oliver Yes, I remember.

Magda Well then, put it on.

He does.

You going to feed the animals?

Oliver No.

Magda You going to talk to Brook? You going to take Hector out? He could do with the exercise.

Oliver No.

Magda Well, what are you going to do then, for goodness' sake?

Oliver Walk. I'm just going for a walk.

Magda Well, if you must go out in this Godforsaken weather you may as well take a basket with you. Here.

Oliver Mother. The sun is shining. Why are you giving me this?

Magda For collecting plums. And if the sun is shining you won't be needing that hat, will you?

She holds out her hand; he gives the hat back.

Oliver 'Bye.

Magda 'Bye-bye, my darling. I love you.

She hugs him as though he were going off to war. She releases him and he replies dutifully.

Oliver Love you.

He goes.
    As they both exit, Olive enters.

SCENE SEVEN

Olive, walking, comes across a plum tree (in fact, two actors, one on the other's shoulders).

Olive Oh plums. Food.

She circles the tree; there's no way she can reach the fruit. She collapses underneath it, closes her eyes, and holds out her stumps.

Dear God. I know I don't believe in you, but . . . I'M STARVING.

The tree bends down and a plum drops into her hands. She stares at it, then at the tree.

What?

Oliver walks by, unseen by Olive. He sees her.
    Olive holds her hands out again. The tree bends again and another plum falls into her hands. She eats it hungrily.
    Oliver can't believe his eyes. He approaches Olive, who holds her skirt out to catch more fruit. She turns and sees him. A beat.

Oliver Who are you?
Olive Nobody. Who are you?
Oliver I live here.
Olive Oh, I'm sorry, I was just –
Oliver No, it's fine, you help yourself, please – how do you do that? That thing with the plums?
Olive I don't know.
Oliver Your hands! What happened?

Olive Oh – that happened ages ago.

Oliver They're bleeding. You should get them seen to.
Come, come –

Olive No, that's plum juice.

Oliver – with me. Plum juice?

Olive Yes, it's just plum juice.

Oliver Oh. I thought . . .

Olive No.

Oliver Oh. I see. What are you doing all on your own in
the middle of the woods?

Olive I had an argument.

Oliver With?

Olive Everyone.

Pause.

Oliver Well, still you must come.

Olive Where?

Oliver To my house.

Olive You own that pile?

Oliver Well, no, I mean, yes, but I don't actually, oh,
you know.

Olive No.

Oliver Will you come?

Olive Why?

Oliver I'd like you to meet my mother. She'd like to
meet you.

Olive If you want me to come, I'll come. But I don't
want to come just because you're taking pity on me
because I have no hands and no friends and nowhere
to live.

Oliver No, no, of course not.

Olive That's understood then?

Oliver Absolutely. And we'll say I met you in town, shall
we? We met in town at the baths, something like that,
and you just dropped by, an old friend.

They begin to walk off together.

Olive You don't want to tell her you found me stealing
at the bottom of your orchard.
Oliver Not really, no.
Olive Fair enough.

After walking together awhile, Olive stops abruptly.

No, actually, I'd rather you told her the truth. Otherwise
I have to pretend I know you.
Oliver You do.
Olive I do?
Oliver You will.
Olive I will?
Oliver I do.
Olive I'm sorry?
Oliver What did you say your name was?
Olive Olive. What's yours?
Oliver Oliver.

Pause. They stare at one another.

Oliver The basket! I forgot the basket. You stay there –

*Olive remains where she is while Oliver returns to the
tree and retrieves the basket. He looks at the tree,
holds his hands out: nothing. Shakes it. Still nothing.*

SCENE EIGHT

*The letters are rearranged to create seating indoors.
Oliver, Olive and Magda sit. Ella, a young girl servant,
serves tea.*

Oliver We met in town at the baths and she just
dropped by, you know.

Magda How delightful. And what did you say your
father did?

Olive I didn't.

Magda Ah. Perhaps he is a diplomat passing through
on important business. A delegate from the new
Convention. Or a member of the armed forces,
maybe? A particle physicist? A volcanologist? Or
a travelling musician newly come to town.

Olive My father's dead.

Magda A tragedy! And you so young! Your mother?

Olive She died when I was born.

Magda What a coincidence!

Olive Coincidence?

Magda To die the same minute that you are born. Oh
you poor orphan.

Oliver Mother.

Olive It's alright.

Magda What?

Oliver You don't say orphan.

Magda Why not?

Oliver It sounds –

Magda Orphan. It's what she is. A small unloved person
left alone in a world that doesn't care.

Oliver Oh, God.

Olive No, it's fine. I was brought up by a mother and
father who loved me more than all the sea in Mina.
As far as I'm concerned, they are my real parents.

Magda How nice. What an emotional little soul. And
where do these loving people live?

Olive Pieland.

Magda I see.

Silence.

You speak our language very well. For a Piel. They
usually get their w's mixed up with their g's and their

b's with their v's and I can't understand a word they
say. But you don't really have an accent, do you?

Olive That may be because my adoptive parents are
both Eritropan immigrants. But my father was
brought up this side of the river and my mother's
parents sent her to school in Leandis, so she speaks
very good Swinnish.

Magda Oh oh oh.

Ella rushes to her aid.

Olive Are you alright?

Magda suddenly notices Olive's hands.

Magda Hah! Your hands!

Oliver It's alright, Mother, it happened a long time ago.

Magda What happened a long time ago?

Oliver It's plum juice.

Magda What?

Oliver It's not blood. It's plum juice.

Magda What's plum juice?

Oliver That.

Magda Huh! Blood!

Oliver No. It's not blood. That's what I'm saying.

Magda She's dripping. (*to Ella*) Quick, a cloth, a cloth.

Olive Oh no, that is blood. I cut myself trying to get the
plums.

Magda What plums?

Olive At the bottom of the garden.

Magda Our garden?

Oliver No.

Olive Yes.

Magda She comes all the way here for tea and steals our
plums at the bottom of the garden? I think I'm going
to go and lie down.

Oliver Mum. She didn't come all the way here for tea.
She just dropped by and –

Magda I asked her if she wanted tea and she said yes.
If she didn't want tea she should have said, I don't
want tea. We have other things. Maybe she prefers
coffee. Then she should say, I prefer coffee. We have
coffee and tea. And hot chocolate and cold chocolate
and orange juice and apple juice and cranberry juice
and lemon juice and angostura bitters! We have everything! I don't want her leaving here and going around
saying, 'They made me have tea.' What will people
say? I'm going upstairs to put my head on a pillow, if
you'll excuse me.

*Magda goes. Ella makes to follow, but Magda signals
for her to remain and listen.*

Olive Sorry.

Oliver No, I'm sorry.

Olive I always think it's best to tell the truth.

Oliver Yes.

Olive Don't you?

Oliver Of course. But . . .

Olive But?

Oliver Some people can't take it. My mother. I can't
explain.

Olive Your mother loves you very much and is
threatened by the presence of a girl in her house. She
has already imagined that I will come between you
and her – which of course is absurd: we've only just
met – but it's my job to put her at her ease.

Oliver Are you real?

Olive Of course I'm real. I'm thirsty. I'm afraid I can't
hold a cup. Could you –

Oliver helps her drink.

Oliver I've never done that before.

Olive I've never asked anyone to do that before. You
don't get out much, do you?

Oliver Oh, I think so. I took Hector round the field a couple of times yesterday. I'm always out there, overseeing the land. I've been across the river a couple of times to Podwold. I go to market once a week.

Olive And people?

Oliver People?

Olive Do you know many?

Oliver Oh I always stop and talk to them, yes. Why are you looking at me like that?

Olive I've never met anyone so . . . unworldly before.

Oliver And I've never met anyone like you. Do you like anchovies?

Olive Yes. Why?

Oliver I could never marry anyone who doesn't like anchovies.

Olive Marry?

Oliver What?

Olive You said marry.

Oliver Did I? I meant to say something else.

Olive Like what?

Pause.

Oliver The important thing is, you like anchovies.

SCENE NINE

Magda and Oliver.

Magda If you like her then of course she must stay until she feels better. I won't have people saying I threw a convalescent out into the streets now, will I?

Oliver She's not convalescing, Mother. She's fine. She's just got no hands.

Magda Oh, that's normal, is it?

Oliver I didn't say normal. I said fine. Look, if you really don't like her –

Magda I don't! I don't not like her. I'm just pointing out to you that she's a foreigner, an orphan, a mutant and a thief, that's all.

Oliver That is not all.

Magda You mean there's more?

Oliver I mean you've just selected the adjectives that suit you to describe her. That is not what she is.

Magda And what is she then, son and heir to my estate?

Oliver She's kind. She's wise. She's amusing. She likes me?

Magda That's not a description, THAT'S NOT A DESCRIPTION! It's a trap! What does she want from you, ask yourself that. A girl like her, she can only go up, and I don't want her upping herself on you. Your father would turn in his vault. I would rather cut off your inheritance than have you cavorting with an urchin.

Oliver She likes me. That's all I said. Is that so strange?

Magda So does Florence. And Mathilde. And Kitty. And they all have hands.

Oliver They do not.

Magda Well what would you call those things with fingers at the end of their arms?

Oliver They do not like me. They're nice to me. That's all.

Magda They love you. Why are they always calling you, visiting you, bringing you gifts then?

Oliver Because I'm the richest man in the canton.

Magda Exactly, and being the richest man in the canton you can choose whoever you want to marry. You don't have to make do with any cripple, bastard, orphaned, half-Pielish –

Oliver Mother! And who said anything about marriage?

Magda You did.

Oliver I did not.

Magda Yes, you did.

Oliver I did not.

Magda You did.

Oliver I didn't.

Magda Yes you did.

Oliver I didn't. You did.

Magda I did not.

Oliver You did.

Magda What? What did I do?

Oliver Oh, for God's sake, I'm going out.

Magda No, don't leave me. And with those words! How could you be so cruel? Like your father before you – those very words – 'I'm going out,' he said, and never came back. Are you trying to provoke disaster? You want me to be alone again? Your mother – 'the woman who was left alone'.

Oliver I'm going to feed the cows. I'll be back in five minutes. And you are not alone. Olive is upstairs.

SCENE TEN

Olive, pacing. Finally she drops to her knees.

Olive Oh God. I know I don't believe in you, but . . . What do I do now? I don't like anchovies. I mean, they're okay, in pizzas and stuff, but on their own – yuk. What was I thinking of? Oh, Oliver. He's kind and gentle and when he smiles it's like swimming with dolphins. Oh God. I know I don't believe in you, but . . . If you could just swing this one. Amen. Or whatever.

Magda enters the room.

Magda Are you alright, my dear, sitting on your knees like that? Let me help you up.

Olive No, I'm fine, I was just –

Magda Praying?

Olive Picking something up, no, no, I wasn't praying.

Magda No.

Olive Don't believe in it, religion, load of old crap. Makes you feel better, like a sugar pill, shuts you up, then smacks you in the face and kicks you up the arse at the same time and says, here y'are, have another pill. Bollocks to that.

Magda Well I believe in what I see. And at the moment I see a poor young girl whose heart is about to be broken. Don't be alarmed. It's as well that I tell you now before the damage is done.

Olive My heart?

Magda Yes, my dear, I can hear it. I can hear it in your voice when you talk to him, I can see it in your eyes when you look at him because oh, I have heard that heart before, oh yes, I have seen it many times. The look, the falling in love, the rejection, and the girl who walks out into the night, dragging her broken heart behind her in a trail of blood. Oh yes, I've seen it all before. Because it shames me to say it, but Oliver, my only beloved son, is not what he seems.

Olive What? What is he?

Magda Fickle. He's in and out of love like a cuckoo in a clock, can't devote himself to anyone because he has a flaw, you see, he can't love anyone except – he has a hole in his heart, a vacuum, a nothing, a great big nothing. Oh, I'm so sorry. Forgive me for being blunt. I thought it would be kinder. It usually is in the end.

Olive No, of course. Thank you. I see. Thank you very much.

Magda Such lovely girls too, all of them, but his standards are so high, you see, with him being the only surviving Malion, he has his family to think of, his blood and his ancestry, it's hardly surprising they don't live up to his expectations. And the hole, the hole in his heart left by the father who walked out into the night. The father who promised him the world, but threatened to curse him should he ever abandon his family. Oh the legacies we bear. So all I can do is leave you to your prayers, my child, and wish you well.

Olive I wasn't praying, I was –

Magda No, of course. Looking for something.

Olive Yes.

Magda I hope, my dear, you find it.

SCENE ELEVEN

Oliver crouches in the garden, transfixed by something. Olive enters.

Olive What are you doing?

Oliver The sunflower. Just looking at the sunflower.

Olive Why?

Oliver It's growing.

Olive You're watching it grow?

Oliver I want to catch it as it turns its head towards the sun.

Silence.

I'm so glad my mother likes you.

Olive ?!

Oliver She said she found you very receptive.

Olive Receptive?

Oliver I knew she would. You're different.

Olive From the others?

Oliver The others?

Olive The others.

Oliver Oh, the others. Well, there's a girl called Florence who I've known since I was born. But Mum doesn't like her. She holds her fork in the wrong hand, pronounces kitchen with two i's and dresses like a trollop. She says.

Olive Do you pity me?

Oliver Sorry?

Olive Is that why you asked me here?

Oliver No. That's not why I asked you here. (*Pause.*) Do you pity me?

Olive No. Why should I?

Oliver People do. (*Pause.*) Sometimes I think there's a piece of me missing. I don't know what it's called but it's the thing that joins you to the rest of the world. But you make me feel it's there, it's alright, I'm not . . . alone. (*Silence.*) So you're a believer?

Olive ?

Oliver She said she found you praying, my mother.

Olive No, I'm not. I wasn't.

Oliver It's alright. I don't mind either way.

Olive No. I had it once. Now I'm immune.

Oliver To religion?

Olive Like chickenpox. Once you've had it, you can't get it again.

Oliver What's wrong with it?

Olive Makes you live in hope.

Oliver Isn't that good?

Olive I don't want to hope. I don't want to trust. I don't want anything from anyone.

Oliver Then you don't want to live.

Silence.

That miracle –

Olive Wasn't a miracle.

Oliver It was pretty weird.

Olive Weird isn't miracle.

Oliver What is it then?

Olive Just weird.

Oliver The tree bent down and gave you its fruit.

Olive It was just the wind. In the trees . . .

Silence. He takes her hands and, at first, she makes no resistance. He kisses them. Then, suddenly, she pulls away.

Oliver Olive. I don't believe your heart is made of stone. Despite your name.

She looks at him. Then turns and runs. Into the next scene.

SCENE TWELVE

Ella brushes Olive's hair.

Ella First off I thought, what's the matter with him? I'd be there, make-up, no knickers, and he wouldn't so much as give me the nod, I said, he's a friend of Dorothy's, no question. Then once upon a time I went, right, let's brazen it out then, and I walked in on him without me kit while he's having his bath. So we're both standing there raw as oysters – and *he* apologises, starts trying to put my clothes back on, all polite like it was his mistake. Uh-oh, I'm barking up a cat-flap here, I thought, but then I found out about Florence and I worked out he's not a blouse at all, he's just a gentleman. A gentle man.

Olive Florence?

Ella His fiancée, yeah, *she* doesn't know about it, Magda, but I've heard them whispering in corners. They've known each other since they were born, you know.

Olive I know.

Ella Shame. Seeing him in the buff, yeah, I'd dance on his mattress any day of the week. (*Pause.*) Does that answer your question?

Olive It's a bit more information than I needed. But cheers, yeah.

SCENE THIRTEEN

Music. Olive goes to plum tree, stands underneath it, hopeful. Nothing. She walks away. Turns and stares at it.

Oliver What are you looking at?

Olive The possibility that I am alone. That we are all alone and nothing means anything.

Oliver I thought you were looking at that tree.

She nods. They both look at it.

That tree bent down for you.

Olive It won't now.

Oliver You don't need it to.

He picks a plum off the tree and offers her a bite. She refuses.

SCENE FOURTEEN

Magda, Oliver, Olive, and Lady F. Oliver looks uncomfortable, distracted; Olive looks at Lady F, keen.

Magda I thought a little garden party would be nice. Lady Florence – they've known each other since before they were born, haven't you, darling, splashing about in each other's swimming pool, and playing your lovely music all over the place – she is a terribly talented musician – such beautiful hands. Would you like a scone?

Lady F Yeah, great. I love scones. (*pronounced the other way*)

Magda winces.

Magda Ella! Oh, Ella! (*to herself*) What is the girl doing?
Lady F You look fab, Ollie. I love your shirt. Where d'you get it? Looks like one of Dyetti's. Hey, what do you think of my new Venus bod? Funky or what?

She opens her cardigan to reveal the skimpiest of bodices. Magda stares; Oliver doesn't look; it's left to Olive to respond.

Olive It's lovely.
Lady F What are you looking at, Ollie?
Oliver That.
Lady F That?
Oliver Yes.
Lady F You mean the sheep?
Oliver No. I mean the ceanothus.
Lady F Yeah, I love red.
Oliver It's blue.
Lady F Of course it is.
Oliver Amazing it's survived at all. Considering.
Lady F You mean the winter?
Oliver No. I mean the weeds.
Lady F Are they alive?
Oliver The weeds?
Lady F No. The sheep.
Oliver Of course.
Lady F They're not moving.
Oliver It's too hot.
Lady F Yeah, I should take this off.
Oliver I mean for them.
Lady F You mean the sheep?
Oliver I mean the sheep.
Lady F I thought you did.

Silence.

Magda They get on so well together, those two. They've known each other since before they were born, you know?

Olive I know.

Magda I think we'll leave them alone for a minute. I'm sure they've got things to talk about. Go and see what Ella's doing with those scones.

Magda goes, expecting Olive to follow her. Olive hovers a moment, then nips up behind Oliver and Lady F to a point from which she can hear them, but remain invisible.

Lady F I've got something to tell you, Ollie.

Oliver So have I. You know how we always said we'd tell each other everything.

Lady F Yeah, and how we always thought we were similar.

Oliver And how we promised never to lie to each other.

Lady F And how we said we were made for each other.

Oliver And that we planned to marry and spend the rest of our lives together.

Lady F Oh Ollie, the thing is, right, I've met the person I want to –

Oliver No, listen, because I've met the person I want to marry –

Lady F – marry and it's not you.

Pause.

Oliver It's not? But that's fantastic!

Lady F Wicked.

Oliver So you don't mind?

Lady F Of course I don't, you twit. I can be happy for both of us now.

They embrace.

Here. To you and Olive.

Oliver To you and – how did you know?

Lady F Get off, you might as well have it written on your forehead.

They toast each other with their teacups.
    The letters 'OLIVE' are rearranged behind them to spell 'LIVE'. In the process Olive is revealed. She stands, looking out into the garden.

SCENE FIFTEEN

Music, quiet at first, but joyful.
    Ella enters carrying a white dress and a white suit.
    Lady F walks away from Oliver to receive the white suit from her. They wait, observing Oliver and Olive.
    Oliver crosses to Olive.

Oliver What are you looking at, Olive?

Olive That.

Oliver Clematis.

Olive It looks like a question mark, doesn't it, the way it scrambles up the wall?

Oliver It does. And that looks like an answer.

Olive What is it?

Oliver It's called a bride plant.

Pause.

Olive Florence is perfect. She's beautiful. She's kind. She's understanding.

Oliver There's more to it than just a list. What are you looking at now?

Olive remains looking out.

Olive You.

Oliver And what do you see?

Olive That I was wrong. What are you looking at?
Oliver You.
Olive And what do you see?
Oliver That I was right.

Silence.

Olive Oliver. I've got something to tell you.
Oliver What?
Olive I don't like anchovies.

Pause.

Oliver So what?
Olive So what?
Oliver I can live with that.
Olive You can?
Oliver I will.

Ella dresses Olive and Lady F dresses Oliver while they speak. The music builds to a triumphant climax, suggesting the wedding ceremony itself.

Olive You will?
Oliver I will. Will you?
Olive I do.
Oliver You do?
Olive I do. Do you?
Oliver I do.
Ella Hooray!
Lady F Hooray!

Both Ella and Florence shower them in white flowers. Oliver and Olive embrace and dance together, in sync. But as the music becomes wilder, so do they. All four of them dance the music out and exit.

SCENE SIXTEEN

Magda enters with a broom and a basket. Angrily, she clears the strewn flowers, then takes a scythe from the basket and starts hacking away at a plant.

  Olive enters. No longer wearing white.

Olive What are you doing? Magda, what are you doing?
Magda Weeding.
Olive That's not a weed. It's a plant. It's the bride plant.
Magda It looks like a weed.
Olive It has flowers on it. Stop it, please.
Magda The place is a mess. And you just stand there like a scarecrow. (*Magda stops what she's doing; looks at Olive.*) Well, I suppose you could keep the starlings off the lawns, yes, that might be your job, standing on the grass with your little stumps out, you could pass as a scarecrow. Got to find something for you to do now that you're *family* – I suppose you think it's destiny, don't you? *Olive, Oliver* – aieugh – ugh.

  Magda moans and collapses. Olive goes to her.

Olive What is it, what's wrong?
Magda Stay away from me!
Olive You look white.
Magda I feel white.
Olive Are you anaemic?
Magda There's a permanent taste in my mouth like iron filings. My legs feel rusty and my body is like someone else's carcass. Anaemic is the least of it.
Olive Are you tired?
Magda Are you stupid?

  Pause.

I need whisky.

Olive Whisky?

Magda Neat. Coffee. Black. Chocolate. Dark. Now.

Olive They'll make you worse. In the end.

Magda I'm not talking about the end. I'm talking about now. I want them now.

Olive But they're all so bitter. How about something sweet and healthy? Shall I get some plums?

Magda You leave my plums alone.

Olive Your immune system gets low if you have an excess of one kind of food. I don't know, but maybe if you supplemented some of those things in your diet –

Magda My immune system has been in this family for hundreds of years. It was passed on to me in my mother's milk. My mother, the Duchess of Malion, and you stand there without your hands and dare to talk to me of immunity! A girl from Pieland, for whom my son has rejected one of the most eligible women in the country, talks to me of sweets and food supplements.

Olive I understand that you resent me because I'm not good enough for your son. I agree with you. But I am just saying what you eat may reflect on how you feel. There may be a connection / between –

Magda Connection! Reflection! Nothing and no one is connected! To anything or anyone. We are alone, all alone, surrounded by idiots.

Silence.

Magda And what about you? Is there a connection between what you ate and your stubby withered hands?

Olive Of course not. I've told you what happened.

Magda Ah, but have you? Have you told me everything?

Olive Yes. I have told you.

Magda I've forgotten.

Olive Look. I know I'm not what you planned for your son. I'm not asking you to like me. But if you don't respect me, you don't respect him.

Magda Oh, that's what it's all about. We're supposed to give you respect, you *young* people, as well as all the years of slavery and abasement while we get under the table and beg for an occasional crumb of affection in return. Respect! What about responsibility? What happened to responsibility? The world is upside down and we're all going to fall off because you *children* – (*Magda takes objects from her basket and begins to hurl them on the floor in her frustration.*) – you scavenging *magpies* – you filthy horrid *parasites* –

Oliver walks into the room. Magda changes her tone immediately.

– it's a question of gravity, you see. So if you drop this on the floor – (*She drops another garden implement.*) – it stays there. Or this – (*She takes a lemon from the basket and drops it.*) – or, indeed, this. – (*She drops a tomato.*) Pulls it back down to earth with a splat. Hello, darling, just having a little chat about Newton and all that.

Silence.

Oliver Did Olive tell you our plans?
Magda Plans?
Oliver Yes. We were thinking of going away together.
Magda How lovely. I haven't been away for years.
Oliver No. I mean 'we'. Olive and me.
Magda You?
Oliver Us.
Magda Away?
Oliver Together.
Magda You've never been further than our estates.
Oliver Exactly.
Magda Are you mad? Leaving me in this condition. Ah! Oh. I can feel it again. Oh, my heart, my heart. How could you? A doctor. I must see a doctor.

Oliver She's not well. She fainted earlier.
Magda Aggh. My legs. My back. My God.
Oliver What's wrong? What is it?
Magda A doctor! I WANT TO SEE A DOCTOR!
Oliver What kind of doctor?
Magda Just a doctor.
Oliver What shall I tell him?
Magda That I'm ill.
Oliver But what with?
Magda EVERYTHING!

> *Olive grabs Oliver and leads him off. After a moment,*
> *Magda straightens up. She goes over to a cupboard,*
> *opens a drawer and takes out a packet of sweets. She*
> *eats one. Then another, and another, and another. She*
> *remains where she is, impassive, while the focus moves*
> *to Olive and Oliver who stand, waiting, next door.*

SCENE SEVENTEEN

Olive What's wrong with her?
Oliver Don't know. He's been in there for over an hour.
Olive She said some terrible things to me.
Oliver Oh, it's just her way. She likes you really. How
could she not?
Olive Things you just don't say.
Oliver She's excessive, that's all. She gets very emotional.
Olive Oh, Oliver, how can someone like you come from
someone like her?
Oliver She has suffered.
Olive You defending her?
Oliver Living every day without someone who's just
disappeared – you can't mourn properly, you can't
love properly, and you can't hate properly. But you try
to do all three at once.

Olive Yes. Yes, I know. My mother.

Oliver She's in limbo, that's all.

Pause.

Olive She could be my mother. If she would let herself.

Oliver Yes. But you can't be her husband.

Olive No. But neither can you.

Magda enters their room.

Magda The doctor says I must have peace and quiet and sweetness and light and be looked after every minute of the day in case of a relapse and not be left alone. At all. Ever.

Oliver Ah.

Magda So let's all go into the garden, shall we, and watch the sun set. Wouldn't that be nice?

She puts her arm around Oliver and they walk off, leaving Olive to follow. She doesn't.

Olive Oh God. I know I don't believe in you, but . . . This is a nightmare. How can I possibly convince her I'm harmless if she's already made her mind up? (*Pause.*) HARMLESS, I said. I know your hearing's crap. Look. I'm not asking for trumpets and angels. Just a bit of a hand up. I don't want to be afraid any more. Forget what I said before. I want to live.

SCENE EIGHTEEN

Olive is handed a lump of dough. She starts to knead it on the kitchen table.

Magda enters a room next door, furtively opens a drawer, gets out a packet of sweets and starts eating.

Olive overhears the noise of sweet wrappers being unwrapped. She notices Magda in the room next door.

Magda picks up a photo of her husband and stands, staring at it.

After a while, Olive approaches. Magda hardly reacts on seeing her. She is lost to the world.

Olive Tell me. What was he like?

Magda He was like light. Luminous. He shone. Like a lantern in the garden on a hot summer night. Every insect in the world wanted to dance in his beam. But he didn't want them. He didn't want the world. He wanted me.

Silence.

Olive What happened to him?

Magda He asked me where his shoes were. I said, 'Which shoes?' He said, 'My brown ones, you know.' I didn't. I ignored him. He must have gone out the back door, because he didn't kiss me goodbye. He always kissed me goodbye when he went anywhere. He wasn't planning on going anywhere. Just to feed the chickens, he said.

Silence.

'Try and forget,' they say. But how can you bury someone who might still be alive?

Olive He has a beautiful smile.

Magda Oliver's smile.

Olive Yes. Oliver's smile. (*Pause.*) I don't want to take your son away from you, Magda. That's not my plan.

Magda starts to cry. Olive embraces her.

I have a photograph I'd like you to see too. (*She gets out a photo of her mother.*) It's black and white so you can't see the colour of her eyes, but they're bright, not tired at all, I'd just been born, she was alright then, she looks so happy, stroking my head like a kitten, see. My mother.

429

Magda Plan?

Olive Sorry?

Magda You said 'plan'. 'That's not my plan.' You said.

Olive No. It's not.

Magda But you might?

Silence.

Magda Promise me you will never take my son away
from me.

Olive Whatever happens, Oliver will always love you,
I'm sure of that.

Magda Promise me.

Olive I can't promise –

Magda Promise me you will never take away what's left
of my heart. Promise me!

Olive I promise I will try not to.

Magda Goddam, you to hell and may you shrivel and
die if you don't promise me now.

Olive I can't account for the future. I can't make
promises on his behalf. I can't. I only wish –

Magda I want you to swear on the Book, on your life,
that you will not take my son away!

Olive I can't.

Magda Then I curse the day he set eyes on your mutant
body. I curse every minute you spend with him, and
every day you live in this house will be as wretched as
if you were already dead. And if you try to leave this
house with him I will kill you and anything that issues
from your womb.

Olive starts to vomit. Magda remains impassive.
It becomes dark. Music.
    Olive looks up at Magda and, as she does so,
Magda turns round to reveal her father. They are
standing back to back. He holds out a hand to her.
He speaks gently.

Father *Talitha com. Na hisbiato me. Shnea pola. Shnea.*
Shnea.

> *He turns to reveal Magda again, glaring, malevolent.*
> *She turns to reveal her father again. He is angry.*

Father *Haja te karamush. Ni ko fasa menka gallish.*
Wok ne pisha ratsip. Ha.

> *He threatens her with a knife. Father and Magda*
> *separate and return to their places.*
> *Olive vomits again. Oliver enters.*

Olive I believe in God, I believe in hope, I believe in
trees, I believe in good, I believe in grass, I believe in
love, I believe in everything.

Oliver What's wrong?

Olive I think I'm pregnant.

Oliver Oh my God.

Olive Help me.

Oliver A baby! (*He embraces her.*)

Olive Help me, Oliver.

Oliver I will. Of course I will. Do you feel sick? What
can I get you? Water? Rice? Spinach, isn't it?
Cornflakes? My mother, I'll get my mother, she'll
know. We must tell her, come on, come.

Olive No. We mustn't tell her.

Oliver We have to. She'd be –

Olive No. Not yet. It's too early. Wait. Wait until it's
safe. Three months.

Oliver Why?

Olive Anything could happen.

Oliver It won't.

Olive No, but I'd like it to be our secret, just ours, for
now. Please.

Oliver Alright, yes, okay. A baby. It's a miracle. How?
I mean, I had no idea – I mean, of course I know how,
but – just like that. A baby. Wow.

He stares at her stomach in wonder. But a ghost walks over her grave.

SCENE NINETEEN

Olive stands under the plum tree, eyes closed, expectant. Nothing. She closes her eyes again and holds her arms out, beseeching. A plum is put into her mouth. She opens her eyes. It's Ella.

Ella You trying to do, scare the crows? Been looking for you everywhere, I have. You doing down the bottom of the garden? Dinner's up.

Olive Mmngh o ungee.

Ella Yeah, people who talk with a plum in their mouth always talk crap.

Olive takes it out.

Olive I'm not hungry.

Ella You sure? You can't survive on a bit of old rice cake for lunch, you know. Nor can the babe.

Olive It'll be fine. If I eat now, I'll only bring it all up again.

Ella You got it bad, girl.

Pause.

Olive Do you believe in curses, Ella?

Ella 'Course I do. Best words in the language, swear-words. You wanna know what my favourite is?

Olive I mean curses, like black magic. Being cursed.

Ella No. You make your own luck, good and bad.

Olive And if it's bad?

Ella It'll come round.

Olive And if you don't get what you want?

Ella You get what you need. Not what you want. I'm
not after working here all my life, but for the moment
it pays the baker.

Olive Can't they ever be the same?

Ella In your dreams.

Olive How long have you worked here, then?

Ella Long.

Olive You like Magda?

Ella I do what she wants.

Olive You trust her?

Ella I do what she wants.

Olive Even if she asked you to, say, pick her nose for
her?

Ella She does. No, but even if she asked me to stand at
the bottom of the garden in the effing cold begging
you to come and eat.

Olive She sent you?

Ella He did.

Olive I don't want any supper.

Ella You might not want it, girl. But you need it. Come
on.

SCENE TWENTY

*Olive and Magda. Olive is pushing her food around her
plate. Magda scrutinises her.*

Magda So when's it due then, the little bastard?

Olive He told you?

Magda Don't need to be told. You've been clutching
your stomach like a gold purse all month. So, whose
is it?

Olive Oliver's, of course.

Magda Don't be ridiculous.

Olive What?

433

Magda I've seen you fraternising with the shepherd in the woodshed. Or was it that half-wit who comes to collect the milk on a Thursday?

Olive How dare you?

Magda How dare *you*, come here, ensnare my boy into marriage, then skip around without your knickers on behind his back!

Olive You know you're making this up. I know you're making it up. Why?

Pause.

Magda Do you have a complaint about my food?

Olive No. I just –

Magda Then eat.

Olive looks at Magda, blank. Magda, remembering that Olive can't feed herself, starts to put food in her mouth. More than she can possibly swallow.

Magda Got to feed the baby. Give it a chance, poor little cripple, here, give it a drink –

Olive Please, I feel –

Magda Never mind what you feel, it's him from now on, the baby wants this, the baby needs that, mind the baby, watch the baby –

Olive I can't – please – stop feeding me!

Magda Don't do that to the baby oh look how he's grown aren't you lucky look you can sit around and enjoy the emptiness now he's all grown up and buggering off, there there. What's the matter with you?

Olive chokes and dribbles the food and drink that's been forced into her mouth.
    Oliver enters.

Oliver What are you doing?

434

Magda The girl refuses to eat. She's threatening to get
rid of the baby just because it isn't yours and I'm
saying it won't do. A baby is a baby.

Oliver Say that again.

Magda A baby is a baby.

Oliver Olive?

She can't speak; she has her mouth full.

Magda Exactly. Nothing to say.

Oliver She can't speak. She has a mouthful of food. Are
you mad?

*Oliver helps Olive take food out of her mouth and
regain her composure.*

Olive I WILL NOT BE MALIGNED BY THIS WITCH WHO
CALLS HERSELF YOUR MOTHER BUT HASN'T GOT A
THOUGHT IN HER HEAD FOR ANYONE BUT
HERSELF. (*to Magda*) I WILL NOT BE TRIPPED AND
PRODDED AND POKED AND TORMENTED ANY
MORE. I AM NOT YOUR DOG.

Magda Well, we haven't seen this before, have we? This
explains everything. Is she saying I'm not your mother?
She's mad.

Oliver looks at Olive.

Olive If you think this baby could be anyone's but yours
then you don't know me. And if you don't know
me . . . I no longer know myself.

Oliver looks at Magda.

Magda What can I say? I saw them together in the
cornflowers, her and some bottom going up and
down, and it wasn't you obviously, no, this was a
short, dark, squat person. Oliver, don't look at me
like that.

After a while, Oliver speaks.

Oliver I would like to talk to Olive.
Magda You can ask her what you like – I know –
Olive Alone.

Magda is compelled to leave. But stops a moment at the door.

Magda She'll deny it, obviously. Conversation will get you nowhere.
Oliver Alone.

She goes. Silence.

Olive Don't ask me why. She hates me more than she loves you. That's all I know.
Oliver How can anyone hate more than they love? How can anyone be that afraid?
Olive Afraid?
Oliver Of love.
Olive A long long time ago, I used to believe in things. I used to believe the world was a lovely round blue ball, you are what you eat, and there was a thing called truth.
Oliver And now?
Olive Now I know that truth is just a piece of wet soap.
Oliver And the world?
Olive A balloon with a slow leak.

SCENE TWENTY-ONE

Oliver rushes about, getting ready to go out. Magda helps him with his coat.

Oliver Tell her not to worry.
Magda I will.
Oliver I'll be back soon.

Magda Absolutely.

Oliver Where are my shoes?

Magda Which ones?

Oliver My black ones.

Magda You're wearing them.

Oliver Oh God.

Magda Don't you worry about Olive. She'll be fine, and you'll sort it out in no time.

Oliver What happens if she goes into labour early?

Magda She won't.

Oliver Tell her not to worry and – oh, where is she? – tell her I'll be back soon.

Magda I will, darling. Off you go now. Love you.

Oliver Yeah, you too.

Oliver goes. Magda retreats to her rocking chair and her supply of sweets. She eats ravenously. After a while, Olive enters.

Magda Oh, Olive, darling, where have you been?

Olive I told you. I went to feed the horses.

Magda Of course you did. How are they?

Olive Fine.

Magda Now you really must sit down and put your feet up. All this walking around feeding animals. You're making me feel lazy. Boiled sweet?

Olive Where's Oliver?

Magda Oh, trouble on the other side of the estate. That woman's refusing to leave Minton House and the new lot are moving in tomorrow. He's gone to sort her out.

Olive Oh.

Magda Don't worry. He'll be back tomorrow.

Olive Did he say anything?

Magda He said not to worry and you're to get a good night's sleep. Can I get you a little drink before bed?

Olive It's only five o' clock.

Magda Oh, but I remember what it's like, all that kicking and squirming going on inside, it's exhausting. What would you like, my dear? Raspberry-leaf tea? Cocoa? Fizzy water?

Olive Vodka and tonic.

Magda Oh very good, vodka and tonic, yes, can you imagine! Oh, it's such a long time since we just sat, you and me, and had a good laugh, isn't it? Such a long time.

She smiles warmly at Olive. Olive smiles back, nervous.

SCENE TWENTY-TWO

Music; foreboding. It's the middle of the night. Olive is asleep.
  Ella appears at her bedside, wakes her and gets her out of bed. She starts dressing her.

Olive Has it started? What's happening? Am I in labour? I can't feel anything. Ella? Ella? What are you doing?

Ella Put your shoes on.

Olive My hospital bag. Where's my hospital bag?

Ella Coat.

Olive Nappies, camomile cream. It's in the bathroom.

Ella Scissors.

Olive But I'm not. I'm not in labour. I should be waking *you*. This is all wrong. Scissors?

Ella Come on.

SCENE TWENTY-THREE

Music. Olive and Ella wallking through a wood.

Olive If you asked me now whether I was dead or alive, I'd say dead. (*Olive collapses.*) In which case, who are you?

Ella stops, satisfied that they've come far enough.

Don't tell me, you're just obeying orders. It's the middle of the night, we're miles from anywhere, what now? We going on a bear hunt? – aagh – oh, God it's starting – aagh.

Olive clutches her stomach. Ella starts to walk away.

Where are you going? Ella? Ella! Please.

Ella You're having someone else's baby and it will be deformed. Yes, I'm just obeying orders.

Olive I'm not. That's a lie. I'm not, Ella, it won't, it's a lie, she's a liar!

Ella She saw you.

Olive She saw nothing.

Ella You're a liar.

Olive Ugh. Please, no.

Ella The scissors were my idea.

Olive Don't leave me. I'll die out here. Please no. No. No!

Ella goes.
    The letters are rearranged to spell 'O EVIL'.
    Oliver shouts out at the same time as Olive's last 'No!':

SCENE TWENTY-FOUR

Oliver *No!*

Oliver is on the floor, beside himself. Magda is putting on black.
    Ella stands nearby, stiff and silent.

Magda I should have known, if only I'd guessed, I mean she talked about the sea and drowning and I thought, well, of course, she's upset, the baby was blue and cold and stiff and so dead, but who would have thought, really, just like that, in the middle of the night she went, oh, I know, to think of it, both of them at the bottom of the sea, it's too much, too much to bear. Come here to me, my son, come here.

Oliver doesn't move. Nevertheless, she embraces him.

Oliver What was it?
Magda What?
Olive A girl or a boy?
Magda Oh. A boy. Yes. A boy. (*She gets out her sweets and starts to eat them, rapidly, one after the other.*) Would you like a sweet?

He ignores her and starts to walk off.

Where are you going? We have to talk about the funeral. I know it's hard, darling, but it has to be done – phone calls, flowers –

Oliver exits. Magda notices Ella standing nearby.

So. That's it then?

Ella makes no reply.

That's it.

Ella goes. Magda devours the sweets like they're going out of fashion. She finishes the last one, is still a moment. Starts to gag.

SCENE TWENTY-FIVE

The sound of a baby crying. Then silence.
Olive stands by a river, her baby round her neck in a sling. A young girl stands the other side. She is deaf and signs all her responses.

Olive Who are you?
Girl I live here.
Olive Will you help me? Please. Can you help me?

The girl nods.

A nod must mean yes.

The girl smiles. Olive smiles back.

Yes. I need some water. But I can't cup my hands. Could you help me get some water?
Girl No.
Olive No, don't worry, I'm not asking you to take my baby. Just help me get some water. I'm dying of thirst.
Girl No.
Olive No, you don't understand –
Girl You get the water.
Olive Look. All I want –
Girl Do it yourself.
Olive Oh, this is so – what I'm trying to say –
Girl I know what you're trying to say. But you must help yourself.
Olive Look. Look! My hands are withered. I can't.
  I can't / cup my hands! Are you blind as well as –
Girl / Put them in the water.

Olive – dumb? No, I'm sorry, but are you, because it's quite obvious my hands are useless.

Girl Put them in the water.

Olive I can't! Look, I can't do anything with them! Look!

Olive puts her hands in the water by way of demonstration and the baby falls in.

My baby. Don't just stand there! Help!

The girl doesn't move, so Olive plunges her hands and herself into the water.

Oh my baby, my God, my baby. My daughter.

She manages to grasp the baby and lift her out of the water. She smothers her in kisses. It is a moment before she notices her hands. They are no longer withered. The bandages are off and they are perfect, as before.

My hands. My hands! (*She looks up at the girl.*) Who are you?

Girl I live here.

Olive My hands. My daughter. My hands.

She is lost in wonder at both.

SCENE TWENTY-SIX

Magda is trying on various black hats. Ella holds them for her.
Oliver sits nearby, vacant.

Magda I hate to say this, but it seems her second name isn't her real name – well, it wouldn't be since she's adopted, I suppose, but she's taken her mother's maiden name – who's dead – so that's no good to anyone. And even if we could find any of them they live the other side of the world, so it's going to be quite an intimate affair. Oh, but Florence is coming, you'll be glad to hear.

The doorbell rings. No one moves.

No, don't you go, I'll get it. More flowers, I expect. (*Magda demonstrates two hats for Ella.*) This one. Or this one. What do you think?

Ella doesn't look at her.

Ella Yes.

Magda goes.

About eighty miles away, not far from Hallidon, there's a wood. It's called Blackcomb Wood. It's big. But in the middle there's a small tunnel. It's made of trees and it's about half a mile long. Follow it and if you get there, if you get there, you may, God knows how, but you may find . . . peace.

Oliver remains impassive.

A nice place to go for a walk anyway.

Ella goes. For the first time in the scene Oliver stirs, looking after her as she goes.

SCENE TWENTY-SEVEN

Oliver starts making his way through the forest.
Meanwhile, elsewhere in the forest, Olive sits with the young girl, who peels a satsuma. The baby is asleep nearby.
Oliver appears through the end of a tunnel. He follows a length of bandage which he rolls up as he goes.

Olive Yes, I do feel much stronger. And look, my hands
are obeying me properly now. I agree, it was good to
rest, I needed to recover, and she's feeding well now
too. It's lovely here, you've made it very cosy. Must
be cold in the winter though. I really do feel much
stronger. You've looked after us so well. (*Pause.*) I want
to go home.

*The girl offers her the satsuma. Olive closes her eyes.
The end of the bandage stops short of Olive. He
stares at her. She opens her eyes. She rushes to him.*

Oliver Are you real?
Olive I knew you'd come, I knew you would. At last.

The girl slips away, eating the satsuma herself.

Oliver Your hands! This is a dream, right?
Olive I thought you'd come, I hoped you would. How
on earth did you find me?
Oliver If you asked me now whether I was dead or alive
I'd say dead.

*Olive throws herself at Oliver, hugging and kissing
him.*

Olive Does that feel dead? My God, I thought you'd
never come.
Oliver Your hands. Your hands.
Olive And something else. Another miracle. (*She shows
him the baby.*)
Oliver It's alive!
Olive Of course she is. She's smiling at you, look, she is!
Oliver The baby. Oh, my God. It really is.

Olive hands Oliver the baby.

She?
Olive A girl, yes, she's a girl.

Oliver She said it was a boy.

Olive What else did she say?

Oliver That you were dead.

Olive I've never in my life felt more alive. And it's all thanks to – where's she gone? (*She looks around for the girl, who has gone.*)

Oliver Your funeral is tomorrow afternoon at three.

Olive I'll make sure I'm there.

Oliver I'm going to kill her.

Olive No, Oliver. Don't think of her now, please.

Oliver She is not my mother. I am not her son.

Olive I am your wife and this, look, this is your child. That's enough for me. Please. I'm too happy to think of punishment.

Oliver She wanted you dead.

Olive But I'm not.

Oliver We might never have seen each other again.

Olive But we did.

Oliver (*gesturing at the baby*) She would never have been born.

Olive But she was.

Oliver How can you be so *reasonable*?

Olive Because I know what it is to be alive. (*She embraces him.*)

SCENE TWENTY-EIGHT

Magda, sitting down, while Oliver stands over her. Ella hovers nearby.

Oliver What exactly did it look like?

Magda Oh. Oliver, is this a good idea? Going over it all. So painful. For both of us.

Oliver What did it look like? Exactly?

Magda Blue. Just blue. And black and all scrunched up and yes, I'm sorry to say it had no hands and no feet. I didn't want to tell you that, but there it is.

Oliver I see. And then she picked it up and walked into the sea. Is that right?

Magda No, I told you, no, it happened in the middle of the night. She said she wanted to be left alone with it – we respected her wishes. God knows I wish we hadn't now, but who could have known? We only found out in the morning – she was gone and then we had the witness on the beach come round.

Oliver And how do you sleep at night?

Magda What?

Oliver How do you sleep at night?

Magda Well, you know, I've always been a bit of an insomniac. But I usually put a bit of camomile under my pillow. Why?

Oliver Have you heard of a place called Blackcomb Wood?

Silence.

Before you go and kill yourself there's someone I'd like you to meet.

Magda What? What did you say?

He doesn't answer.

Who?

Olive appears. Magda reels back in horror.

Olive It's alright. I'd want to kill anyone who threatened to take my baby away, too.

After a moment, Olive steps towards her. She offers the baby for Magda to hold. Magda backs away from them both.

Magda Ella! Ella!

Ella doesn't move. Magda grabs at the air for support. She falls to the ground and scrambles off.

Oliver I swear, if she doesn't kill herself I'll do it for her.

Olive My being here alive is shame enough.

Oliver Are you defending her?

Olive I think she believed she was acting in the interests of the family, her family.

Oliver I am not her family. She is not my mother.

Olive Maybe not. Mother is a verb. Not a noun. Oh Oliver, I haven't got the energy.

Oliver For what?

Olive For hate.

Silence. The baby stirs. Oliver contemplates her.

Oliver I hope she's more like you than me.

Olive No. No. We haven't even got a name for you yet, baby.

Oliver Little Olive. Olivetti.

Olive I used to hate my name. When I was small. I thought of myself as a small bitter little starter.

Oliver And now?

Olive Now I like the taste, I like the name.

Oliver What does it mean?

Olive No idea.

In the background the letters of 'OLIVE' are rearranged to spell 'I LOVE'.

Magda appears briefly with a suitcase, scuttles across the stage and off. Oliver makes to follow her.

Oliver What's she doing now?

Olive Leaving. Let her go. Oliver. Let her go.

He does.

Olive I love the way your nose flares when you frown. I love our baby. I love you. I love my name. I *love*.

Oliver What?

Olive I just do.

A pear rolls along the floor to land at their feet.

Where did that come from?
Oliver Must be the wind. In the trees.

Oliver picks up the pear and, between them, they eat it.

The End.

STARSTONE

Christian Martin

translated by Penny Black

Characters

Fool (Hanswurst)
Starstone
Engelhart
Husband (Schoolmaster/Father)
Wife
Anna
Schoolchildren
Zealot
Soldier
Artist
Farmer
Captain
Whore
Military Padre
Soldiers and People

Stage

The platform or 'stage' of a band of travelling players
(five to eight players). They perform the story of
Starstone set in the Thirty Years War in the style of
Hanswurst, a crude and comical figure whose origins were
in Austria at the beginning of the eighteenth century.
He was based on Harlequin and Merry Andrew/
Jack Pudding. However, unlike in commedia dell'arte,
he always appeared alone and was not part of
the ensemble. He moved complacently amongst the
players and commented on the action for the audience.
To find out more go to www.aeiou.at

PROLOGUE

Fool
    let's play a game
    peace or war
    heads or tails
    no choice no more

    sunshine brings flowers
    dreaming is fun
    a belly looks for freedom
    once the rain is done

    no one knows whither
    our lives will go
    to the doors of heaven
    or the darkness below

    heillihollahollaho

SCENE ONE

Fool
    bah
    we're all fools
    god be willing
    a play for the world
    taratarataratara
    yessir (*Disguises himself.*)
    did you see that
    me
    yes I

am now
hanswurst
his very self
Hanswurst
everything has one end
only sausages have two
sausages have two

'growl'

helphelp a wolf
wants to eat me alive

'nonsense
it's only me
your belly'

youhoo

'fool
don't you know me
I'm starving
hungry as a bear
do something
or we'll both snuff it'

but

'but what'

I've nothing
nada niente
not a farthing

'at least try'

hmmm hmmm I
might have an idea

'at last
not a moment too soon'

a wig a hat and
a cloak – so
I am now
hanswurst the judge
his very self
and gatekeeper to heaven
we are at the frontier
he who wants to enter must pay
to soothe his conscience
oho two pick-a-backs
to set the ball a'rolling
'Soldier'
giddy up slow coach
I'll make your legs move
'Judge'
collapse
more likely
'Farmer'
I can't go on
'Soldier'
stupid nag
we're nearly there
'Judge'
HAAAALT
'Soldier'
have we arrived
at heaven's gate
'Judge'
your dick can't wait
bubut
tell me first
how many
how many you have killed
I I I
the highly holy judge
will know if you lie

and then oh then
the fires of hell will burn you
'Soldier'
errr one hundred
'bout a hundred
a hundred for sure
'Judge'
a hundred what
I want to know exactly
'Soldier'
catholics that's what
'Judge'
that
that lot'll cost a penny
and you
'Farmer'
not one
I promise
all my born days
I've just ploughed and slaved
'Judge'
so so you slave
that's also a penny
'Farmer'
but
'Judge'
no buts
you pay a fine
because all your born days
you've dragged that scrounger
around with you
come come come away with you
the next lot are already
on their way
another mule

'Farmer'
  the way to heaven
'Judge'
  on the nose
  pay a penny
'Farmer'
  why
'Judge'
  why
  is there a crack
  or a hump on your back
'Farmer'
  because
'Judge'
  look up
  speak up
'Farmer'
  because a good for nothing
  murdering sod
  is clinging to my back
'Judge'
  exactly
  I have helped to
  shine a light
  and that costs
  (*to the 'Soldiers'*)
  and now you
  filthy cowards talk
  only the truth mind
  or else the fires of hell
  sooo
  how many notches in your sword
'Soldier'
  a hundred lutherans
'Judge'
  that's another penny

455

and off you go
oxen to the slaughter
aha who do I see coming this way
herr schwarz his very self
I thought
you were long dead
(*to the audience*)
that clever crackshot
invented gunpowder
and one day puffffff
the whole world will explode
'Schwarz'
ppppppure chance
an experiment
not my fault
'Judge'
aha chance
the game is hard and fast
and if chance is shuffling the deck
reason always loses
confess
curiosity pure and simple
drove you
'Schwarz'
yes but yes but
if I'd had any idea of the harm
well then well then
'Judge'
bla bla bla bla
that if if if
was and is the rogue
no ifs for men
poor wretches
hand it over man
till it hurts
eleven pennies

hand them over
and get out of my sight
or you'll feel my boot
'Schwarz'
phew
that was lucky
'Judge'
chance and money
rule the world
aha who
who do my sad eyes espy
hey angel
your senses
appear confused
surely you don't want
to return to earth
'Gutenberg'
yes
'Judge'
and why
'Gutenberg'
because
what I see from up there
I can't stand it any longer
this hell on earth
'Judge'
now we're talking
but are you not
the good lord himself
in disguise
'Gutenbcrg'
go on with you
he's busy today
'Judge'
as always
so he sent you

457

'Gutenberg'
　I came of my own accord
'Judge'
　funny fellow
　d'you have a name
'Gutenberg'
　johann gutenberg
'Judge'
　oho
　the inventor of the printing press
'Gutenberg'
　I've also printed the bible
　many times
'Judge'
　what good's that done
　war's gone on nearly thirty years
'Gutenberg'
　that's why I'm bringing
　good news
　negotiations are going on
　in osnabrück and münster
　to bring peace
'Judge'
　liarmouth
　don't make me laugh
　your efforts are in vain
　man has learnt nothing
　and meanwhile
　withorwithout books
　it's every bellyhead
　for himself
　my belly is mine
　and mine alone
　and it's grumbling and growling
　like a bear
　never satisfied

d'you hear it
it's full of intent
(*Throws off his disguise as the judge.*)
murderous intent
so flit back up
to your heaven
before I eat you
grrrr
'Gutenberg'
heeeeeelp
Hanswurst
go on scream
scream your head off
perhaps the world'll wake
out of its dark slumber
and if you believe that
who knows
(*Puts the Fool's costume back on.*)
anyhow
my business of the masquerade
has paid off
thirteen plus
one plus two
fifteen pennies
off to the inn
to get a bellyful
everything has one end
only sausages have two
but wait yooooo
fool for a hanswurst
you're taking the piss
this is fool's gold
you'll get nothing for it
mmmmm
so what next
a real play

a story a real one
with a beginning and an end
of course
what else
that's why you're here
so sit up take note
we would like to present
the story
of a young man
called starstone

SCENE TWO

A starry night, snowy path.

Wife
what is it
what is it now
keep going
pull that cart
it's heavy enough
Husband
d'you hear nothing
Wife
hear what
the cannon's roar
this far out
madmen
half the town
but rubble and ash
and wasteland
Husband
there
and there again

the quiet mewling
of a babe
Wife
not ours
Husband
over there
in the bushes
Wife
careful
Husband
a tightly-swaddled
bundle
frozen to ice
it's a child
left behind I think
during the exodus
Wife
holy mother this war
people become
worse than animals
Husband
give me a blanket
I'll try wrapping
it again
Wife
gently now
Husband
I know I know
a boy
he's still warm
his voice hoarse
Wife
he's hungry
hand him over
Husband
no name nothing

all alone
without a name
on this earth
Wife
how he gulps it down
hey little wriggler
leave some for our young 'un
Husband
that there is the moon
around it stars without number
and during the daytime
the sun shines
s – u – n
Wife
head in the clouds dreamer
he's but a couple of months old
he won't understand you
Husband
I wish
it was springtime
Wife
what
what are you looking at me for
Husband
and you me
Wife
four
four mouths in all
can we do it
Husband
I don't know whether
this world still
needs schoolmasters
hasn't helped much so far

Wife
  preachers and sermonisers
  are always wanted
Husband
  I can't be
  holier than thou
Wife
  you have to remember
  'to eat this bread
  I must sing of this song'
Husband
  mm
Wife
  when there's peace
Husband
  when (*Pause.*)
  here we have
  precious new life
  not one but two
  the future must come
  it must
  what does it say in the scriptures
  'suffer the little children
  to come unto me
  and turn them not away' (*Pause.*)
  can you think of a good name
  for the boy
Wife
  for our daughter
  it was easy
  anna 'the gracious'
  but there's time enough
  for the boy
Husband
  we found him
  by starlight

like a small stone
in the snow and ice
god wanted it so (*Pause.*)
starstone

Wife
starstone it is
and we will rear them
as brother and sister
snuggle him in

Husband
their four little eyes
gleam and sparkle
as if they understood
woman
let's go

Wife
but where

Husband
what do I know
just over the mountains
our backs to the war

SCENE THREE

Schoolroom.

Master
forty-five times forty-five
starstone

Starstone
two thousand and twenty-five.

Master
listen and wonder
all of you
how the answer shoots out

464

as from a pistol
work it out yourselves
on paper (*Pause.*)
well
you there
Schoolchild
he's right
forty-five times forty-five is
two thousand and twenty-five
Master
so
so now I'll let you in on the secret
of working it out in your head
let's see four times five is
you there
Schoolchild
twenty
Master
now simply add on the twenty-five at the end
so forty-five times forty-five is
Schoolchild
two thousand and twenty-five
Master
exactly
sixty-five times sixty-five
anna .
Anna
four thousand two hundred and twenty-five
Master
zickzack
six times seven
Schoolchild
forty-two
Master
and add twenty-five to the end
you

Schoolchild
four thousand two hundred and twenty-five.
Master
good
now let's follow the principle through
take the one at the front times
the next highest number
then add on twenty-five
thirty-five times thirty-five is therefore
you
Schoolchild
errr
one thousand two hundred and twenty-five
Master
exactly
fifty-five times fifty-five is
Schoolchild
five times six is thirty
add on twenty-five
three thousand and twenty-five
Master
eighty-five times eighty-five
Schoolchild
seven thousand two hundred and twenty-five
Master
there you are
works like a dream
what is it
Schoolchild
but why
why should we have to do it
quickly in our heads
sir
Master
er why

what sort of a question is that
well ummm

From 'outside' drums and pipes can be heard.

Schoolchild
soldiers
it's soldiers

The children run to the window.

Master
what are you thinking of
sit down
sit down please
are you all deaf
there's nothing to gawp at
Schoolchild
look at him
that one at the front
with his helmet and plume
Schoolchild
look how it sparkles
so brightly in the sunshine
all silver and gold
Master
anna starstone
go back to your seats
is it all in vain
or
look at me now
the ten commandments
anna the sixth
loud and clear
Anna
thou shalt not kill
Master
precisely

away from that window
you deaf fools
for the last time
goddam

Anna
father the third

Starstone
ring the bell
we want to go to the fair

Anna
please

Master
out of my sight
all of you
that's enough for today

The children run 'out' yelling and shouting.

SCENE FOUR

Fairground. Anna and Starstone wander from stall to stall.

Zealot
go on laugh
laugh at me but
he who laughs last
laughs most terribly
ye are all damned
and accursed
because your memory
has consumption
it forgets about satan
till the bitter end
till the last judgement
ye stinking brood of vipers

    hypocrites and liars
    go to hell

Soldier

    go to hell yourself
    you vicious-tongued cripple
    pile of pus you pestilent worm
    even heaven holds fairs
    so
    don't spoil my fun

Zealot

    go on hit me
    spit on me
    kick me
    into the dust go on go on
    aahh the pain does me good
    don't stop don't stop
    whether you want it or no
    my truth
    is witnessed by god
    for I am saint paul
    the apostle
    and truly I say unto you
    no stone of this city
    not one single one
    will remain standing
    blood and ignominy
    destruction
    sodom and gomorrah

Soldier

    paul don't fall
    shut your gob
    ha

*He beats him up even more. Starstone tries to help
the Zealot.*

Anna
    stop
    please
    don't interfere
Starstone
    but
Anna
    I'm afraid
    afraid of them both and
Starstone
    afraid for me ha
Anna
    don't laugh
Zealot
    the church makes out
    the body is sinful
    the men of of of
    science say
    the body is a machine
    it is business
    the whores whisper and call
    and the fools brag
    it was nothing but a ball
Soldier
    a ball a banquet
    what a banquet
    more like a fortress
    every man every one
    is a fortress unto himself
    wanting to be stormed
    get it you idiot
    don't drivel
    the whole world
    is crying out to be laughed at
    crying out to be shot

Zealot
    betrayal
    eats into the flesh
    and the power of darkness
    tears it asunder so
    (*He rips his shirt.*)
    into a thousand pieces
    if ever we allow it
    in our bodies
    we live far from god
    because only death
    is truly great
Soldier
    that's what I say
    haha (*Marches off.*)

    far from home
    and unshaven
    polished angels
    seek a haven
Starstone
    the things
    that flash through
    the minds of men
Anna
    it's a mad world
    don't listen
    come let's go

(*Silhouette Artist can be played by the Fool.*)

Artist
    over here
    come on over here
    gather around
    don't be afraid

I don't bite
well only my scissors
Starstone
we've no money
Artist
who does
but art simply emerges
unbidden
out of the soul
those are the best moments
they need nourishment
or else the fire is extinguished
I noticed you a while ago
been watching you
dewy-fresh
untainted lovers
are rarely found
in these times
you could say
the only beam of light
Anna
but
Artist
yes yes
money is not everything
please
brighten my life
both your faces
are like a blessing
and faith hope love
everything that's genuine
is to be found in art
well what is it
the silhouette's a present
a remembrance
and one day perhaps

when you're married
you'll think of me
be still still now
ants in your pants
makes your heads wobble

Anna
  we are twins
  not
  what you think

Starstone
  but
  not identical

Artist
  aha I see
  two separate
  eggs on a plate
  are you making fun of me
  or what

Anna
  why

Starstone
  yes
  why

Artist
  I might ask you
  that
  your heads your heads
  my eye is true and
  unerring
  brother and sister ha
  love devises
  all manner of pranks
  it's really droll
  you both have
  striking profiles
  two dispositions

essentially different
have you not
but opposites
are known to attract
man and wife
so that you become one
one flesh and blood
so spake the lord
just like adam and eve
and yet
he still drove them out
of paradise
the rogue
and that was that
done with
that's knocked you huh
straight into the unknown
well then
don't just pretend
you're seeing each other
for the very first time ha
scarlet-faced
I told you
it is a present
Both
thank you
Artist
good luck
I have never seen
such naivety
Starstone
why
are you looking at me
like that
Anna
like what

474

Starstone
   so strangely
Anna
   me you

   Hall of mirrors.

Soldier
   so tell me
   what do you say
   that pretty mirror monkey there
   would be just right
   such a budding rose
   ready to be picked
Anna
   ha look at you
   longlonglong and thin
   like a runner bean
Starstone
   and you
   fat and round ha
   like a pancake
Anna
   hey stupid mirror
   I am in fact
   slim and slender
   am I not
Starstone
   s'true
   you're a liar
Anna
   and
   look at our tongues
   big as cloths
   I wouldn't want to kiss
   you
   with that

Starstone
  and this
  ugly mug of a face ugh
  it's not really you
Anna
  nor is it you
Starstone
  in
  in reality you're
Anna
  go on say it
  hey stay
  don't run away
Soldier
  what do you say my lovely
  to us two
  I'll pay
  whatever you want
  go a'courting
  slake a thirst
  feverishly I see
  your cherry-red mouth
  and after the hosanna
  come
  my dowsing rod
  can find the source
Anna
  but I
  where
Soldier
  come now
  he's long gone
  and who knows what
  the morning brings
  what do we care
  let's live for today

Anna
I'd
I'd rather not
Soldier
hello let's go
and blow my pay
Starstone
hey hey
let her go
get your filthy paws off
Soldier
huh
want to get your hands
dirty on me
heel hound
we soldiers are
furies of might
milksop
and dog dangerous
to crossssss
I'd stab out the eyes
of the blind
cut off the ears
of the deaf
rip out the tongues
of the dumb
huuuhuuuuh ha
we are maniacs
in the bedlam of men
yet unbeaten in love
there's another clout
not had enough yet
leave go
Anna
please please
please mister soldier sir

leave my brother
alone
Soldier
brother soso
brother and sister ha
believe that and you'll
go to heaven
well I wish you happiness
I'm no monster
don't be afraid
I won't be the first
to slice your unshaven chin
because you young witch
are a beauty
say thank you
go on move it or else
she won't recognise
your visage
Starstone
ththth
Soldier
don't bother
I'll find another
sister ha (*off*)
Anna
what a
revolting brute
does it hurt
Starstone
course not
Anna
you defended me
like a real cavalier
Starstone
maybe

madam would you
proffer me you hand
Anna
but certainly kind sir
my whole arm
if you wanted

They exit, arm in arm, laughing.

SCENE FIVE

Room.

Father
well
are they asleep finally
Anna
yes
Father
you're like a mother
to the young ones (*Pause.*)
that she too
had to die so young (*Pause.*)
what is it
help yourselves
what's left is for us
Starstone
you eat it
Father
not hungry
you
everywhere
there is less and less
cupboards are bare
I can't conjure with air
and now the soldiers

479

not a good omen
hopefully
the town will be spared
I can't envisage
that either luther or the pope
wanted it so
back then
I always thought
we were christian folk
nothing between us
one like the other
and that reason will win
one day
oh well (*Pause.*)
why so quiet
was there nothing to amuse
at the fair
starstone
you usually bubble over
like a spring
Anna

Anna
this here
this silhouette
was given to us

Father
that so
the profiles are very fine
a small work of art

Starstone
for you

Father
thank you
I'll hang it
over my bed

Anna
 father
Starstone
 we
Father
 starstone
 my decision is final
 you won't be a soldier
 not ever
 d'you hear
 not even if the recruiting officers
 knock me about a bit
 we'll hide you
 with a farmer
 give him a strong helping hand
 and you'll not need to starve
 what is it
 what is it with you
 cat got your tongue
Starstone
 I
 you ask
Anna
 father
 you always say
 that the world outside
 loves only appearances
 that it
 lies and deceives
 its children especially
 but that you don't
Father
 what are you on about
 what is it you're after
Starstone
 are we

    anna and me
    brother and sister
    I mean
    blood relatives
Anna
    please please
    tell us the truth
Father
    alright then
    it's not escaped me that (*Pause.*)
    but it is also true that
    friendship and love
    are like twins
    little brother little sister
    you could never get enough
    of that fairytale
Starstone
    but
Father
    don't worry
    I'm not avoiding the issue
    I just want to get used
    to the idea
    of you two as
    young lovers (*Pause.*)
    but what will the
    neighbours think
    and say
    they know nothing
    come here

SCENE SIX

*Room. Anna is at the window staring out. She sings
quietly to herself.*

Anna
  look the snow is falling
  tho' the time is not yet ripe
  to duck the boys' snowballing
  as the neighbours start to snipe
Starstone
  no anna
  not a sad song
Anna
  you're awake
Starstone
  have been for ages
  and don't cry
  please
Anna
  afraid
  I tried to sleep
  last night
  but all I could hear
  was the heavy tread
  of our hearts
Starstone
  don't be afraid
  don't be afraid
  I will come back
  I promise
  cross my heart
  and
  you'll see
  time will fly by

Anna
    I don't know (*Pause.*)
Starstone
    the stars up there
    let's choose one
    agreed and
    in our minds' eye
    we'll think of each other
Anna
    yes yes
    I'll wait I'll wait
    I'll do waiting
Starstone
    there look
    the sun is coming up
    your song is not yet over
Anna
    I want to sing it
    with you
Starstone
    thank you lord
    for creating a world
    as indescribably beautiful
    as my anna
Anna
    flatterer
Starstone
    our love
    is our faith
    and if needs be
    without forgiveness
Anna
    oi you
    kiss me

SCENE SEVEN

Field.

Farmer
go on don't stop
one more furrow
what is it
tired already
not used to it
out of breath
I'd pull it myself
but you can't guide the plough
not yet
you should eat some bread
your face is covered in sweat ha
good
time to draw breath
time to eat

Starstone
all my bones
hurt

Farmer
soon pass soon pass
and one day
when the seedlings grow
your heart will smile

Starstone
today you're talking
like a waterfall

Farmer
nearly as much as
townsfolk

Starstone
  get on with you
  not half as much
Farmer
  because they don't know
  really
  what they want
  no peace no quiet nothing
  that makes sense
  but all the time
  it's seething and swirling
  then bubbles over
  like a witches' cauldron
  satan's very own
  venom and spite (*Pause.*)
  rats plague war city
  somehow
  somehow
  it all fits together
  I can't explain why
  and I don't want to be all
  doom and gloom but
  I feel it
  a great undoing (*Pause.*)
  the world out there
  has become one
  one big hurry scurry (*Pause.*)
  tell your father the schoolmaster
  not so much adding up
  not so much science
  feeling that's what
  and noticing the seasons
  a present from god
  the eternal cycle
  nature
  living dying being

so that one day
we don't flee death (*Pause.*)
ha look at those two beetles
how they muck about
how they play (*Pause.*)
yes
then there's love
then there is love
root of all life
you're in love aren't you
ha you're going red as a beetroot (*Pause.*)
let's back to work
no one else will do it

SCENE EIGHT

Ruined farmhouse.

Engelhart
speak dog
go on
where've you hidden it
your pot of gold
spit it out you stupid pig
you've nothing else to lose
save your pathetic miserable life
fire away huh
your wife and children
are praying from the other side
that you'll spill the beans
Farmer
if that's so
then kill me too
Captain
wait

he'll sing soon enough
tie him up
hands behind his back
hold him tight
up and down
ever so nicely
through his tongue
with a bodkin and horsehair
Engelhart
filthy farmer
go on scream louder
through you bloody mouth
where is it hidden
where where
Starstone
nothing
he has nothing
let him go at once
Engelhart
hey hey hey
and which hole
did you crawl from
boy
killing needs practice
your scythe on your neck
Captain
leave him
fellows like him
make good soldiers
I'm listening
you want to live
your choice
with us or
Engelhart
straight to hell

Farmer
    starstone go
    everything is over
    here (*Dies.*)
Engelhart
    hell's blood
    the old man croaked
    on his pain
Captain
    so
    we're left with the livestock
    the spoils are hardly worth it
    damn and shit
Engelhart
    and still
    my stomach hurts
    come on boy
    up you get
    walk ahead of me
    and don't get any ideas
    about absconding
    I'll catch you
    sooner or later
    then you'll die like him
    or even worse
    my name means hard angel
    starstone eh
    how romantic
    go on go on
    I'll teach you to use
    sword and pistol
    the war needs men
    not lanky johnnies
    ha

SCENE NINE

Room.

Anna
    mercy mercy
    dear lord
    grant us grace
    that we'll be together soon
    starstone and me
    I am wilting wilting
    like a flower
    without water
    don't ever want
    to be sad again
    and forsaken
    every single day
    this melancholy
    never leaves
    and the long
    dark nights
    full of grim grimaces
    I can't shake off
    those foul faces
    simply can't shake them off
    and no singing
    my lips let
    no song pass
    please just let me
    fall asleep
    dear lord and father
    so that longing
    does not eat me up
    eat me up
    amen

SCENE TEN

Manoeuvres in the field.

Engelhart
  come on
  let it out
  your rage
  attack
  is and always will be
  the best defence
  that's right
  but not too
  hot-headed
  you should always try
  to keep your cool
  remain sanguine
  come on come on
  I am the enemy
  I am the ogre
  you have to kill
  or else
  it will get you
  and
  careful now
  fight back
  parry
  weakling
  that's how you'll be beaten
  every time
  now you're using theory
  no fire in your belly
  ufff (*He trips.*)
Starstone (*overcomes him*)
  you bastard

   you murderer
   you torturer
Engelhart
   look at that
   who'd believe it
   thrust it through
   go on
   you've taken hold of me
   like the plague
   you could be free
   maybe
   the murderer starstone
   (*Overcomes him.*)
   fool
   take note
   too much thinking
   ruins the mind
   and body
   never hesitate
   mercy is
   emotional wishwash
   first me then nothing
   then me again
   a soldier wants to live
   no matter how
   victory
   is his duty
   rule number one
   go on get up
   at me
   one last time
   puppy taste blood
Starstone
   let me
   I

I would like to
you know
Engelhart
what do I care
time was ripe
go and meet your faerie sprite
but one thing I'll say
don't get caught
I know nothing
and as a traitor
I'll hang you myself
got it
got it
Starstone
yes

SCENE ELEVEN

Room.

Anna
the siege is
truly terrible
but many are hopeful
of the allied forces
Starstone
they're still far away
Anna
of an evening
from the city walls
I look down on the hordes
of your army
a thousand camp fires
I hear the sound of drums
the shout of orders

barbaric
is it not
what
what will happen to us
to us all
I don't understand
don't want to understand
it might not be far
the end of the world
starstone

Starstone

from all sides
we're caught in a trap
the noose tightens
it will crush us
like a metal-clad fist
without mercy
flight anna
is out of the question
and me
I am a traitor
whether here or there
if only father knew

Anna

you are not
not for me
kiss me
kiss me
I want to forget
where we are

SCENE TWELVE

Camp fire.

Fool
if I serve one
then there's no gold
if I serve t'other
the world becomes cold
if I serve on water
weeks become years
if I serve on land
there's nothing but tears
if I serve the devil
I'm straight down hell's hole
if I serve god
it's my conscience and soul
if I serve myself
fight hard here and now
my booty the soil
the sabre my plough

Engelhart
hey starstone
sing along
my booty the soil
the sabre my plough
thus spake the devil
to all soldiers
the earth be your bed
the sky your blanket
a cloak your house
and wine – your good health
the best of all lives
dancer of dreams
what are you staring at

there's nothing there
the moon is bloody
and sharp as a sickle
head off chop
and the stars glint
ice-cold
nothing but deception
from a black hell
come on
drink up
glug it down
or give me your ration
I can take it
cheers – faintheart

Starstone
idiot you know
this is my hometown
and I

Engelhart
don't keep stuffing my ears
full of drivel
home town home town
what's that then eh
for us soldiers that means
money money a tidy sum
that's what we fight for
that and nothing else
and
of course
comfy winter quarters
to warm and fill
our bellies
and rest bones tired
from our exertions
till the next slaughter
got it

better tell me why
'your' town
doesn't capitulate
run up the white flag
false pride is fanatical
and thirsts for blood
on both sides
but we'll squash that
obstinate insect flat
no mercy now
believe me

Starstone
well what do you say
will you help me

Engelhart
help yourself
for no one else will

Starstone
promise me
on your heart

Engelhart
your 'anna'
for ever and three days
burt lurrve
never dies
you know what a
real soldier is
he bores into any hole
even the devil's own
beauty is a luxury
he doesn't give a damn
because the last womb
he buries himself in
is his grave
for only there

497

does he find true peace
cheers and prost *
I have spoken
Captain
so men
what is the general mood
Engelhart
good captain good
Captain
the lull before the storm
will you command
the first raiding party
tomorrow
Engelhart
thank you for the honour
I'll get along without it
Captain
I didn't say this
but you take the plunder
from those you kill
Engelhart
if that's so
well then
I'll kill the lot of them
now if you want ha
Captain
ha Engelhart
you always were
a witty brawler
d'you know this one
a sly soldier
on meeting death
his very self

* *prost* – prounced as in 'pro and con' – means good health,
cheers, to us all, etc.

says to him
'no one is ever spared
I know that
but I have one last request
grant it me'
the devil says
'I suppose so
it's granted'

the soldier 'promise'
the devil 'I keep my word'
the soldier 'then
do not kill me till I have said
the lord's prayer'
and mister d
has been waiting
ever since ha
Engelhart
ha I must remember
that joke
Captain
so in battle
keep your wits about you
Engelhart
we will
this particular life
comes at a heavy price
hey starstone
Starstone
rosengasse
the first house on the left
near the town hall
please promise
Engelhart
what
not this again

Starstone
    spare anna
    the whole family
Engelhart
    aaaalright I'll do it
    if I live
    myself
    sleep now

SCENE THIRTEEN

Soldiers before battle, sunrise.

Engelhart
    ha
    he's going to preach at us
    he's as loaded
    as a gunbarrel
    just as I said
    it's all a jest
    the world reels
    into the abyss
    and we can only follow
Starstone
    remember
    do you remember the street
    the house
Captain
    calm your prick down
Starstone
    say it
Engelhart
    town hall gassenros
Captain
    shut it

Military Padre

so my brothers
the battle lies ahead
but do not do as others do
and say
I'll take the money
and serve the devil
because you
you are noble and brave warriors
serving the honour of god
you believe in righteousness
you fight for the holy fatherland
but
the enemy is real
and is entrenched
behind walls of stone
and its jeers are
weighted with hatred
it alone wants
to destroy us
and so spake the lord our god
'look
I will stretch out my hand
against the philistines
and smite them
and revenge myself upon them
and punish them cruelly
that they might know
that I am the lord their god
and I will revenge myself
upon them'
but ye shall
behave and fight
as true christians
show mercy
spare the innocent

so now the time has come
unsheathe your swords
and fight
in the name of the lord our god
amen

All

amen

Soldier

in the morning I always
say my a b c out loud
let the lord his very self
make a prayer of it

Engelhart

I fart loudly
the blessing then
stinks to high heaven

Captain

so men
pull in your balls and at 'em
atttaaaaaaacck
drums and trumpets
sing

Fool

let's all sing
and make dying easier
tops of your voices

    our god is
    a fortress

SCENE FOURTEEN

Destroyed quarter of the city, occasional battle noise,
Anna dead, violated and crucified against a house door.

Engelhart
    give
    give me that knife
    d'you want to maim yourself
    mad dog
    steady now friend
    slow and steady or else
    what
    why stare you so
    too late
    we got here too late
    that there was er
    her own people
    believe me
    a note
    yup we found a note
    round her neck
    or pinned to her breast
    on it
    'I am a whore
    I betrayed the city
    to the enemy'
Starstone
    liar
    show me
Engelhart
    burnt
    burnt in hell's fires
    what sort of madness is this

rouse yourself
your anna will be avenged

Captain
quick quick follow me
the rats have barricaded themselves
in the church

Engelhart
let's torch
those priestly pigs

Starstone
stop it
will you please stop

SCENE FIFTEEN

On the streets. Rowdy noises.

Captain
aaaah
an arc of piss
gleams and steams
like a comet's tail
into the icy night
if only one knew
its destination

Engelhart
the captain
being sentimental
is quite simply
in at one end
out the other
but always downhill
yet my dowsing rod
is randy as a dog ha
looking and looking

for a warm burrow
to spend the winter
we've done it
Captain
that
that engelhart
is best forgot
in strictest confidence
for your ears only
before chaos breaks
Engelhart
as a grave as a grave
Captain
we've just caught
an enemy messenger
in two or three days
we'll be surrounded
by a much greater power
then there will be a bloodbath
without end
Engelhart
hell and damnation
with our losses
we've no chance
Captain
as I said
and the people here
are for the other side
and the land far and wide
will stay ravaged for years
even if war does cease
and it will
but without me
I've had it up to here
and privately ha
my conscience is saying

stay ahead of the disaster
I'm off
to France
dukely duty calls
my relatives there
will take me in
for my coat of arms
hangs on my umbilical

Engelhart
d'you
d'you have room
for a comrade

Captain
ha engelhart
you've gone all
starry-eyed
each man for himself no
separate births
separate paths
was ever thus
and must so remain
a nobleman has his venison
the judge his sop
the farmer his harvest festival
and every dog ha
his nuptials
any questions

Engelhart
and the soldier

Captain
work it out yourself (*off*)

Whore
well dearie
any money left or
or have you spent it all on booze
standing there like an idiot

Engelhart
ha dearie
don't jest
I'll show you
Whore
then pay up
beforehand mind
Engelhart
hey hey
goods first
then the money
Whore
not with me
I've had a couple of bad experiences
flesh is flesh
and mine
soldier dear
is not for free
it's pretty tough though
Engelhart
I can see that
Whore
and I can see
that you are in dire need
of a drop of solace
Engelhart
ha solace
solace costs now
is that what we've come to
Whore
what do I know
business is business
and the world
oh picture of manhood
was not devised by woman

so
payment yes or no
Engelhart
there
let's go

SCENE SIXTEEN

Graveside.

Engelhart
what is it
cowering there
like a noxious child
are you a soldier or what
time heals all wounds
Starstone
not mine
all dead
all of them
the whole family (*Pause.*)
and anna my love (*Pause.*)
I feel
as if my soul
has been extinguished
for ever
in the day I wander
as if I am my own shadow
and at night
I howl at the moon
and lament this terrible misery
Engelhart
aaaaalright
that's enough

Starstone
    what
    what does life
    hold for me
    what (*Pause.*)
    and where
    will I feel at home
    without anna
    tell me
    you who have an answer
    to everything (*Pause.*)
    I am now
    alone in this world
    alone

Engelhart
    so what
    pathetic wretch
    all alone ha
    we all are
    from the very beginning
    barely do we glimpse
    the world's light
    and no one cares
    we simply exist
    whether so
    or so
    come starstone
    we are alive
    we live
    whether you want to admit it
    or no
    until one day
    we take ourselves to hell
    that'll wait awhile (*Pause.*)
    everything that lives ha
    eats up time

and itself
hey
a tiny small thought has come to me
we'll desert
huh we're dogs
betrayed and spat at
come let's go
away from here
from this
icy embrace (*Pause.*)
what is it now
want to grow roots here
come on come on (*Tries to drag him away.*)

Starstone
let me gooooo
bastard piece of filth
hangman's henchman
let me be or else
(*He swings at him, Engelhart ducks.*)
I
I will stay
and hand myself over

Engelhart
stupid idiot
dung for brains
what do you think
they'll do to us huh
after our rampage here

Starstone
you
not me

Engelhart
you and me I
where's the difference
do you think anyone'll bother
with it

they'll torture us to death
treat us both the same
I loathe the rack

Starstone
I don't care
sorrow is sorrow

Engelhart
no one cares d'you understand
let's go come on
be a good boy
you must know a cunning way
out of this town
let's make tracks
before it's too late
the dead remain dead
caterwauling does not help

Starstone
then
till the last judgement

Engelhart
ha
good joke
better idea save ourselves
flight
always fleeing
let's go (*Drags Starstone with him.*)

SCENE SEVENTEEN

Open fields, heavy snow.

Engelhart
where there's a will
a way can be found
damned storm

just what we needed
two lost souls ha
without dwelling
what a joke
let's keep
looking
don't hang back
Starstone
I'm tired
so tired
Engelhart
my arm
hold it tight
at the very least
we have to find
a barn for the night
or we'll freeze
to death
come on eh
we'll do it
the two of us
damned servants of god ha
Starstone
quiet
can't you hear
the angels singing
Engelhart
you've gone off again
the storm is howling
like a pack of wolves
must keep moving
or we're supper
Starstone
shush
just for a moment

I want to hear
anna's song
Engelhart
fantasist
you're dreaming a'foot
keep going
we'll hold up each other
don't sleep don't
don't go to sleep or else
talk talk talk
anything
Starstone
when
when peace comes
I will be a farmer
in spring
plough the fields
in summer
animals on the meadows
in autumn golden
the harvest (*Pause.*) yes
and harm no one
rest in winter
from all the travails
the sun
I can see the sun
Engelhart
heyheyhey
open your eyes
farmer starstone
I won't let you rest for
I
I will form a band
yup a band of wild bandits
born out of war
and learning is learning

I am master of the craft
nothing else
everything stays the same
you slave
and I'll take it away from you
that
that is
true friendship
and love
in this world of men
ha

*They fall asleep. The winter storm gets wilder and
wilder – amongst the noise there is a suggestion of
sirens howling. Abrupt end.*

EPILOGUE

Fool
    once the winter's over and
    dreams draw us home on the plains
    there is an end to hunger and pain

    once the last ice has melted and
    the first flowers have begun to bloom
    the first signs of hope start to loom

    once the lark's up and singing
    and fields submit to the plough
    the darkness of night can end now

    heigh-ho those with faith
    sing paradise's praise
    heigh-ho those who've not
    go straight to hell to rot

in terrible times there is seldom a happy end
nevertheless if you liked my story
please clap your hands

TAKE-AWAY

Jackie Kay

Characters

Darcus
tap-dancing poet

Kimberley
works in the take-away

David
Kimberley's big brother

Mitzi
Kimberley's mother, works in the kitchen downstairs

Tyrese,
young angry man

Ruth
Tyrese's girlfriend

Jatinder
Ruth's mother

Kirk
onion addict

Mohammed
Kirk's friend

Kenneth
oddball loner

Eve
young woman

Ivy
Eve's best friend

Gang

a bunch of young people (any number from three up)
of different backgrounds and nationalities.
The Gang performs the same function as
a Greek chorus. They are invisible to everybody
except each other. They comment on what is happening.
If a very large cast is available, the Gang could be
split into two or more groups. Each gang could speak
alternate lines or words, so that a complex choral effect
is built up. Sometimes the gangs could speak together
and sometimes singly.

Onion Pushers

minimum of two people, possibly more

Onion Johnnies

two people who sell onions on bicycles and have
long strings of onions hanging over their handlebars.
They wear French berets and sell the onions door
to door. They can speak when the Pushers speak.

Mr McDonald *and* Mrs Morrison
Onion Commission
(two people, could be more)

Dancing Girl
just one at the moment, but could be more

A Note on the Set

The set should give the idea of a part of a city.
There should be a river running across the set;
a take-away with an upstairs and downstairs;
several corners or doors for people's different homes;
a table for the town council's onion commission.

A Note on the Onions

Onions could be used imaginatively.
Onion street lamps, onions rolling across the stage,
perhaps an onion tree.

If it is possible, the Onion Johnnies should cycle
across the stage with strings of onions hanging from
the handlebars. The Onion Johnnies should speak
in a French accent. If only a small cast is available,
the Onion Johnnies are not necessary, they simply
add texture.

The onions in the play are metaphors for what is
potentially dangerous and destructive in our society:
drugs, addictions, obsessions, sadness, depression,
violence . . .

It would be good to use *real* onions,
bearing in mind that they are also symbols.

SCENE ONE

Place: a Chinese and Indian take-away, with a Chinese menu and an Indian menu, in the city.

Time: Bitter Friday night in winter

What's happening? All the young people are out in shirts with no coats. There are Onion Pushers and Onion Johnnies on street corners, everywhere.

Darcus is tap-dancing towards the city from a long way off.

He has plans to make the city a better place.

He is going to get rid of the onions in the East End.

Darcus (*tap-dancing as he talks and looking at his watch*)
The river nice. I hear tell about it, now.
The river pretty in the city
plenty fishy in there, flipping and flashing
their tales in that tea-brown water.
The river snakes its dark coil
round the city, you can see it everywhere
you look, a sparkle of the river's glitter.
The river always busy heading someplace.
Never lazy, never slowing down a pace.
Boats sail down the river.
Children skip flat stones
one, two, three, four,
like a promise, like good news coming.
The flat stone, like a little girl
skipping to school
in her smart black shoes,
a little shipping girl singing
her sad onion rhyme.

A Dancing Girl dances around Darcus singing:

Dancing Girl

Cry baby cry,
Watch the onion fry.
Cry baby cry,
Someone's going to die.

Darcus

I feel attracted to this city:
a wide deep river, a frisky West End
a busy bustling shopping street
and the best take-away
in the country. Of course I is not forgetting
this city's big onion problem in the East End.
That's where I am heading.
I am going to do something.

The Gang is standing in a long queue outside the take-away. They are trying to pretend they aren't cold.

Gang

Tandoori Chicken, Tandoori Chop, Poppadom,
Paratha, Mango Chutney, Lime Pickle, Boti Kebab,
Kidney Kebab, Chicken Pakoda, Chicken Kashmiri,
Onion bhaji, Samosa, Pakora, Prawn Cracker, Won
Ton. Dim Sum. Har kau, Spring Roll, *Naaaaaaaan.*

Egg Fried Rice, Pilau Rice, Chow Mein, Chips,
Peshwari Nan, Pommi Nan, Keema Nan, Roti,
Chapata, *Naaaaaaaan.*

Chicken Vindaloo, Lamb Do-Piaza, Chicken in Black
Bean Sauce, King Prawn in Oyster Sauce, Cantonese
Duck, Pancakes, Braised Beancurd, *Naaaaaaaaan.*

Chicken Jalfrezi, Lamb Shah Jani, Chicken Madras,
Sweet and Sour Chicken, Sweet and Sour Pork, Sag
Chicken, Karachi Gosht, *Naaaaaaaan.*

Lobster Masala, Lamb Hot Pot, Keema Peas,
Beansprouts, Mushroom Chop Suey, Mushroom

Chow Mein, Rogan Josh, Bhuna Gosht, Lamb Dansak,
Lamb Tikka Masala, *Naaaaaaan*.

Chicken and Aubergine, Chicken and Pineapple,
Aloo Gorbee, Bombay Aloo, Sag Aloo, Tarka Dahl,
Asparagus, Mutter Paneer, Sag Paneer, Stir Fried
Vegetables, Steamed Vegetables, Brinjal, Bhindi,
Naaaaaaaaaaaan.

Cucumber Raita, Chinese Cabbage, Green Tea,
Jasmine Tea, Kingfisher, Kobra, Irn Bru, Coca Cola,
Sweet Lassi, Sour Lassi, Banana Fritter, Pineapple
Fritter, Mango, Lychee, Kulfi, Burfi, Gulab Jaman,
Ice Cream, *Naaaaaaaaaan*.

No dirty knives, no dirty hands, no dirty boards,
no dirty woks. Clean pots. Clean cooker. All above
board. No germs, we are very hygienic. Very good
meal. Good take-away. Good carry-out. Best in the
country. Have a taste. Treat yourself. We're good.
Yes, yes. We are very very good.

*People are jostling with each other to try and get
forward in the queue. Two Onion Pushers walk up
and down the queue trying to tempt people to buy
onions.*

Kenneth I was before you.
Tyrese No you weren't, you liar.
Ruth Don't get involved, Tyrese.
Kenneth Shift or I'll shift you.
Tyrese Funny guy!
Ruth Ignore him, he's a complete nutter.
Gang (*circling the queue*)
The biggest problem in this city is the onion rings.
This city can't control the onion rings.
Mountains of onions on the main streets.
Onions sprouting from the city walls.
Onions sitting on double-decker buses,
Onion-eyed pushers inside offices,

Hanging around outside schools.
Onion johnnies with their long strings
Cycling down the narrow lanes,
Onions rolling on the football fields,
Onions bumping downstairs in the town hall
Onions on church pews, people praying for onions.
Kids stealing from their mothers' purses
To get their fix of onions.
Unmarked onion vans in side streets.
Onions in bathrooms at parties.
Onions being downloaded on the Internet.
They don't know who is bringing the onions in.

Summer onion. Autumn onion.
Winter onion. Spring onion.
Sybies. Sybies. Sybies.
Shallot. Shallot. Shallot.

The onions are destroying our confidence.
They've got the city police onto it.
The teachers are on red alert.
Everyone has been told to be vigilant, you bet.
Yet, yet yet,
So far not one single person
Has been done for onion possession.

Darcus is dancing towards the long queue. The two
Onion Pushers hold out some bags of onions. They
run alongside Darcus holding out the bags.

Onion Pushers Five pounds a bag, cut-price onions
Onion Johnnies (*in French accents*) Terrific, wonderful,
   fantastic onions. Without onions there would be no
   cuisine. Dream the onion dream.
Darcus
   A man in the south told me
   about the city in the east
   with the big onion culture.

I'm attracted to a place
with a bad problem
like a bunion on a toe.
Darcus is your man, I said.
Then took off for the city.
(*to the Onion Pushers*)
Not for me, thank you.

*Darcus pushes the Pushers and they both fall down.
Their onions roll everywhere. They look perplexed
and shocked.*

Onion Pushers Did you see that? Did you see that?
We're having him. Who does the man think he is?
Who is he? He's a stranger. We'll catch him later
Onion Johnnies My goodness. Did you see that man?

*Inside the take-away: David and Kimberley are taking
the orders.*

Kenneth How did you decide chicken chow mein would
be Number 23? Why didn't you make chicken chow
mein Number 27? That's my birthday. 27 November.
Chow mein is my favourite. Why did you make
Number 27 sweet and sour pork? I don't like sweet
and sour pork. Why don't you switch the numbers?
Twenty-three is the date my mum died. I don't like
Number 23. Can't you switch the numbers, big man?
Tyrese Hurry up!
Ruth Tyrese! I don't want you getting in more fights.
Please.
Tyrese (*to Ruth*) Shut it!
David (*speaking non-fluent English*) We can't switch
number. (*gently*) We got menus printed. You say 27
and we bring Number 23? No problem.
Kenneth (*angry*)You think that helps?
Tyrese There's a big long queue here! Come on! Come
on!

527

Kenneth Why not? Is it a lot to ask? I'm falling apart here.

Kenneth stomps off.

Ruth (*quietly*) You've got to feel sorry for that man.
Kimberley What's eating him?
Tyrese He's barking, barking.
David Number 23 is eating him.
Ruth My favourite is mushroom chop suey. My favourite number is nine. But mushroom chop suey is not Number 9. That's life. We can't all go about getting our favourite numbers on our favourite meals.
Kirk (*to Mohammed*) What are you having? I'm having chicken madras and pilau rice.
Mohammed You always have the same.
Kirk That's the point about take-aways, to always have the same. It's a comfort.
Mohammed You never needed comforts before you started on the onions.
Kirk I didn't realise the beauty of the same thing, again and again.
Mohammed Kirk, I think you've become a bit strange.
Kirk No I haven't. I'm just the same bloke eating the same curry on a typical Friday night.
Kenneth (*turning back*) Why can't we? It's only a small thing to ask. I mean, I'm not asking to win the bloody lottery. (*to Tyrese*) What did you call me?
David No trouble. We don't want trouble in here.
Tyrese I'm not making any trouble. He's the one you should be talking to.
Kimberley (*to Kenneth*) Tell me your order and stop this nonsense.
Kenneth (*quickly*) Chicken chow mein and a can of Coke.
Kimberley Chicken chow mein and a can of Coke. Take a seat, please.
David What wrong with me?

Kimberley You give in too much. You need to be strict
with a silly man like that one there.
David Sssssh!
Kimberley He isn't frightening me. I've got more things
to be frightened of than a man who doesn't like
Number 23.

Darcus is tap-dancing outside the take-away

Darcus
The onion problem is a problem
For the whole of society.
The dogs don't like the onions
When they turn up in their bowls.
The teachers don't like the onions
When they roll into schools.
The women don't like the onions
Spoiling their conversations.
The policemen don't like the onions
At the end of their truncheons.
The footballers don't like
To take penalties with an onion.
The basketball players don't
Like the onion falling through the hoop.
The snooker players don't
Like the onions in the pockets.
The electrician and the optician don't like the onions
In the sockets.
The doctors don't like the onions
On the end of their stethoscopes.
The astrologers don't like onions
Forecast in the horoscopes.
The weather man don't like
The onion rain falling.
The whole society can't cope
With the invasion of onion,

The onion invasion.
The terrible times we are living in.
Eve What you having?
Ivy Mushroom chop suey.
Tyrese Chicken chow mein. (*to Ruth*) What about you?
Ruth Tandoori chicken and a paratha, please.
Kimberley Okay. Anything else?
Ruth That's me.
Ivy Shall we get a banana fritter?
Eve No.
Ivy No banana fritter? Aw, come on.
Eve It's up to you.
Ivy Two banana fritters, please.
Eve I'm not eating them.
Kenneth God!
Tyrese What!
Kenneth I just saw another one, skidding across the
    floor. It went that way.

*Kenneth chases the rolling onion and puts it in his
pocket.*

Darcus Many old people have cited onions the biggest
    of their fears.
    All the city people hate the onions when they are
    reduced to tears.
    The big worry is those who have fallen in love with
    the onion
    Those who are addicted to ripping off its brown skin
    Till they get to their pearl moon, eating, eating
    The whole onion raw like you'd eat an apple and ting
    Those whose breath stinks of onion, bitter in the
    morning,
    Who go to sleep dreaming onion dreams, rings and
    rings, never ending,
    Those who believe the moon is an onion.

Those who wake up in the morning weeping and crying.
Take an onion. Peel it. Look at its many layers.
Can you comprehend the problem
The oniony East End is facing?

Darcus dances past the Dancing Girl

Dancing Girl
Cry baby cry,
Watch the onion fry.
Cry baby cry,
Someone's going to die.

SCENE TWO

*David goes outside to try to clear the onions away.
Many onions roll around on the street. Some have lost
their skins. It is slippery. David tries to sweep his street
clean.*

David What you think you doing?
Onion Pushers We're selling onions.
Onion Johnnies Oui, oui, precisely.
David Not outside my shop. Leave my shop alone!
Onion Pushers Or else?
Onion Johnnies What then?
David I call police!
Onion Pushers Call the police! There's plenty onions in
the police. You can try but don't be surprised if you
find yourselves under investigation with the Inland
Revenue, for instance.
Onion Johnnies No, no, no, no, no. Is it possible to be
amicable? To have a place for everybody, no?
David I'm telling you last time. Last warning!
Onion Pushers (*sarcastically*) Ooooh we're very
frightened.

Onion Johnnies We are. We freely admit. *Nous avons peur.*

Gang
We've seen deaths on the streets
Sights we wish we hadn't seen,
Wherever we've gone, wherever we've been,
We've seen how rival onion rings operate
We've seen people frightened to co-operate
And every investigation evaporate
There is no stopping them,
They have no shame.
Once this was a good city.
Terrible pity, terrible pity.

Mohammed and Kirk are outside in the street under the onion street lamps. As they talk, the Onion Pushers dance around them in a circle faster and faster, like their conversation.

Mohammed Don't buy the onions!

Kirk I want some onions.

Mohammed No, don't buy the onions. They are bad for you.

Kirk I need onions.

Mohammed You don't need onions! Don't be silly. How can somebody need an onion?

Kirk I do need onions. If I can't have onions, I feel depressed. I've got no purpose. Nothing to look forward to. Friday night is boring without onions.

Mohammed Yeah, but you're starting to eat onions every night of the week.

Kirk No I'm not. Only have them for a treat.

Mohammed No you don't. I've seen you. Sometimes, three, four, five whole onions a night.

Kirk Thing is, I can't sleep without my onions. I can't get to sleep. If I could get to sleep, I wouldn't take them any more. I'd give them up.

Mohammed That's pathetic.

Kirk Come on. Go on. Have a bag, it won't do you any harm. I've never had flu since I started taking them. They're good for you.

The Onion Pushers approach Mohammed and Kirk.

Onion Pushers We're selling this batch off cheap. Five bags for a quid.

Kirk Cool! Five bags, pal.

Onion Pushers They're hot. Watch your back.

Kirk (*rips the brown skin off quickly and munches into it raw*) Ahhh! Nothing like it. Nothing like it. Have some –

He offers a bag to Mohammed, who takes an apple out of his pocket and munches it as Kirk munches the onion.

Mohammed I couldn't, mate. It revolts me. You stink. Look at you. God's sake, man, you're crying.

Kirk (*crying*) I'm not crying.

Mohammed You are, what's this?

Mohammed touches Kirk's tears.

Kirk My eyes are a bit watery that's all, no problem. (*Kirk has a big sneezing fit.*)

Mohammed You need help. This is so sick it's not true.

Kirk blows his nose.

Kirk (*transforming*) Chill out. Hey! You should try this. Nothing like it. Raw's the best. Some people fry them and roast them and shit, but I like them raw. Nippy. Hot. Bitter. Pure white-hot heat.

Mohammed How long for? How long before the onion rings take over? How long before we've got no choice at all.

Gang (*very fast, like a rap*) Chicken Dopiaza, Vindaloo, Korma, Madras, Methi Ghost, Lamb Jalfrezi, Chicken Sag, Red Chicken, Yellow Chicken. Lamb Dopiaza. Bhuna Ghost. Chicken Begham Barhar, *Naaaaaan*.

You come back from holiday. What do you want. You want a curry. A bottle of beer. A vindaloo. A Kashmir.

Kirk You're talking nonsense. That's just panic talking.

Mohammed Not from what I've been hearing. Not from the word on the street.

Kirk What? What are you on about?

Mohammed I heard the onion pushers are planning to close the take-aways down. They are working on a big attack right now. That's what I've been hearing.

Kirk Why would they want to do that?

Mohammed So that they can sell more onions, obviously.

Kirk Are you on something? You're talking mad.

Mohammed Me mad? I'm just eating an apple here. It's you on the onions. Kirk, can you not see yourself? You've changed. All you care about is knowing your onions. They are going to destroy you. I'm your mate. I'm concerned for you.

Kirk Look at the fucking moon up there. It is one big onion. Look at the stars, they are bright little chopped onions. Look at the night sky, Mohammed. It is sparkling. The stars are fizzing and frying in the sky. Look at my skin, it's translucent. I can almost see through myself you know. I'm a many-layered guy, Mohammed. The world's a complex place. If I didn't eat these onions, I wouldn't see its beauty or its complexity. (*Kirk has another sneezing fit.*)

Mohammed You're talking bollocks. That's the onions talking. You are off your onions. Look at the state of you! Why can't you see it?

Kirk All you care about is the superficial, Mohammed. What is a little bit of sneezing, a little allergical reaction, to understanding the meaning of life?

Mohammed Which is?

Kirk Life is complicated.

Mohammed Is that it?

Kirk And some other stuff. I forget. Listen to the moon
singing. Isn't that beautiful? Smell the stars. Sniff the
night's sweat. That's the meaning of life. Live in it,
Mohammed. In this moment right now with your
friend Kirk. I love you, Mohammed.

Mohammed I told you. This isn't you any more. This is
the onions talking.

Kirk No, it's not. It's the truth. The onions peel away
the bullshit till you get to the truth. This is the truth,
Mohammed. (*Sneezes again.*) You are the best mate an
oniony guy could have.

The Dancing Girl dances past them in the dark.

Dancing Girl
Cry baby cry,
Watch the onion try.
Cry baby cry,
Someone's going to die.

SCENE THREE

*Downstairs in the take-away's kitchen. Mitzi is cooking
in the woks fast and putting the meals in take-away
boxes.*
*The Gang run round the stage collecting the meals
and taking them to David upstairs. The Gang could give
some meals out to the audience.*

Kimberley (*crying*) I'm fed up working here, being stuck
down here half the day and stuck up there half the
night with all these mad people out there. I'm fed up
getting my skin burnt with fat from the woks when

my friends are watching *Friends* and nobody else is
working. I don't know if I'll ever fit in properly when
I spend so much time down here. I'm tired at school
from working down here till midnight. I'm falling
asleep in my lessons.

Mitzi Nothing we can do. Don't worry about fitting-in
thing. Who care? When we get enough money, we go
back.

Kimberley I don't want to go back. How can I go back
when I've never been there?

Mitzi You are from there!

Kimberley I am from here.

Mitzi You can't forget yourself.

Kimberley I can't remember myself.

Gang (*suddenly freezing into statues*) Remember. Forget.
Remember. Forget. Remember. Forget. Remember.
Forget. Forget. Remember. Forget. Remember. Forget.
Remember.

Mitzi You are confuse.

Kimberley I was born here, Mum.

Mitzi You are from there not here.

Gang (*rushing around again*) Here-there, here-there,
here-there. There-here, there-here, there-here.

Kimberley My brother is getting in a state up there. He
can't take the orders without getting into a fight with
some mad person in the queue.

Mitzi Dear Kimberley. Always worry. Always think
family. Don't worry. Everything okay. Your brother
okay. Your father okay. (*laughing*) Everybody okay.

Kimberley But I do worry. I have a bad feeling about
our shop. There is a strange atmosphere out there
tonight.

Mitzi Friday night. Always busy Friday night. Always
drunk people, crazy people Friday night. Hospital
busy Saturday morning because of Friday night. Don't
worry, my girl.

Gang (*the whole Gang dances*) Friday night in the city. Disco dancing. Pub-crawling. Boys and girls snogging. Boys drinking. Girls drinking. Everybody dancing. Friday night, Alright, alright. Everybody's out on a Friday night.

Kimberley Why don't I believe you? Why don't I feel reassured?

Mitzi Have some har kau. I just made them. Nice and fresh. Have some green tea. Relax. Sit down a minute.

Kimberley I can't, we've got a massive queue up there. I better get back upstairs.

Mitzi You are a good girl, Kimberley.

Kimberley I'm not. I have bad thoughts. I can feel a nosebleed coming on again.

Mitzi Ask David to call in somebody.

Kimberley Joy gen.

Mitzi See you later.

Gang (*whispering*) Good girl, bad girl, good girl, bad girl, good, bad, good, bad, good, good, good.

Kimberley cries all the way up the stairs. Gang follows her up.

Kimberley (*to herself*) I can't seem to stop this weeping all the time. I can't stop the feeling of sadness. My heart is heavy. A sad feeling across my chest. Time is so slow in here. We can't take away time.

Gang (*slowly*) Tick tock tick tock tick tock tick tock tick tock . . .

SCENE FOUR

Eve and Ivy leave the take-away with their order and walk down the street. Enter Onion Pushers.

Onion Pushers Do you want some of this?

Eve No, I'm not interested

Onion Pushers Come on, you haven't tried them raw, have you? They are pure.

Eve We don't want any. We're going home.

Ivy I'm a bit tempted –

Eve Ssssssh!

Eve and Ivy walk on. Onion Pushers follow them and circle around them. The Onion Pushers are dressed in clothes of many brown layers.

Onion Pushers (*stripping off some of their layers*)
Try the edible rounded bulb.
Munch the concentric close coats.
Taste the powerful pungent flavour.
Sniff the strong smell.
Underneath one ring, another ring,
Underneath that ring, another ring.
Crunch the edible rounded bulb eaten since early times.

Ivy It won't harm us to try the once. It's Friday night. I'm bored.

Eve No, Ivy, don't be silly. You can't even trust these guys. They might be rotten onions. You don't even know where they got them.

Ivy Eve! I'll be able to tell if they're rotten.

Eve How?

Ivy I'd smell, of course.

Eve You're mad, leave me out of it.

Onion Pushers We're selling them cheap. It's a bargain. An onion hung in a room will ward away disease. Put an onion under your pillow and dream of your lover-to-be. Rub an onion on your bottom when you've been hit with the cane, to alleviate pain. If you can't decide which man to pick, then scratch the name of both men on two separate onions, leave them in a warm place, whichever sprouts first will tell you the strongest love!

Ivy (*suddenly excited*) Give me a bag!

Eve Ivy!!

Ivy You're such a girl. Grow up!

Eve You think it's grown-up to do this?

Ivy Oh come on, Eve, just this once. You heard him! They're amazing!

Ivy buys a bag from the Onion Pushers. Ivy and Eve walk off quickly, looking behind them, for home.

Ivy Smell that! Somebody's frying onions. Ahhh. Nothing like that smell. Please let me have onions for my tea.

Eve It used to be such a nice innocent thing, eating onions on hamburgers, on sausages. It's all changed now. It's not the same. Nothing is innocent any more, not even onions. Don't you see, Ivy? You shouldn't have bought them. Throw them away quick! Before it is too late.

Ivy You've gotta be joking! What do you take me for? I've just paid good money for these.

Eve I've got a bad feeling, a bad omen.

Ivy You and your silly omens! You are the most superstitious girl I know. Come on. Let's get back to my place and try these.

SCENE FIVE

Ruth and Tyrese stand playing a game of catch-the-onion, back and forth, back and forth. Jatinder, Ruth's mother, is getting incensed.

Jatinder Can't you two do anything else?

Ruth We're having fun.

Jatinder I'm fed up watching you.

Ruth Don't watch.

Jatinder Don't be cheeky!

Ruth How's that cheeky? You said you're fed up watching me and I said, 'Don't watch.'

Jatinder I know what I said. I said don't be cheeky. Cut it out! (*to Tyrese*) What are you staring at? She wasn't like this till she started with you. I want my lovely girl back.

Tyrese Not you too. Everybody's good at blaming Tyrese. I think it is blame-Tyrese season.

Jatinder Have you ever thought why, Tyrese?

Tyrese doesn't answer, just scowls.

Jatinder Time for you to go, anyway.

Ruth Let's just finish this game. We're at a good bit.

Jatinder No. Time for him to go.

They continue to play.

Ruth I'm going with him when we're finished. We'll go when we're ready. Back off.

Jatinder You are not going anywhere, madam. You have homework to do.

Ruth Our lives are ruled, you know. Think about it. You tell us what to do and we're supposed to do it. No wonder everybody's on onions in this city.

Jatinder I let him come here. I let you both stay in. I let you go out. I don't know what else to do. Why can't you give me some respect?

Ruth and Tyrese are still throwing the onions faster and faster.

Tyrese My mum doesn't bother.

Jatinder Well I do bother! I care. I care about the pair of you wasting your life. All you do is play with the onions. You don't read. You don't have any interests. You don't have any hobbies. You don't seem to care about anything but playing with those silly onions.

Ruth They're fun.

Ruth throws a wild pass at Tyrese. Tyrese leaps to catch it.

Tyrese Cheeky guy!
Jatinder (*practically driven mad*) Will you STOP THAT?

SCENE SIX

Kenneth on his own in a corner, ordering onions in a neat row. He cuts the top off each onion and sniffs along a line of onions.

Kenneth I used to like when I was a little fellow playing with an abacus and arranging the colours. And then I liked those puzzles where you had to arrange the numbers in squares. And then I liked those cube things where you had to get a whole side of yellow and a whole side of red. I was good at all that. And my mum used to buy me lots of those metal puzzles and I was good at those too. And then my mum died. She just died. And I'm not good at anything now. I'm good at onions. That's what I'm good at. (*Kenneth obsessively plays with the onions, rearranging them into different configurations.*) I liked that girl in the take-away tonight. She got me to say what I wanted, not like the guy. She had something nice about her. Not like him. He was a fool. But she was nice. If I see her on her own I'm going to ask her if she'll go out with me. My mum said if I had friends I would be happy and I said she was my friend and she said she wasn't enough and then she died and she definitely wasn't enough. Maybe that girl would like me. Maybe she'd like my onions.
I never had many special friends. Some people don't.

I was always a bit of a loner, a bit of a freak, a bit of an anorak. Just when I try and do something normal, I spoil it, at the last minute, and say something weird. I can't help myself. I know when I'm going to do it, like you know when you're going to fall and then you fall anyway. You can't stop yourself. It's something to do with gravity.

SCENE SEVEN

Ivy gets four of the onions, peels them with a small knife. She cuts the name Sam into one and the name Greg into the other.

Ivy Sam. Greg. Now, who do you fancy? Who is it between? You like that guy Tyrese, don't you, that Ruth goes out with?

Eve No I don't!

Ivy Who then? Come on, this is fun.

Eve Put Mohammed and –

Ivy Mohammed! You're joking!

Eve I'm not doing this.

Ivy Okay, okay, okay, Mohammed and . . .?

Eve Kirk.

Ivy Kirk?

Eve Yes.

Ivy We'll leave these ones here and whichever sprouts first, that will be our men.

Ivy peels the last onion, then cuts it into a quarter.

Eve I told you. I don't want anything to do with this.

Ivy Everybody does it.

Eve I'm not everybody.

Ivy Yes you are everybody. There are no individuals any more, Eve, get real. We are all everybody. That's it – end of story.

Eve I don't agree with that.

Ivy Listen to you! You don't agree. It's not about whether silly little Miss Eve Rain agrees or does not agree. Don't you see? Aw, stop it. I'm doing this.

Ivy sets a match to a quarter of the onion, then she eats it.

I'm telling you, Eve. It's delicious. You should try it.

Eve Why?

Ivy Because you are my friend. And if you don't try it we won't be the same any more. Don't you see, Evie, we'll be different and we won't be close or anything.

Eve Stop it, you're frightening me. We are close!

Ivy Not if I've tried onions and you haven't tried onions.

Eve Oh, all right then, just this once.

Ivy Excellent! Excellent news.

Ivy lights a match and roasts Eve a quarter. Eve takes it from her slowly and is scared to eat it.

Go on! It won't bite.

Eve takes the onion and eats it.

(*starts laughing hysterically*) It's good, isn't it! It makes you feel so good. What did I do before, I wonder, to make me feel this good? Do you remember when we were little we were happy with playing hopscotch! Hopscotch. (*She is laughing till the tears pour down her cheeks.*) Is that sad?

Eve slumps immediately and her eyes glaze over.
Enter the Gang on tiptoes, they walk around Eve. They whisper.

Gang

> Here goes another one. Whose will is done?
> Here goes another one. Who bit the sun?
> Here goes another one. What was her name?
> Here goes another one. All for a game.

Ivy (*still laughing hysterically*) Do you remember how
we used to like to wear the same clothes and we'd get
our mothers to buy us the same things! Aw, those red
shoes! Remember them with the buckles! Those tights
with the giraffes down them from Sock Shop! Fancy
wearing giraffes on your legs! You should wear
giraffes on your neck if you're going to wear giraffes.
(*killing herself laughing*) Oh God, that's funny. Do
you get it, Evie? Giraffes on your neck?

> Do you remember how we used to walk to school
hand in hand and that big girl Anne Kerr always
wanted to come between us? She always wanted you,
Evie, as her best friend, but I wouldn't let her. Cheeky
cow, trying to steal my pal! Why did she want to steal
you, Evie, Evie, Evie?

The Dancing Girl enters and dances round Eve.

Dancing Girl

> Cry baby cry,
> Watch the onion fry.
> Cry baby cry,
> Someone's going to die.

*Ivy suddenly notices that Eve isn't responding at all.
She panics. She starts to shake her.*

Ivy Eve! Stop messing around. This isn't funny. Evie!
Come on. Don't do this to me. Come on, Eve! Wake
up. Wake up, Eve. Oh God, oh God, oh God. What
have I done? (*Ivy rushes around clearing all the
onions up from her corner, shoving them in the bin,
or hiding them. Then she picks up the phone and*

dials 999. Screaming) A girl here has collapsed! Quick!
You've gotta send an ambulance!

SCENE EIGHT

In the take-away, downstairs.

Mitzi I have something to tell you two. Your father and
I are going home and we are going to leave you to run
the take-away. We trust you. Soon you big enough to
go away from school.

Kimberley I don't want to leave school. I'm only fifteen.

Mitzi Soon, you will –

Kimberley I want to go to university.

Mitzi There are things we all want to do. I am a good
artist. I never paint. In China I paint. Here no time.
No time to have life. I miss my people. Miss speaking
my tongue. This country no country for a Chinese
woman to grow old. Take-away look after you.

David It's okay by me.

Kimberley Well, it's not by me! Look at the queue
tonight. We can hardly manage, never mind without
you and Dad.

Mitzi We'll get more help.

Kimberley I wish I had my own life.

Mitzi Everyone wishes they have own life. Everyone
have responsibilities. Too many onions in this city.
I am started to dream them at night. Time to go back.

*Onion Pushers enter and start to peel off their layers
very slowly in a dreamlike trance-dance.*

Mitzi In my dream I peel off layers of my skin. Down to
my own bone. When I got to my heart, I pulled it out.
I ate my own heart. (*Starts weeping.*)

545

David Ma. Don't be silly, it only dream. We don't do onions. They are selling them on the black market, but Kimberley and I don't buy them.

Mitzi No, thank God.

Kimberley We still get affected by them, I'm sure that's the reason we weep.

David You can't blame us for them.

Mitzi I don't blame you. I just say I want home. I don't like dream. I am old woman. Tired. I want to spend last days in China. Sad without China. Not myself here. I look in mirror, I am surprise at myself. I look wrinkled. I wonder what has happened my life?

Kimberley You chose to come over here! You can't come and leave us.

Mitzi You come back too when the take-away makes enough money.

David Our mother deserve this. She work hard.

Kimberley It will be me that does all the work while you go out to Chinese film and Chinese gambling. I will be making the money and you will be spending it.

David Rubbish. I don't gamble.

Mitzi No, he doesn't gamble. He only like mah-jong.

Kimberley I don't think it's selfish of me to want to go to university.

Mitzi You are a girl.

Kimberley Yes? And? So?

David Don't talk like that to your mother.

Kimberley I feel trapped.

Mitzi Don't be silly. You save, you come back home. No problem.

Kimberley I can't speak Cantonese properly any more, or Mandarin.

Mitzi Don't worry. You learn fast.

Kimberley Somebody has just come in. I'll go and take the order. (*Kimberley runs up to the order counter.*)

Mitzi She has never been easy, never easy child. Always argue and complain.

David She be okay. I look after her.

Enter Kenneth into the take-away.

Kenneth Number 27 please

Kimberley Chicken chow mein??

Kenneth (*clearly pleased that she has remembered he doesn't like Number 23*) Yes, thank you.

Kimberley Anything else?

Kenneth A can of Coke, please.

Kimberley You okay now?

Kenneth I think about you.

Kimberley You think about me?

Kenneth Yes, yes I do.

Kimberley (*laughing*) What do you think about?

Kenneth I just think about you.

Kimberley What about me?

Kenneth Your eyes.

Kenneth jumps up and sits on the counter. Several onions roll into the take-away. An onion light comes down from the sky.

Kimberley You are a bit strange.

Kenneth I know. I've always been odd.

Kimberley Why are you strange?

Kenneth I don't know. Would you like to . . . ? I mean would you consider . . . ? Oh, never mind.

Kimberley (*gently*) What? What?

Kenneth Would you like to go out with a strange guy?

Kimberley Depends on the guy.

Kenneth I mean me. Would you go out with me?

Kimberley Go out where?

Kenneth I don't know. I know! A surprise. When is your night off? I will come and take you out for a surprise somewhere.

Kimberley I'll try and get off tomorrow. You won't forget?
Kenneth How could I forget when you have those eyes?
Kimberley (*laughing*) I like strange guys.
Kenneth Why?
Kimberley Because you are too strange to be boring.
Kenneth Thank you very much.

SCENE NINE

Meeting of the special Onion Commission. Darcus is tap-dancing towards them.

Mr McDonald We've got to wise up tae the fact. We've a real problem here. And it's no going away. It's getting worse. I was down in the East End yesterday and I saw onions everywhere. Children as young as eight with onions in their pockets. It's no joke. I saw them selling onions outside the Chinese carry-out. If we don't rack our brains tae tackle this problem, it's going take over our whole city. Already Councillor Jones has told me there have been five hundred onion-related attacks with people having severe onion allergies. The breath of our people stinks, by and large. The biggest problem is nobody seems to know how they are getting into the city. Some just roll in on their own. Others have people selling them. We don't know where they get them from.

Mrs Morrison That's what I've been saying for the past two years. I warned of this ages ago. What we need now is not talk. We've had enough bloody talk and bloody commissions and special meetings and executive councils – ENOUGH. What we really need to do is put our minds to this and think of a solution.

We need to act not talk. What is that saying? Actions speak louder than words? Let's think now.

They sit in silence, racking their brains. Darcus tap-dances around them.

Mr McDonald If only we could just get rid of them altogether.
  If we could get some vast net and scoop them all up and throw them into the sea.
Mrs Morrison You wish. It's not that easy.

At that moment, they suddenly look up and notice Darcus, wearing a long coat, smiling. He stretches his hand out and shakes Mr McDonald's and Mrs Morrison's.

Darcus
  I hope you won't mind me barging in on your meeting.
  It's only that I couldn't help but overhear the problems you are facing.
  I have come to offer a solution.
  I have ways and means of ridding your city of onions.
  People call me Darcus.
  I is the man with the promise.
  I have been around this whole country
  Cleaning the litter from Liverpool,
  The midges from Mull, the druggies from Manchester, the luvvies from Edinburgh.
  Any place with a problem, Darcus is your man.
  If you pay me just one bar, a thousand quid
  In other words, you can kiss goodbye
  To the culture of the onion
  And welcome a new civilisation.
Mrs Morrison A thousand pounds! We'd pay you fifty thousand pounds.
Mr McDonald Or fifty bar, as you'd say, since you come from afar.

Darcus
No, no, no. I insist. One bar is plenty.
Darcus is not the man to take advantage.
Darcus will not exploit the situation,
Your onions are causing worry for the whole nation.
One bar, let's shake on it.
By tomorrow morning your city will be glorious.
Darcus will be victorious. You watch. You wait.
You will see. Believe me. Darcus is your man.
Darcus is the only man to solve the situation.

Darcus dances out into the street and sings in scales,
holding his hands on his mouth.

Darcus Ai and Ai, Ai and Ai, Ai and Ai, Ai and Ai –

The Dancing Girl comes on again, dancing, almost
taunting Darcus. She sings her song.

Dancing Girl
Cry baby cry,
Watch the onion fry.
Cry baby cry,
Someone's going to die.

SCENE TEN

The Dancing Girl follows Darcus, dancing along behind
him.

Gang
Into the street the dancing man stepped
Smiling a wide smile
His eyes lit up, clapping his hands,
Tapping his feet, singing his strange little song,
Come along, come along.

Darcus

Come all ye onions joyful and triumphant
Come all ye onions to the promised land.

Gang

Into the night, the dancing man stepped
Wearing his long bright coat,
His dark black hat, clapping his hands
Tapping his feet, singing his odd little song,
Come along, come along.

Darcus

Come, all ye onions, joyful and triumphant
Come, all ye onions, to the promised land.

*The entire cast dance around the stage, following
Darcus. They catch the onions and throw them from
one to another to Darcus, who puts them in a big
brown sack and carries them on his back to the river.*

Gang

And suddenly out they came
from the cupboards and pans
from the trees and the fridges
from the earth and the land:
the onions from France,
the onions from England,
brown and white and gleaming onions
following the dancing man,
rolling and skidding and sliding along,
with the man singing his odd little song.

Darcus

Come, all ye onions, joyful and triumphant
Come, all ye onions, to the promised land.

Gang

The weeping and the stinking onions,
the sneezing and the smarting onions.
The bulbous and the pungent onions,
the Welsh onions, the wild onions.

They left the cupboards and the jars
the salad bowls and the frying pans
the window sills and the chopping boards
the vegetable racks and the bicycles.

Darcus

Come, all ye onions, joyful and triumphant
Come, all ye onions, to the promised land.

Gang

Dozens and dozens of long strings of onions,
solitary spring onions, scallions, shallots,
pickled onions, long green leeks, garlic.
Red onions, white onions, fried onions, sybies.
Roast onions, onions in their brown skin,
bare naked onions, onions in bulbs,
onions from French onion soup,
gay onions, straight onions,
onions from onion bread.
Every onion that had ever led an ordinary life
rolled along, following the man and his song
all the way to the river bed
the onions hurried along.

Darcus

Come, all ye onions, joyful and triumphant
Come, all ye onions, to the promised land.

Darcus rolls around on the floor, forward rolls,
picking up all the onions.

Gang

You should have seen the East Enders
running around, ringing their bells,
poking out those onions with long poles
till every last onion had left the East End
and floated on the river.

Darcus

(*standing by the river, throwing one onion in at a time*)
Watch the onions float along the river

like lily pads in a pond.
Watch the onions bob along waves
like buoys in the sea.
See the onions appear on the water
like small white boulders.
Notice the onions catch the light
like crystal balls.
Wait for the onions to tell the future
like pearls of wisdom.

The onions are leaving the city
small white fishing boats going out to sea,
down where the river leads to the estuary,
where the sea will open its big mouth
and gargle those onions down.

One day the sea will taste of onions, not salt.
The sea's waves will froth with onion juice, not spume.
One day the sea will sweep every last memory
   of onion away.
Onion ships out at sea.

So watch the onions ride on the sea's galloping back.
Up, down, up down, up down, and away, away, away.
The onions are leaving this town.

Gang (*gathering around the river*)
No more bitter breath
No more iffy kisses
No more salty tears
No more coughs and sneezes
No more danger, no more violence
No more sudden attacks
No more disappearances.
The brave East End is safe again.
Come and join the celebration.

There is a street-party atmosphere, music, drums,
fireworks. Ruth and Tyrese dance happily. Kenneth

arrives at the take-away to take Kimberley out.
Jatinder is dancing with Mitzi. Kirk and Mohammed
are engrossed in conversation. There could be a short
improvised conversation between each grouping,
showing how the onion-going has made them happy.
Kimberley is laughing.

Only Ivy is not happy, sitting in a corner with Eve
lying at her feet.

Mr McDonald and Mrs Morrison toast themselves.

SCENE ELEVEN

Darcus dances through the middle of the celebrations,
splitting the crowd. He approaches the Onion
Commission.

Darcus First, if you please, my thousand pounds!

Mr McDonald A thousand pounds! I don't think so. Who
said anything about a thousand pounds? Do you realise
that would cost the council a significant part of next
year's budget which could go towards better things?

Darcus What is better than ridding the town of onions?

Mrs Morrison The council has some entertaining to do.
We have celebrities coming to the East End. We'll need
that money for wine.

Darcus We agreed one thousand pounds. We shook
hands on it.

Mr McDonald We're happy to give you something to
eat and drink. Throw in fifty quid. But to be frank,
we never ever said one thousand pounds. Are you off
your head? Anyway, the deed is done. The onions are
gone. Pity, but there's not a lot you can do about it.
If you heard us say one thousand pounds, what you've
done is take a joke seriously. This has been a hard
year. Fifty quid maximum. Take it or leave it.

Darcus Don't muck me about! Or you'll regret it.

Mrs Morrison How dare you threaten us? See, this is the problem with you people. One second sweet, the next second aggressive.

Darcus A deal is a deal. A promise, a promise.

Mr McDonald Look, take your idle threats and get out. There's the door! You don't scare us. You're all talk. The onions have gone. You can't exactly swim in the river collecting them all up again. Moan as much as you like. Fifty quid, top!

Gang

Once again the dancing man took to the streets,
with a hey hippity hop and a bee bippity bop.
And he cried out three long notes.
His voice sweetened the air.
His notes enchanted the atmosphere.
It seemed like no time at all
before all the young people gathered outside the hall
and followed the dancing man

Kirk, Mohammed, Ivy, Eve (as a ghost), Kimberley, David, Ruth and Tyrese follow Darcus. Kenneth tries to catch up but gets left behind.

down the street, up that one, and down another,
left, left, right, left, right, right.
His hands clapping, his feet tapping
singing his strange little song.
Out came the East End youth
with a curl in the hair and a gold tooth,
Jiving and break-dancing and skimming along
following the music from the dancing man's song,
listening to his big sounds, getting in the groove,
slip-sliding along with the song.

Mr McDonald and Mrs Morrison, Jatinder and Mitzi stand still as statues, unable to move.

Gang

All the adults froze to the spot
Watching their children skip on by.
Not a single adult could move her foot
To follow the dancing man's cry.

Ruth and Tyrese and Kimberley went by
happy as the day is long,
Kirk and Mohammed followed
the dancing man's song
Eve and Ivy, friends to the last,
Held hands on the way to the river bed.
Only Kenneth couldn't keep up.
Only Kenneth missed out on the water party:
the waves and the spume and the white horses,
the surge and the gush and the rush,
the combers breaking, the surf spraying.
It was Kenneth who did not hear
the incredible music of the deep blue sea:
the babble and bubble, the burble and gurgle.
Kenneth missed the choppy party
in the river that leads to the sea
where the dancing man took the youth that day.

All the young people fall into the sea.

It was a day of cross-currents
of whirlpool and maelstrom.
It was the day when the waves surged and rushed and
    gushed
and all of the youth shrieked and swallowed and
    swallowed and swallowed too much, too much.

This is the ebb and flow.
This is the life we know.
This is the flow and flux
These are the facts.
A promise is a promise.

The dancing man took our children.
The dancing man took our children.
The dancing man took our children
away, away, away, away out to sea.

Jatinder, Mitzi, Kenneth, Onion Commission, Onion Pushers and Onion Johnnies form a circle holding hands. They all scream at the same time. A long scream into the dark that rises and falls.

Kenneth Just when I had fallen in love, my love was taken away. Just when I'd got up the courage. We were going to be meeting that day, Kimberley and I.

I was trying to work out if I should kiss her on the first date or leave it to the second. I knew what I was going to wear. She was beautiful, Kimberley. She made me feel normal. She made me like myself. Now I don't feel normal any more. I'm back to Kenneth the sad loser. I can feel myself unravelling, like a long piece of string.

But Kimberley wouldn't like that. She wouldn't like me falling to pieces. I know she wouldn't. Maybe it's enough that I was nearly loved.

Mitzi I can't go back now. I have to stay here, here where I lost my children. Now the only connection I have to them is this bit of the sea. There are so many things I never managed to say. Where am I from? I am from the place where my children died.

Jatinder What did it matter? What was it all about? I wish we'd never bothered about the onions. I wish I'd never got angry. I wish we'd left it all alone. Now look what we've done. We've rid our whole town of its young people. The place is dead. There is no music. I'd like the fights again. I'd like to hear them arguing. I'd like to see them hanging around the street corners, smoking and joking. I'd love one to kick a football through my window. I'd give anything for one to rip

my fence off. I need one to curse and swear at me.
I'd die for one to steal my purse. Go on, take it! I crave
a massive phone bill. Go on, ring, ring, ring. I'm
desperate for the hot water to run out. I want an
empty shampoo bottle. I want a messy house. I want
wet towels on the floor. I want all the biscuits eaten
immediately. Eat them! I want the homework undone.
I want somebody to say, 'Where's my book? Where's
my shoe? Where's my jacket?' I want them back!
Now! I need the young people back. I'll never moan
about them again. I'll never complain. I promise. I
didn't know I was born. I didn't know I was living. I
will love them. I will love life, please. Just bring them
back, dancing man. Bring them back.

*Darcus stands with his back to Jatinder and his arms
folded.*
   *The Gang comes in with a huge brown parcel. They
throw it around the audience. Everybody rips a layer
off. When it gets down to the bottom, an onion is the
present, a huge onion. Mr McDonald and Mrs Morrison
gather round the onion. They peel it and cry.*

Mr McDonald
   If only we had kept our promise
   If only we had never lied
Mrs Morrison
   If only we had been true to our word
   If only we had paid the price
Mr McDonald
   If only we hadn't turned our back
Both
   We would have our kids back.
   We would have our kids back.
Mrs Morrison
   We would have our town happy with live voices
   We would have our teenagers

Filling our city with vivid laughter,
With sport, with booming music.

Mr McDonald

Now the East End is silent.
All we can hear is the terrible hush.

Both

SSSSSSSSSSSSSSSShhhhhhhhhhhh.

Mrs Morrison

The awful silence of the dead, the disappeared.
All we can feel is the ghost of what was.
All we can taste is the bitter taste of despair.

Mr McDonald

They were here. Now they are gone.
SSSSSSSSSSSSSSShhhhhhhhhhhhh.

Mrs Morrison

What have we done? What have we done?
We who live in the ghost town
Have nothing left but our memories.

Mr McDonald

Memory is everything now.

Both

We have our photographs.
We have the time when, and then again the time when.
Apart from that we have nothing.

Mrs Morrison

We are the nothing people now
Without our children, our teenagers, our girls and boys.

Mr McDonald

No balls, no bicycles, no games, no toys.

Both

The worst thing? We have ourselves to blame.
We hang our heads in shame. We hang our heads in
shame.

The Dancing Girl dances around them.

559

Dancing Girl
  Cry baby cry,
  Cry baby cry,
  Cry baby cry,
  Cry baby cry.

Mr McDonald weeps out loud.

Darcus
  The river nice. I hear tell about it, now.
  The river pretty in the city
  plenty fishy in there, flipping and flashing
  their tails in that tea-brown water.
  The river snakes its dark coil
  round the city, you can see it everywhere
  you look, a sparkle of the river's glitter.
  The river always busy heading someplace.
  Never lazy, never slows down a pace.

The End.

TEAM SPIRIT

Judy Upton

Characters

Lucas
Tania
Tom
Melanie
Jayne
Ronny
Stuart
Anne
Joel
Jake
Philippe
Tania's Mother
Tania's Father
Doctor

Chorus

Act One

The yacht Team Spirit *takes up the stage. A video camera is clamped to the ship's mast, another in the below-deck area. A projection screen, back, shows scenes of yachts in Plymouth harbour.*

Champagne corks, popping flashbulbs. Tom looks all in, he is sipping champagne.

When (later) the Chorus speak to Tania, it is many voices in loud overlapping confiding whispers.

Tom moves to the side of the stage, starts a mimed conversation with his neighbours. Lucas and Tania cross the stage.

Lucas The photographer needs you to go outside to get a couple of shots, Tania.

Tania Again?

Lucas It's a different photographer.

Tania Oh . . .

Lucas And try not to stand with your arms folded this time.

Tania Does it make me look too stubborn?

Lucas Stubborn is good, Tania, but we call it 'determined'. No, I'm more concerned about them seeing all of your jacket.

Tania Oh, the logo.

Lucas Precisely. Now don't keep them waiting.

She starts to move away.

Attagirl. (*Lucas heads back to the side of the stage. Calls after her.*) And try to smile a bit more naturally, eh?

Tom crosses, meets up with Tania.

Tania Got to do another photo, Tom.

Tom Great, terrific.

Tania I can't wait to be gone.

Tom Just try to be sociable for once, eh, love?

Tania I am . . . It's not . . . It's just I'm too wired up, raring to go. I'm not . . . a person, I'm part of *Team Spirit* . . . part of the boat . . .

Tom Just a few more minutes, Tania.

Chorus Tania, Tania, the photographer's waiting!

Tania clambers up onto Team Spirit *and poses.*

News Report Favourite to win is the British solo yachtswoman, Tania Travers . . .

Jayne's mother (Melanie) appears on screen, looks directly at Tania on the yacht, and calls to Jayne.

Melanie Jayne! It's on the news. The race.

Jayne There! There she is. I want to meet her. When she wins.

Melanie You and ten thousand others. We can go down there when they arrive, but I doubt we'll get close enough to speak to her.

News Report *Team Spirit* has on board all the latest technology to allow people from Plymouth, Halifax and worldwide to watch Tania on the Internet throughout the race. You can also talk to Tania via e-mail –

Jayne Write it down, Mum!

Melanie What?

Jayne The e-mail address. Quickly!

Melanie She doesn't look very strong, to sail a yacht all that way.

Ronny Tania!

Tania looks towards Ronny.

Chorus Look at the camera. Tania.

Ronny The live broadcast is going to be a first for our
station.

Tania A first for me too, Ronny.

Ronny Won't it be great, to have all our viewers at your
side throughout the race?

Tania I guess so.

Anne Tania! Tania . . .

Chorus Look at the camera, Tania.

Anne Just want to wish you *bon voyage* on behalf of all
our readers.

Tania Thank you, Anne.

Anne I'm looking forward to that special exclusive
interview on your return.

Tania (*less sure*) Me too, Anne.

Chorus Tania, it's time to prepare. All the competitors
are on their yachts. Set the sails and be ready to weigh
anchor.

Tania The wind's risen slightly, like it's growing impatient,
wanting me to hurry and weigh anchor, so it can carry
us towards Halifax. I must adjust the mainsail . . .
(*She does so.*)

Chorus All the yachts have set their sails, the tugs are
ready to take you to your starting position.

Tania moves to weigh anchor.

Be ready, Tania.

Tania Weighing anchor, and *au revoir* but not goodbye,
Plymouth.

*She waves. Sounds of cheering. On the screen
Plymouth fades into an image of the sea.*

Chorus The yacht is moving.

Tania Heading out past the docks into Plymouth Sound.
The Hoe and the Citadel are becoming smaller behind
us. (*She looks at the camera.*) Hope you can hear and
see me okay, at home.

Tom walks across the stage, picks up a champagne bottle, a party popper. His mobile rings, cheesy sea-shanty ring tone.

Tom Yeah, hello?

Ronny comes on stage. Although they are both on stage it's obvious it's actually a phone call.

Ronny We can't get the video link, Tom. We're wanting to use it in the live broadcast. Is there some kind of problem?

Tom What time is . . . No, no she just hasn't switched it on yet. She's got to get clear of Plymouth Sound. I'll call you back as soon as we're up and running. It'll only be a couple of minutes now.

Ronny It'd better be if you want Tania to appear on the midday news.

Tom I do, I most definitely do, Ronny. It's gonna be great, it's gonna be fabulous.

Ronny It had better be, Tom.

Ronny goes back to the edge of the stage. Tom switches the phone off. It rings again. Anne comes on stage.

Tom *Team Spirit*, hello.

Anne Yeah, 'Hello' is the problem, Tom. What the hell do and you and Tania think you're playing at? Our deal was an *exclusive*! God knows we're paying you enough. Then I hear you're gonna be in *Hello*. Shit, Tom.

Tom Anne, trust me. I wouldn't jerk you around. Your paper is the only one with access to Tania, when she docks in Halifax. No one else will be allowed on the boat.

Anne They better not.

Tom Don't insult me, how long do we go back, eh?

Anne And *Hello*?

Tom Are just gonna do a glossy photo spread of me and Tania in our beautiful home . . .

Anne Beautiful home? I thought you had to sell your flat to part-finance the damn boat?

Tania tries phoning Tom.

Tania Oh, get off the phone, you pillock!

Tom Okay, Anne, somebody else's beautiful home. They do that all the time. But we will have a beautiful home . . . soon.

Anne Thanks to Tania?

Tom Hey, and her go-getting publicist boyfriend here.

Tania gives up trying to ring Tom.

Tania Oh sod you, then. (*Tania returns her attention to steering* Team Spirit.)

Chorus Steer into the wind.

Tania We're bearing along at a good speed.

Anne Do you ever feel just a little envious, Tom, or resent –?

Tom (*interrupting*) If I told you that, Anne, I'd be giving an interview and your paper's cheque ain't arrived yet. Catch you later, sweetheart.

He dials another number. Tania's mobile rings. She turns to address him directly.

Tania Oh, there you are. We are still talking, then.

Tom How's it feel to be back out there, babe?

Tania Incredible . . . the gulls crying, water lapping the boat, that salty tang on the breeze . . .

Tom Good for you. Me, I'm wrecked, from last night's party, and today's launch party, which is still going on even as we speak.

Tania It's so great to be out here – free – alone.

Tom Alone – without me, you mean?

Tania I didn't mean it like that. You *are* grouchy. Have an Alka-Seltzer. You've got that whole media circus to deal with. Gotta keep a clear head, Tom.

Tom Yes, *mother*. (*A beat.*) It's time to switch the video on.

Tania Not yet, I could do without the distraction while all the yachts are still so close together. Be a disaster, if I'm so busy watching the computer screen that I get in someone's way and get myself disqualified.

Tom You won't be watching the screen, you'll be up on deck.

Tania But I'll still be on camera. I . . . I feel really awkward and self-conscious, Tom. I don't want people seeing me like this . . . We've never had a live camera before and –

Tom (*interrupting*) We've discussed this, babe.

Tania I know . . . It's just . . . just I want to be alone with my thoughts, for a little longer.

Tom And the midday news want their pictures. Pictures equal publicity, Tania, And no publicity, no transglobal voyage for you and *Team Spirit*.

Tania I know, okay?

Tom We don't own *Team Spirit*. The world does.

Tania Okay. I'll switch it on now.

Sounds of going online. Jayne comes on screen and speaks her words, above the sound of typing.

Jayne Hi, Tania, my name's Jayne and I'm in my first year of high school here in Halifax. That's Halifax, Nova Scotia, not the English one. I've a bet on you winning the race. So go, girl! When will you switch on the webcam so I can see *Team Spirit*?

Tania switches on the webcam. Team Spirit *appears on the projection. Cacophony of mobiles and modems again.*

Tania Goodbye, solitude.
Jayne Wow! Hello, Tania.

Stuart, dressed in a strange robe, comes on stage.

Stuart Cosmic greetings, Tania.
Tania (*amused*) Cosmic greetings?

Anne comes on stage, notebook in hand.

Anne Tania, we can see you now. And you do look
terrific. We're planning a feature on waterproof make-
up. You might be able to get some kind of endorsement
or have a range named after you . . .

*Ronny comes on, holding her ear as if talking into a
mike.*

Ronny Preparing for the link-up live to studio.
Jayne Sorry to bombard you with e-mails, Tania, but I'm
so excited. If you've time to get back to me, I'd love to
know what it's like to be a lone yachtswoman. It's
long been an ambition of mine. I'd love to know just
what it feels like.
Tania Dear Jayne, yours was the first e-mail from
Halifax I've received, so I'll answer it first. Like to be
alone? With an inbox already full of messages – 257
to be precise. And I'm only about twenty miles clear
of Plymouth Sound. But I'm not one to shut myself
away. In fact, I'm quite a party girl on shore. I live
with my boyfriend, Tom, my partner in the *Team
Spirit* yacht. He's a sailor himself, but he's put his own
ambitions on hold for now to help me. I'm also very
close to my family, who've always been really
supportive . . .

Tania's mother comes onstage.

Mother Get that life jacket out of the kitchen now – it's
dripping mud everywhere.

Tania Yes, Mum.

Her mother stops Tania leaving.

Mother Tania, I was speaking to Mr Collins up the block, he could do with some more help building his rockery. I thought it might help towards paying for a few more sailing lessons.

Tania (*to Jayne*) Mum used to worry, of course . . .

Mother (*to Tania*) It's no good me telling you not to do something, once you've made up your mind, well, that's it.

Chorus Wind's changing direction, Tania.

Tania Must adjust the mainsail, and steer into the breeze.

Mother leaves. Tania breaks off to adjust the mainsail. She returns to the helm, and addresses Jayne onscreen.

Jayne I'm so thrilled to hear from you. Especially when you're so busy. I can only imagine what it's like – but that's exciting in itself – seeing the pictures on my computer, as if I was right there on the boat beside you. Though I suppose you wouldn't really like that. It must be amazing, just you, the boat and the sea. No one for miles around. I guess you must really like being alone.

Tania Hi again, Jayne . . . I mean you're a normal person, aren't you? What I mean is, I can tell you're real – this isn't another interview where I have to be careful what I say. (*A beat.*) Actually, I do often feel lonely, but not when I'm on the boat . . . Look, this'll probably sound wacky to you . . . but often when I'm with people – Tom, or friends – I just feel shut off, isolated in my own headspace, can you understand that? That's why I do this, I think. More later.

The screen returns to showing the sea. Joel, a scruffy teenager, comes onstage.

Joel Hi, Tania, I've just gone out and bought *Speed
Yacht* – you know, the simulation for the computer?
I mean, how accurate is it, man? How like the real
thing?

Tania I've never sailed a simulator, Joel. It's a lot drier,
I imagine.

Jayne reappears onscreen.

Jayne Another question. Sorry. Do you manage to sleep
on board? And if you do, do you dream about sailing?

Tania Well I hope to get some sleep, Jayne . . . Usually
I can snatch an hour or two at least. But it depends
on weather conditions, of course. Interesting you ask
about dreams. Actually, I have a recurring one . . .
It's of sailing away from Plymouth on a great journey,
to arrive at a new place . . . only when I come ashore,
the new city looks almost identical to the one I just
left. I walk through the streets past the Hoe and the
Citadel, and see some buildings I don't recognise. So
it isn't Plymouth . . . I've not been travelling in a
circle . . . but then it's so like Plymouth it isn't really
somewhere new. I bought one of those books that tell
you how to analyse your dreams. It's not been any
help.

Stuart Maybe you're worried about your true direction,
Tania. You are currently unsure exactly where you are
going . . .

Tania I'm usually a pretty good navigator. Though even
in my car I carry a compass.

Stuart I mean in your life, Tania. Do you know your
fate, your destiny, the path on which your life is
leading you?

Tania (*to herself*) He's gonna start trying to sell me life
insurance . . . or God . . . I just know it.

Stuart Do you often look at your life and wonder about the bigger picture? Do you constantly wonder about the forces that govern your existence, Tania . . .

Tania shoos him off the boat.

Tania Do I have the time to read any more e-mails right now? No. The wind's almost astern and I should boom out the staysail. (*She starts to adjust the sails.*) That'll keep us on course.

Tom crosses the stage, dialling a number on his phone. Lucas's mobile rings.

Lucas Pendragon Holdings. (*Lucas comes onstage.*)

Tom Lucas, have you heard the latest? She's nearly an hour ahead of her nearest competitor now.

Lucas That's great news, Tom.

Tom Yeah, I was wondering whether it was time to go public with the next part of our deal.

Lucas I don't quite follow . . .

Tom I thought maybe we should draft a press release about how your company has generously agreed to part-fund *Team Spirit*'s trans-global voyage . . .

Lucas *Pendragon Team Spirit*'s trans-global voyage.

Tom Of course . . .

Lucas Whilst I share your enthusiasm, I think I should sound a note of caution. There is a condition to us sponsoring the round-the-world trip . . .

Tom I realise it relies on Tania winning the Halifax race, but she's already well ahead . . .

Lucas Well, let's talk about the deal when she's got that medal in her hand, Tom. Now if you'll excuse me, I'm trying to watch the TV highlights.

Tom checks his watch, phones Tania.

Tom (*on phone*) Tania . . . We've a live link up with the South West News Channel.

Tania When?

Tom In ten seconds.

Tania Shit. (*She covers her mouth and looks guiltily at the mast camera.*)

Ronny walks on the boat, talking into a mike.

Ronny Now we can go live to Pendragon Holdings *Team Spirit* –

Lucas (*off*) The boat is called *Pendragon Team Spirit*, you idiot!

Ronny – where Tania Travers, single-handed yachtswoman is, as expected, already taking an early lead in the Plymouth–Halifax race. How does it feel, being in front of the field, Tania?

Tania Brilliant, Ronny, yeah.

Ronny Though after your previous achievements there must've been a certain amount of pressure . . . of expectations . . .

Tania Er, true . . . but I take each race as it comes . . . you're up against the elements. No matter how well you prepare, it's an unpredictable game . . .

Ronny But you are under an immense amount of pressure from certain quarters to succeed?

Tania You mean Tom? No, he just expects me to do my best, not take any unnecessary risks, you know.

Ronny I'm talking about Lucas Miles, who's recently taken over from his father as boss of Pendragon Holdings. Hasn't he said publicly that continued sponsorship from his company depends on *Team Spirit* winning this race?

Lucas (*off*) What?

Tom (*to himself*) Careful, Tania.

Tania I just have to concentrate on sailing. I'll give it my best shot. Lucas knows that.

Ronny Have you heard the latest weather reports for the mid-Atlantic, Tania?

Tania Obviously I'm hoping the wind will have abated somewhat before I . . . and any of the others get that far.

Ronny And who of your fellow competitors do you think poses the biggest threat to your pole position? The Australians have a new design of keel which has shown to be promising in trials, and Philippe Jeunet of Belgium, currently in second place, has won more cups than you in the past year.

Tania It's a difficult field, Ronny. I've just got to keep my head down and concentrate over the next few days and hope luck is on my side.

Ronny Thank you, Tania, and good luck from all at TV South West.

Tania Thank you, Ronny. Gotta get back to the helm.

Ronny leaves. Tania looks relieved that is over, and returns her attention to steering.
Tom's mobile rings.

Steering into the wind. Sun's turning a deep orange over the water. Gonna be in for a cold night's helming.

Tom Yeah, *Team Spirit*.

Chorus Tania, the wind is rising, Tania, adjust the mainsail.

Tania starts adjusting the mainsail but with the wind rising it is a battle.

Chorus Wind is rising.

Tania The squall's making moving the mainsail quite a struggle.

Chorus Wind is rising. Careful, Tania, easy does it.

Tania collides with the jib. It hits her shoulder, knocking her off balance.

Tania Ow! The jib hit my shoulder. Quite hard, in fact.

Lucas Tom . . . (*Lucas joins him.*)

Tom Lucas, just a minute, I'm watching Tania on the telly.

Lucas So am I, Tom.

Tom Isn't it terrific she's already in the lead?

Lucas Yeah, but she didn't sound very confident on TV, did she, Tom?

Tom She is, Lucas, I've never met anyone as single-minded as our Tania.

Lucas She doesn't always come over that way in the media. And image is everything these days.

Tom Image will do you a lot of good in the middle of the Atlantic in a force ten.

Lucas I just wish she'd exude a little more confidence . . . and charisma . . . I mean those awful woolly hats she wears . . .

Tom (*sarcastically*) Whereas high heels and corsets are very in at the moment, aren't they? Maybe she should swap her oilskins for Dolce and Gabbana and –

Lucas I take your point, Tom. I'm just looking at all the angles here.

Tom We're doing our best to make *Team Spirit* repay Pendragon's generous investment, Lucas.

Lucas I'm sure . . . but why I really called is to ask if there's any way you can call TV South West before the next news report and ask them to display the Pendragon logo more prominently. And maybe Tania could refocus the mast webcam so the logo is in focus.

Tom I am not having her go up that mast unless in an absolute emergency, and if you think she should risk her life for a company logo –

Lucas I'm just asking if you think this company does deserve something in return for it's substantial investment –

Tom She'll win the race and your logo will be on every newspaper, every TV screen –

Lucas I hope so, Tom. I hope so.

Chorus Tania, the wind's still rising, wind still rising.
You could go faster, faster.

Tania Got to adjust the sails to increase speed. (*Tania alters the sails to maximise her speed.*) Now we should start really shifting.

Chorus Helm her, Tania.

Tania returns to the helm.

Tania Gotta helm her to utilise the wind speed to its maximum potential. This is a time when I can increase my lead, if I'm skilful enough.

Chorus Ride the wind, Tania. You're going faster.

Tania I can really feel her accelerating.

Chorus Faster, faster.

Tom phones Tania.

Tania Yeah, Tom.

Tom *Future Quest* is looking very dangerous in third. They seem to be gaining on Philippe's *Song Bird*. I think it's Jake the Aussie you'll have to watch, Tania.

From the side of the stage we hear the Australian.

Jake Think you're gonna be first to Nova Scotia, Tania? I'm gonna catch ya, depend on it, mate.

Philippe The Australians are close behind, but they can't beat you, *Song Bird*, my love.

Chorus Watch out for Philippe, he's fast and skilful.

Philippe I think I can gain some distance by veering southerly . . .

Chorus Beware Jake, he's a daredevil who knows no fear . . .

Jake Come on, ocean, I'm ready for yer!

Tania Well, I'm glad someone's gonna give me a run for the money – don't want it to be too easy.

Chorus Keep ahead, Tania. *Team Spirit* must win.

Tom We need to come in first, Tania, not second or third.
Tania I know.
Tom How's your bad shoulder?
Tania A little stiff after the battle with the jib, but fine.
Chorus Look after yourself.
Tom Take some of the anti-inflammatories.
Tania I'm okay. They tend to make me feel a bit groggy
  and slow me down, anyway.
Tom Have you remembered to eat?
Chorus You must eat.
Tania I'll eat later.
Tom I know you, you'll forget. Eat now. Get some beans
  heating up.
Tania Yeah, yeah.
Tom Go and do it.
Chorus Go and cook.
Tania I'm gone.

Tania comes off the phone. Jayne appears onscreen.

Jayne I'll be sitting here glued to the computer all day –
  it's exhilarating watching *Team Spirit* glide through
  the waves. I used to do a bit of sailing . . . years ago,
  when I was really little. I like to imagine you're me –
  living my dreams. Tell me some more about yourself,
  Tania. I know I'm nosey, but I'd so like to be doing
  what you're doing.
Tania Let's get those beans on. (*Tania types on her
  laptop.*) Hi, Jayne, well, I've been at sea for eight hours
  now, and still in the lead, wind carrying me along at
  a nice speed – about eight knots. About me? I guess
  I'm quite ordinary really . . . stubborn, everyone
  says that. And independent. Though then I guess I've
  had to be. You see my mum was ill for a lot of my
  childhood – cancer – they cured it, it came back, now
  finally it does seem to be in remission again. Makes

577

you not take anything for granted. Dad wasn't around much . . .

Tania's father steps onto the boat.

Father Happy birthday!

He tries to hand her a large gift-wrapped box. She walks away. He leaves.

Tania He'd always turn up with a big present on my birthday but I mean, so what, you know? (*Tania wanders across the cabin. To herself*) Those beans are taking a time to heat. Shit. (*She starts typing again.*) Lately, Dad's been cashing in, giving interviews about me to the media . . .

Her father crosses the stage, an arm around Anne and the other around Ronny.

. . . making out that we were close and stuff. I suppose they've been paying him.

Father She always confided in me . . .

Anne That's brilliant, our readers want to know *exactly* what makes her tick . . .

Father Well, now, I could tell you a few things –

Ronny (*interrupting*) It's going to be an hour-long special, Mr Travers . . .

Anne glares at Ronny.

Anne Of course we can't offer *quite* so much if the deal isn't exclusive . . .

Tania watches them leave the stage.

Tania Shouldn't knock it, I suppose – it's all publicity and publicity is what pays for *Team Spirit*. More shortly. Send.

Sound of e-mails coming in. Anne breaks away from Tania's father, comes towards Tania.

Anne Hi, Tania, we've just chartered a helicopter to fly over *Team Spirit* and take some photos of you for the paper. Could you come up on deck and wave to us in about ten minutes?

Tania (*to herself*) Do I have a choice? (*Tania starts typing again.*) So where was I in my life story, Jayne? Oh yeah . . . Living in Plymouth we'd always be watching the ships, the regattas and navy manoeuvres. But I was twelve before I first set foot on a boat. It was a weekend of sailing organised by my youth club and I loved every minute of it.

Tania is joined on stage by the Chorus, raising eager hands, all shouting, 'My turn', 'Me next', 'Let me hold the tiller'. Tania joins them.

Tania Me! Choose me, Mr Tyler. Let me steer her.

The others groan and leave.

Yes! I'm going to be a sailor! I'm going to be a sailor!! (*to Jayne*) I was an obnoxious little thing in those days. More later.

Computer goes online. Sound of e-mails arriving. Stuart strolls serenely in.

Stuart Hi again, Tania, hope you're preserving your magenta aura. I've just read your personal astrology chart for today. Because Pluto has a positive aspect on Mars in your –

Tania Oh bugger off.

She shoos him away. Joel arrives.

Joel I'd love a boat, Tania, but it's only for rich dudes, right?

Tania types.

Tania I'm not a rich person, Joel. Tom and I run a bar to make ends meet. Yachting is a costly hobby, even for the rich . . . and for people like us, to compete professionally, it means thinking fund-raising and sponsorship twenty-four-seven.

Joel Sounds heavy, man. (*He yawns and scratches himself contently.*)

Tania Sometimes I hate our sponsors – I feel owned, here in the middle of the sea surrounded by logos, on my clothes, on my boat – Oh, did I say my clothes and my boat? – I'm sorry, so sorry – our generous sponsor's clothes and boat. I'm besieged by cellphones and this bloody e-mail. I sometimes feel *Team Spirit* is a slave ship. It's floating Big Brother. Do you know, I had to beg the documentary-makers not to put a webcam over my bunk? It's the only place I can get some privacy.

Sound of a helicopter. Tania races up on deck, offers a cheesy grin, waves for all she's worth. Camera flashes.

(*while faking her smile*) Piss off.

Tania comes back below deck again, addresses Joel.

Joel That was cool – you should've mooned at 'em. Shown 'em your arse.

Tania Next time, Joel. (*She walks away from him and the laptop, thoughtful.*) I wish I was a sailor in olden times – what it must've felt like to be truly alone, just you and the ocean. And sailing into uncharted territory, not into another photo session and interview. Don't get me wrong . . . I know this couldn't happen without you, all of you, and so you have the perfect right to peer, snoop and pry into every aspect of my life . . . No . . . no, I'm just tired . . . I'll rewrite this later, Joel, I . . . need to sleep a while.

Tania's mobile rings.

Tania Sleep? I wish. Yeah?

Tom enters, shakes her slightly.

Tom Don't forget to keep checking your messages.
Tania I do need to sleep, Tom!
Tom Sorry, sweet dreams, babe.

He leaves. Tania shakes her head and checks her e-mails. Jayne appears onscreen.

Jayne Hi, Tania, our school is gonna give us the day off so we can watch *Team Spirit* enter Halifax harbour. Of course you'll be in first place and I look forward to seeing you raising the cup in the air.

Jayne is again replaced by sea.

Tania Hi, Jayne, I've never been to Halifax. What's it like? Tell me anything and everything in your next message.

Lucas comes in.

Lucas Just a quick e-mail, Tania, to say I hope Tom's passed on my message about adjusting the webcam on the mainmast to show our logo more clearly . . .
Tania (*to herself*) Oh bugger.
Lucas Tom agrees with me that it is only fair, in the light of Pendragon's continuing financial support of *Team Spirit* . . .
Tania (*to herself*) Yeah, yeah, I get the picture, Lucas, you snivelling little bastard. Gotta go risk breaking my neck to make your company's name global.
Lucas And the name of the boat is *Pendragon Team Spirit*. You keep forgetting the most important part.

Tania Okay, okay.

He leaves. Tania goes up on deck.

Right, I've got to go up there. Just so you can see the logo clearly. I'm not looking forward to this. I just hope I'll be able to get down again.

Tania starts to climb the mast. It's very precarious.

Chorus Careful, Tania.

Tania The wind's ripping into me, and the mast is so slippery. I can't breathe, My hands are going numb.

Chorus Grip tight, Tania.

Sound of e-mail arriving. Jayne appears onscreen.

Jayne Oh my God. That looks dangerous? Is everything alright? Is something wrong with the mast? I'm so worried for you.

Tania It's getting dark . . . and I can't see anything with the spray in my eyes.

Chorus Slowly does it. Careful, Tania.

Tania struggles with the camera, cuts herself.

Tania Shit. Sorry about my language, documentary-makers. Shit. Ow. That's deep.

Jayne Tania, please be careful, please . . .

Chorus Be careful, Tania, slowly does it.

Tania Need to hold on tight . . .

Chorus Hold on tight, hold on tight.

Tania And ease myself down.

Chorus Down you come, down you come.

Tania tries to struggle down the mast. Gets stuck.

Tania I'm stuck. I . . . I can't move. It's my bloody shoulder again, freezing just when . . . I . . . need to . . .

Chorus Hold on, Tania, hold on, Tania.

She slips, but stops herself. Sound of e-mails pouring in. Onscreen, Jayne looks scared. Joel, Ronny, Tom, Stuart and Anne gather at the bottom of the mast, looking up.

Jayne Tania!
Joel Hang in there, girl!
Ronny Is this all on camera?
Tom (*to himself*) Tania!
Jayne Please, God.
Stuart Saturn aspected to Mars . . .

Anne shoves him aside.

Anne Our hearts are in our mouths . . .

Tom dials a number on his mobile. Lucas comes onstage.

Lucas Pendragon Holdings.
Tom There, are you satisfied, Lucas? If anything happens to her. For the sake of your bloody logo!

Tania starts to climb down.

Chorus Take it slow, nice and steady.
Tania (*to herself*) Take it slow . . .
Chorus Nice and steady.
Lucas She's coming down.
Tom Steady, girl, steady.
Chorus Steady. Steady. Nice and steady.

The crowd back away. Tania reaches the deck. Sound of e-mails pouring in.

Tom *and* **Jayne** Thank God.
Stuart As I said, today is well aspected for you.
Anne How do you feel. Tania?

Ronny We've extended the regional news to cover the unfolding drama . . . Could you give as an interview live on air in approximately six minutes?

Tania struggles with the first-aid box. Her mobile rings, she struggles to answer it.

Tom Baby . . .

Tania I can't open the bloody tin.

Tom Christ, I was so scared for you . . .

Tania It's okay now.

Tom is in front of her, furious.

Tom I thought . . . I thought there was some problem with the mast, that you had to make an emergency repair. Not just that bloody camera. Whatever possessed you? Risking your life for a webcam?

Tania Lucas said . . .

Tom (*interrupts*) Sod Lucas! Honestly. He told you you had to go up there, did he? I'll go over there right now, I'll burn his bloody Porsche, I'll punch him –

Tania It was my decision. Listen to me. My decision, right?

Tom And it was nearly your last – just to be on telly.

Tania Just to keep *Team Spirit* afloat, Tom. Without sponsorship . . .

Tom I know, I know . . . I just . . . It's hard you know, watching you onscreen, being so powerless to help. (*A beat.*) Your arm looks bad. The blood . . .

Tania I think it needs stitches. I better try and put a tight bandage on and hope that stops the bleeding. Talk later, babe. (*She takes out a bandage and struggles to bandage her arm.*) Ow, ow! Damn the stupid media. All of you at home watching this. Damn you.

Sound of an e-mail coming in. Jayne appears onscreen.

Jayne Are you okay? Please let me know, I've nothing to do but sit here worrying. Just type Y or N, that'll do.

Tania looks up at her.

Tania I'm okay, Jayne. Gotta go and rig the sails for stormy weather.
Chorus Waves are growing, Tania.

Tania goes up on deck, alters the sails.

Tania Need to reduce the sail. Hopefully the storm jib will cope. No reports yet of how strong winds we could be expecting.

Sound of gulls.

Chorus Gulls are frightened.
Philippe (*off*) Careful, little *Song Bird*, the sea is getting rough.
Jake Strewth, look at all those gulls. Rough seas ahead. *Canberra Queen* to Atlantic Patrol, requesting latest weather update, over . . .
Atlantic Patrol We're about to issue a severe storm warning in your area, *Canberra Queen* . . .

Hiss of static.

Jake You're breaking up, Atlantic Patrol, over? Can you hear me, Atlantic Patrol? Over?
Philippe *Song Bird* to Atlantic Patrol, do you read, over? Atlantic Patrol, do you read, over?
Chorus Get ready, Tania. Get ready.

Tania finishes with the sail.

Tania That should . . . I hope about do it. Those clouds hugging the waves look threatening. I should get back below.

Ronny and Anne approach Tania.

Ronny Can you talk now, live on air, Tania?

Tania I'm sorry, Ronny, feel weak . . . loss of blood
I expect . . .

Ronny And do you think –

Chorus Don't talk. Sleep.

Tania Talk later, eh? I need to sleep.

Anne Our readers are bleeding with you, Tania. Care to
share your thoughts? How bad is it? Are you in pain?

Chorus Tania, sleep.

Tania No comment. Not now. Later, Anne.

Chorus Sleep now. Sleep now.

*Anne and Ronny leave. Tania goes below deck, settles
down to sleep. Jayne appears onscreen.*

Jayne Tania, it's Jayne again, can't see you onscreen
now, so I suppose you must be asleep. I wish I could
sleep – but I'm scared. (*A beat.*) You asked me about
Halifax . . . so what I did was I used my Dad's
scanner and made you a kind of photo collage . . .

*Pictures of Halifax and surrounding area on screen,
some captioned – 'Citadel', 'Docks', 'Truro',
'Dartmouth'. Tania rouses, winces, squints blearily
at the screen of her laptop.*

Tania What? Pictures of Plymouth? Devon? Someone's
sent me some pictures of home. Let's see who . . .
Jayne? I thought she was going to send me pictures of
Halifax. Must be a different Jayne, not the Canadian
one.

Stuart Your stars for tomorrow look more favourable,
Tania, but you must avoid hurting the feelings of
someone close to you.

Tania No one is close to me, you idiot. I'm in the middle
of the ocean.

Tech Support We are currently experiencing a few
difficulties here at your server . . .

Joel Did you get my last message? One hundred jokes about women sailors.

Tania No, Joel. I don't think I did. (*to herself*) And I think I can live without it, somehow.

Joel What's the specifications of your laptop? I'm gonna send you this brilliant new game but it might take a while to download . . .

Tania (*to herself*) Spare me.

Ronny starts to enter.

Ronny We're coming up to the midnight news bulletin.

Chorus Sleep, Tania.

Tania ushers Ronny off Team Spirit.

Tania Sorry, Ronny, need some shut-eye.

Tania clicks back to Jayne's pictures.

Tania (*to herself*) Home sweet . . . No . . . wait a minute . . . (*She looks through the pictures again.*) Hi, Jayne, where is this? It looks exactly like Plymouth . . . can only be Plymouth . . . or the city in my dream . . . Can I really have dreamed of Halifax, without having ever been there?

Tech Support Problems at your server mean there may be a delay in delivering your mail. Please bear with us.

Chorus (*quietly*) Storm is coming. Storm is coming.

Tania settles to sleep. The wind is getting up. Suddenly a bell starts ringing. Jayne appears onscreen.

Chorus Waves are growing, waves are growing.

Jayne The camera on the mast is showing the sea getting rough. I wish I could phone you and warn you.

Jayne is replaced onscreen by a rough angry sea.

Tania Thanks, Jayne, I'm awake – I've a bell in the cabin that rings if the boat is listing too much. Recently I've convinced myself that I could sleep through a hurricane. I don't know why I always get so tired. I need to get the mainsail down before it gets any worse. It's gonna be a struggle as it is with the state of my arm.

Chorus Take down the sail. Storm is coming.

Tom's mobile rings. Tania goes back up on deck, starts to struggle with the sail. Tom paces, agitated, Ronny following.

Ronny Tom, we hear that several yachts are in trouble, are you concerned for Tania?

Tom She's fine.

Tania When the sail's this wet from the spray, it weighs so much . . .

Tania struggles to take the sail down.

Chorus You can do it, you can do it.

Tania Come on.

Ronny Don't you feel kind of helpless, knowing there's a storm and nothing you can do to help her?

Chorus Come on, you can do it.

Tania It's coming.

Chorus You can do it.

Tom She's very capable. But of course I worry . . . when there's anything to worry about . . . but there isn't. *Team Spirit* is riding the storm and still in the lead.

Ronny Still, you'll be glad when she reaches Halifax?

Tom I'm flying out in a couple of days to be there when *Team Spirit* docks.

Tania There. It's down.

Chorus Waves are rising.

Tania Back to the helm for a fight with the tiller.

Ronny It sounds like there's gonna be quite a welcoming committee – all the local schools and colleges have the day off, there's gonna be a band, TV crews, the mayor of course . . .

Tom And our chief sponsor to hand us the contract for Tania's next project – her attempt at breaking the record for sailing solo round the globe.

Ronny In *Team Spirit*?

Tom Of course.

Chorus Storm is rising, storm is rising.

Ronny You must be keeping your fingers crossed Tania brings her into Halifax safely.

The sound of the storm is rising.

Chorus Tania, the storm is rising!

Tom It's Tania's safety that's my primary concern, Ronny.

Ronny Of course. Is it true you plan to marry after the round-the-world attempt?

Chorus Tania!

Tom I can't talk about that, Ronny.

Ronny Because of your exclusive deal with *Hello* magazine, by any chance? Have you already sold the rights to cover the wedding? Does that include TV rights, Tom, because it could be very lucrative . . .

Chorus Tania!

Tom Excuse me, Ronny, I'm watching the webcam footage and it's looking rough out there.

News Report Here in the Atlantic, the weather is causing extremely hazardous conditions for the crews in the Pelican Alliance Plymouth-to-Halifax race. The German yacht is in difficulties, and the Swiss has had to turn back after suffering damage to its mast. Of Belgian yacht, *Song Bird* there is no sign, and concern is growing for sailor Philippe Jeunet. Search and rescue efforts are being hampered by the bad weather.

Jayne appears onscreen.

Jayne I just heard the news. Tania, I'm worried, hang on in there. Let me know if you are okay, Y or N.

Jayne is replaced by stormy weather again. Tania's mobile rings.

Tania Hello?
Tom Tania?
Tania Hello? Tom?
Tom Tania?

Static hiss grows louder. Tom tries to redial.

Phone Voice The mobile you are trying to reach is not currently responding, it may be switched off . . .
Tania Shit.

Jayne reappears.

Jayne Tania, my server says you aren't currently able to receive messages . . . so I guess I can send this without taking up your time. When I said I'd be in Halifax to meet you, I was trying to believe that. I will see *Team Spirit* arrive . . . I'm sure, but it'll be on the TV here in my ward, that's if my operation takes place on time. I know I'm gonna get through this thing and see *Team Spirit* enter the harbour in first place.
Melanie Leave that now, Jayne.

Melanie appears onscreen beside her daughter.
Joel enters.

Joel Why've you taken the sail down? On the sim, you can go really fast if you just pitch straight into the eye of the hurricane.

Tania's mobile rings again.

Tom Tania.
Tania I'm here, Tom, can hardly hear you.
Tom You're okay?
Tania I'm fine, yeah . . .
Tom Well, you take care of yourself now . . .

Tania Don't I always . . .?

Tom I know, babe, it's just, I worry, you know?

Tania (*to herself*) About me or the boat? (*to Tom*)
I know. Miss you.

Tom I know you do.

Tania (*to herself*) Wouldn't hurt him to say, 'I miss you
too,' would it?

Sound of a flare.

Tania That sounded like a rocket.

Tom How's your arm?

Tania The cut's still bleeding, but it's something to think
about tomorrow.

Static hiss rises.

Tom Listen to me . . .

Tania You're breaking up . . . just tell me you love me.

Tom What?

Tania You never say . . .

Tom Sorry? What?

Tania Never mind.

Sound of another flare.

Tania That *is* a distress flare!

Tom What? Hello.

*Static hiss drowns him out. Tania goes below deck.
She puts on the shortwave radio.*

Philippe Mayday mayday . . .

Tania *Team Spirit* to Atlantic Patrol ship, do you read
me, over?

Atlantic Patrol Hi, Tania, is everything okay, over?

Tania Just saw distress flares and heard a mayday
message, the flares in a (*Checks compass.*) south,
south-west direction, over.

Atlantic Patrol Affirmative, we've also received a
mayday message. Unfortunately the nearest craft is
nearly thirty miles away and that's you, *Team Spirit*.
Over.

Tania Have you any idea of what kind of vessel it is
sending out the signal, over?

Atlantic Patrol Negative, Tania. Though from its
position it could possibly be the missing Belgian yacht,
over.

Tania (*to herself*) My God.

Atlantic Patrol We've tried to re-establish radio contact
but there's been nothing since the mayday message,
over.

Tania What about *Canberra Queen*? Isn't she also in the
area?

Atlantic Patrol Negative. She's has had to pull back,
suffered tiller damage.

Tania So I'm the nearest boat . . . Then I've gotta do
something, haven't I, over?

Atlantic Patrol We can't mount a rescue in this storm,
over.

Tania I better go and get rigged, over.

Atlantic Patrol Winds in that area are up to fifty-five
knots and rising. You run the risk of serious damage
if you try to sail into the storm, over.

Tania And if I don't a man may drown, over.

Atlantic Patrol He may have already, over.

Tania No time to lose. Gotta hoist the storm jib. Over
and out.

Chorus Hoist the jib, storm is rising.

Tania Better clamp on the safety line.

*Tania is back on deck, clamps on a safety line before
hoisting the sails.*

Tania Hope I've enough strength in my arm to hoist the
sails.

Chorus Go and save him.

Tania This is madness.

Chorus Gotta do it, gotta do it.

Tania Gotta do it, a man might die.

Chorus You can do it, you can help.

Tania I must, I have to.

Chorus Storm is rising. Hurry, Tania.

Tom dials a number.

Chorus Storm is rising! Storm is rising!

Tom Hi, Technical Support, *Team Spirit* is only intermittently receiving e-mails . . .

Chorus Storm is rising, storm is rising!

Tech Support We think the problem isn't here at your server but due to climatic conditions affecting the Atlantic.

Chorus Change course, Tania . . .

Tania Changing course.

Tom How much am I paying for this support call?

Tech Support Two pounds a minute.

Tom Piss off then. (*Tom dials again.*)

Phone Voice The mobile you are trying to reach is either switched off or –

Tom Shit.

Tania is being thrown about, struggling to stay at the helm. Wind screams deafeningly through the rigging.

Tania Every time the bow dives beneath the waves, I pray we'll come up again. I'm trying to change course –

Chorus Changing course.

Tania – but it's a struggle.

Chorus Changing course.

Tania Into the storm.

Chorus The eye of the storm, the eye of the storm!

Tania (*to waves and wind*) Yeah, come on! Show me what you're made of. Come on!

Chorus You can do it! You can do it!

Tom's mobile rings.

Tom Tania?

Tom strides on stage, Lucas joins him.

Lucas What's going on, Tom?
Tom Can't talk now, Lucas.
Lucas Picture quality's bloody terrible in this storm.
Tom Out of my hands, I'm afraid. 'Bye now.

Lucas leaves, shaking his head. Tom's phone rings again. Ronny enters.

Tom Jesus!
Ronny Tom? We can't see anything onscreen.
Tom (*wearily*) It's just the weather, Ronny.
Ronny Are you worried, Tom?
Tom Of course I'm worried. Look, Ronny, can't talk now, need to keep the line free in case Tania rings. 'Bye.

Tom's phone rings again. Ronny leaves. Enter Anne.

Anne Tom, it's Anne. Is there a technical problem?

Exasperated, he rings off. She leaves.
Tania tries her mobile again. Tom turns to her, relief on his face.

Chorus You can do it! You can do it!
Tom Tania! Are you alright?
Tania The phone was engaged.
Tom How's the arm?
Tania Holding up. Just.
Tom Still in the lead, babe?
Tania Well . . .
Tom What was that? Line's terrible.
Tania I'm turning back.

Tom What?

Chorus She's changed course, she's changed course.

Tania Tom, I . . .

Tom (*interrupting*) You've lost the lead? Is the boat damaged?

Tania No . . . well, not yet . . . Tom, one of the other yachts is in trouble. I'm on my way to help.

Tom Another competitor? Behind you?

Tania We think he's in serious trouble. The coastguard said . . .

Tom Tania, leave it to the coastguard.

Chorus Gotta save him.

Tania They can't get anyone there in time.

Tom Someone else will rescue him.

Chorus Gotta save him.

Tania Who? There's no one else in range.

Tom Air Search and Rescue.

Tania Can't fly in this weather.

The picture comes back.

Tom Tania, it's too dangerous.

Tania What you mean is, it'll put me out of the race?

Tom No, listen to me . . .

Tania The man could die, Tom.

Tom And you could put yourself in danger. Hello?

Tania turns away. Static hiss builds to a climax. Tom's mobile rings.

Chorus Gotta save him! Gotta save him!

Tom Tania?

Enter Lucas, tapping Tom on the shoulder, turning him from staring after Tania.

Lucas We've got vision and sound back.

Tom (*flatly*) That's great.

Lucas Tom, you must stress to Tania that the sponsorship for her round-the-world trip depends on *Pendragon Team Spirit* coming in first.

Tom She thinks a man's life may be in danger.

Lucas And what exactly can she do?

Tom She thinks she might be able to help.

Lucas By capsizing *Pendragon Team Spirit* in the heart of the storm?

Tom I know it's risky.

Lucas Risky? It spells ruin, Tom. Call her back and stop her. For everyone's sake.

Tom dials Tania.

Tom It's me . . .

Chorus To the rescue, to the rescue!

Tania Can't talk now.

Tom Tania, wait a minute.

Chorus Here we come, here we come.

Tania I'll call you back in a while, yeah? (*She rings off.*)

Tom (*to himself*) Shit.

Chorus Gotta save him.

Tania Gotta save him.

Tom's phone rings. Enter Anne.

Anne I've just been speaking to Lucas. If you lose his sponsorship so Tania can't take part in the transglobal, then that's the film rights, TV rights, book deal in jeopardy, isn't it? . . .

Tom Your guess is as good as mine, Anne.

Anne You've quite a dilemma here, Tom.

Tom Dilemma? I've no bloody dilemma at all! Can't get in touch with Tania.

Anne Could this mean the end of *Team Spirit*?

Tom *Pendragon* . . . Oh, piss off and plague someone else.

Anne It's the news, Tom. You might not like it, but you can't stop it.

The tiller almost pulls from Tania's hands.

Tania It's impossible to steer . . .
Chorus Tania, concentrate. Gotta save him.
Tania Gotta save him. (*to camera*) I'll leave the Net link live – maybe some of you watching will understand. Gotta adjust the storm jib.

She moves to the mast. From the radio below deck, a voice is heard.

It's fighting me. It won't move.
Chorus Push it, push it.

Tania adjusts the storm jib, battling it again.

Tania It's barely moving.
Chorus Be strong. Be strong.
Tania Gotta move the jib. Can't . . . gotta push . . .
Chorus Push, Tania. Jib is moving, jib is moving.
Tania It's moving.
Atlantic Patrol Atlantic Patrol to *Team Spirit*, do you read me, over?
Lucas (*off*) *Pendragon Team Spirit*, dammit.

Tania is still wrestling with the sails.

Atlantic Patrol Atlantic Patrol to *Team Spirit*, do you read me, over?

Static hiss.

Atlantic Patrol to *Team Spirit*, do you read me, over?

Tania goes below deck, starts fiddling with the radio. Static hiss.

Atlantic Patrol to *Team Spirit* . . .

Tania rushes below deck.

Tania Yes, I read you, got any news for me, over?
Atlantic Patrol I've made contact with Philippe Jeunet –
he's had to abandon *Song Bird*, after she capsized.
He's on a life raft, over.
Tania Tell him I'm on my way, over and out.

Blackout.

Act Two

Sounds of the storm.

Chorus Storm is rising. Storm is rising.
Phone Message The mobile you have dialled is not
  currently responding.
Chorus Tania.

Tom tries to call Tania.

Voicemail Message The mobile you have . . .

He rings off.

Tom Why don't you ever set up your voicemail, Tania?

Sound of an e-mail arriving. Enter Anne.

Anne What's happening, Tania? We can't see you on the
  camera.
Chorus Tania.

The others enter in a huddle.

Joel Tania.
Chorus Tania.
Lucas Tania
Chorus Tania.
Ronny Tania.
Chorus Tania.
Jayne Tania . . .
Chorus Tania!
Tom Tania, dammit.
Chorus Tania!
Anne Tania . . .

Chorus Tania!
Stuart Tania . . .
Chorus Tania!
Ronny Tania? Are you there?

Tania appears from the stern of the boat supporting Philippe.

Philippe What . . .?
Tania It's okay . . . it's okay . . . you're safe.
Philippe Where's . . .?
Tania Shhhh, don't try to talk.
Chorus You did it, Tania. You did it.
Jayne Thank God!
Chorus You saved him, you saved him.
Tom Oh, Tania . . .
Joel Totally awesome.
Ronny Heroic stuff.
Anne You'll get a medal.
Stuart Bravery is your sign's major quality.

Tania offers Philippe a little water.

Tania Drink this.
Philippe Cold.
Tania Cold? (*She struggles out of her jacket and puts it around him.*) Can you move? We ought to try to get you below deck. (*She tries to move him, without much success.*)
Philippe No.
Tania You're numb with cold. But you can't stay up here very long . . .
Philippe When I've got my strength, my breath . . .
Tania Okay, then.
Philippe Thank you . . .
Tania You'd have done the same for me.
Philippe I'd have tried, yes. But you did it.
Tania There were a couple of times there . . .

Philippe I know . . . I don't want to think how near we
came . . .

Tania But we've made it.

Philippe Yes . . .

Tania I'm tiring you with talking. I'll go below and get
some blankets.

Sound of e-mails arriving.

Ronny Tania, is it possible to clean the mast webcam
lens? We can't currently get any pictures of broadcast
quality . . . and you and Philippe – it's so heart-
warming . . .

Tania types on the laptop.

Tania Is there a doctor out there on the world-wide
web? Can someone give some advice?

Tech Support (*off*) We are currently experiencing some
difficulties delivering your mail . . .

Tania Shit.

Stuart Harmony is in the stars for you today.

Tania Oh, lucky me. Why don't you piss off and bother
someone more gullible?

Stuart looks shocked. He goes.

Shit. I pressed send. I didn't mean to do that. Oh, with
technical problems he won't get it anyway – I hope.

Tania starts typing again.

Tania Jayne . . . I need to talk to you. Are you out
there? I don't know what time it is in Halifax . . .
You're probably at school or asleep. I've probably
blown my chances of having any further career at sea
at all. But what else could I do? I don't know if Tom'll
be able to forgive me. Jayne . . . tell me you, at least,
are still on my side. Love, Tania. (*to herself*) Send.

Sound of e-mail arriving.

Ronny The camera could really do with a clean, Tania.

Tania And my arm is killing me, Ronny. I can't even drag Philippe into the cabin. I've a deep cut, he's got frostbite – and broken bones for all I know, buffeted by a force nine in that dinghy.

Joel Wow, I thought you were a goner, dude.

Tania (*to herself*) Wish I could say the same for you, my friend.

Lucas Tania, we can only see the sea from the mast of *Pendragon Team Spirit* . . .

Tania Congratulations – it's all I've been able to see for days, Lucas.

Lucas Is the yacht safe? Are you still in the race, Tania?

Ronny We've put a request out to all our viewers for a doctor to get in touch right away.

Philippe Hey . . .

Tania goes back on deck, with the blankets.

Philippe Maybe I move a little now.

With great effort she helps him below deck.

Tania I'll get the kettle brewing.

Philippe Coffee. Strong coffee.

Tania Only got tea, I'm afraid.

Philippe What? Tea? You should've left me to drown!

Tania looks at him for a moment, then they both laugh. She helps him out of his boots and jacket, rubs him with a towel.

How is Tom?

Tania Worrying his guts out as usual.

Philippe It's a bad storm.

Tania I ought to call him, tell him we're both okay. Ow.

Philippe You're bleeding.

Tania It's not as bad as it looks – I hope. Supposed to be getting an on-line doctor to help, though what I probably need is stitches.

Philippe Oh yes, I forget . . . you have cameras connected to the Internet?

Tania That's right, this is HMS *Media Circus* – Big Brother on water. Big Brother's a TV programme in England . . .

Philippe In Belguim, same kind of show. So now we are on TV?

Tania We might be. We're certainly on the web.

Philippe You will be a hero – they will have seen the rescue – yes?

Tania Yes, but . . . (*softly*) You're so lucky . . .

Philippe Lucky – I have no boat!

Tania Sorry, Philippe. I mean when you set out on a solo race – you're truly alone . . .

Philippe This time. But now I have no boat? How will I pay for a new one? Sponsorship will only pay for so much. . . . It's the future, Tania.

Tania I think it's the same for mountain-climbers, deep-sea divers.

Philippe Cameras everywhere.

Tania Everywhere but my bunk. I had to draw the line somewhere.

Philippe And people e-mail you?

Tania Wanna see? I'll get the laptop.

She fetches it. Sound of e-mails arriving. The others join them.

Joel Can you get MTV while you're at sea? By satellite or something?

Anne Our hearts were in our mouths.

Stuart Calmer times are on the way for Aquarians like you, Tania.

Melanie, Jayne's mum, joins them.

Melanie Tania, you don't know me, but I believe my daughter Jayne has been following your progress avidly. In fact it's all she's been talking about the last few days. Last night her condition worsened – as she's probably told you, she has cancer and was awaiting surgery. Now a haemorrhage means they will have to operate immediately. She should, however, come round from surgery in five or so hours, and I know she would so appreciate it if a message from you was waiting for her.

Tania My God . . . poor Jayne . . .

Tom's mobile rings. He and Lucas enter.

Lucas Is she still in the race?

Tom Absolutely. And can our heroic rescuer still count on Pendragon Holdings to back her?

Lucas Sure thing. As long as she wins.

They walk off together. Tania starts typing.

Tania Hi, Jayne, I'm coming straight in to see you as soon as *Team Spirit* docks . . . Gotta move the jib more soon. (*to Philippe*) Poor kid. She's the only e-mailer I'm glad of. The rest are just clamour, noise, disturbance.

Philippe You want to be alone?

Tania I mean, it's nice them taking an interest.

Philippe And now I'm here, getting in your way . . . putting you out of the race maybe.

Tania It's not your fault.

Philippe Doesn't make me feel any better. I am useless, I can do nothing.

Tania It could've been a lot worse. In a day or so you'll be up and about. Providing no bones are broken you'll be well enough to walk onshore at Halifax. The

wind's steadying down now, let's see if I can get back
on course. (*She goes and adjusts the jib.*) The jib's
much easier to move now – it felt like pushing a
mountain before. The gulls are swooping on fish
caught up and killed in the storm. They think the
worst is over, and they're probably right. But never
underestimate the sea . . .

Chorus The sea is your best friend.

Tania My friend the sea . . .

Chorus And the sea is your worst enemy.

Tania I love it. The sea. Whatever face it shows me.
I love it.

*Philippe clicks the mouse to make the computer go
online. Sound of e-mails arriving. Ronny and Jayne
enter.*

Ronny Philippe, we watched the rescue with baited
breath. What were you thoughts before *Team Spirit*
came into view? Had you at any point given up hope?

Philippe You are from English TV, Ronny? Talk to my
agent – no interviews for free.

Anne Philippe, we'd love an exclusive.

Philippe Talk to my agent, Anne.

Stuart enters.

Stuart What's your star sign?

Philippe Pisces – and I nearly ended up with the fishes.
Are you real astrologer?

Stuart The only real astrologer.

Philippe Can you draw up my chart?

Stuart My pleasure.

Enter Joel.

Joel Whoa, man, I like watched you sink . . .

Philippe Hope I can say the same for you some day.

Philippe switches the computer off. Everyone leaves. He stretches out. On deck Tania is looking starboard, her mobile rings. Enter Tom.

Tom Jake has a three-hour lead on you now.

Jake (*off*) Kicked that Tania's ass, mate.

Tania It's not as bad as I feared.

Tom You haven't got long to make it up.

Tania I'm not out of the race yet, Tom.

Jake (*off*) The little sheila's dead in the water. Got it sewn up.

Tom There's another problem – the adjudicators are currently meeting – having Philippe onboard when you cross the line will automatically disqualify you.

Tania (*sarkily*) Think I should throw him to the sharks, Tom?

Tom I'm arranging for a rescue boat to collect him – should be with you in four to five hours.

Tania He's in no shape to be hauled onto another ship.

Tom We'll still lose *Team Spirit* and the roof over our heads.

Tania Is that really all that matters?

Tom What else do we have? (*He starts to go.*)

Tania Eh? The signal's going . . . I'm losing you?

Tom You're losing everything.

Tania Hello? (*She continues to struggle with the sail, but her arm is giving her difficulty.*) Ow! My arm . . . it was better while it was numb with cold, but now . . . God, it hurts.

Chorus Be strong, Tania. You can do it.

Tania I can't boom out until I've done something about my arm.

Chorus Try, push, push.

Tania Push. Ow. No. Ow. It's no good.

She comes back inside. Philippe is asleep, she checks e-mail. Enter Ronny.

Ronny Tania, we've got a doctor here in the studio . . .

Tania I need a doctor out here, it's a gaping cut and it's looking angry.

Enter the Doctor. He stands distant.

Doctor Hi, Tania. Do you have suturing equipment?

Tania Yes . . . You expect me to stitch my own arm up, don't you?

Doctor Well, unless Philippe is in any state to . . .

Tania I don't think so . . .

Doctor He needs a medical check-up as soon as possible.

Tania I know, but I think it's nothing worse than bumps, bruises and exposure to the elements. We should reach Halifax in less than thirty-six hours.

Doctor Keep us informed. Now, with your arm, can you start by setting up the sterilisation kit . . .?

Tania I hope the webcam and phone-link hold – so I can see what you're doing as well as take your advice, doctor.

Doctor Okay now, the first thing is to scrub up.

Tania Got ya.

Doctor Now bathe the infected area carefully.

Static hiss rises.

Tania Ow . . .

Doctor backs away a little. Philippe half-wakes.

Philippe What! What are you doing . . .?

Tania Don't get near – this is now a sterile area.

Doctor (*more quietly*) You can see the computer screen?

Tania Yeah . . . though I can barely hear you . . .

Doctor Rest the arm on the table, the needle threads much as an ordinary sewing one does, nice knot at the end of the thread . . .

Philippe I cannot watch.

Tania You can't? What do you think I feel like?

Doctor Start about three millimetres from the edge of
the wound.

Tania What? Like this? Oh . . . my God . . .

Doctor Take your time, don't pull it too tight and
remember . . . (*He leaves.*)

Tania Doctor? Doctor? Don't let me lose the connection
now.

Philippe Keep going, steady, don't stop now.

Chorus Steady does it.

Tania Okay, okay . . . Jesus, it hurts . . . Okay there.
Now what? How do I fasten it off? Maybe a little
knot like . . . this. Bandage . . .

*She bandages her arm. Joel comes across and peers at
it.*

Joel Whoa, well gruesome, Tania! Put me off my burger,
man.

Anne comes over and peers at the wound.

Anne How do you feel, Tania?

Tania I . . . I need to sit down . . .

As Tania staggers, Anne and Joel leave.

Philippe Are you okay?

Tania I will be. Could you do me a favour?

Philippe If I can.

Tania Could you type an e-mail?

Philippe Of course . . . You dictate.

Tania It's the one I started to Jayne. . . . 'As soon as you
are well again . . .

Philippe types.

I'm taking you on a trip on *Team Spirit*.'

Lucas *Pendragon Team Spirit*, which you may no longer
own . . .

Tania 'We can travel round the coast of Nova Scotia
and you can show me the sights. Lots of love, Tania.'
Philippe Send?
Tania Why not?

Computer going online.

Tania Oh, look at this one from the crank.
Stuart Someone close to you, Tania, has feelings they are
afraid to reveal . . .

*Tania looks at the laptop screen over Philippe's
shoulder.*

Tania But no message from Tom, and no phone call. He
must've seen me on the webcam stitching up my arm.
Be nice of him to call.
Philippe Communication problems maybe.
Tania Maybe. We'd just had bit of a . . . not a row,
exactly . . .
Philippe It might be technical problems. (*A beat.*) It's not
easy for him when you're at sea.
Tania Yeah, tell me about it.
Philippe Same thing with my girlfriend.
Tania She misses you?
Philippe Not really.
Tania I'm sure she does.
Philippe I don't think so. (*A beat.*) She has left me for
my brother.
Tania Oh. Oh, I'm sorry.
Philippe Sailors aren't the easiest people to live with.
There's always a third person in the relationship.
Tania (*nodding*) The sea.
Chorus You'll always have the sea.

Philippe stands up.

Tania Careful . . . (*She moves to help him.*)
Philippe I need to get my legs moving.

Tom tries to phone Tania.

Phone Message The mobile you have called may be switched off . . .

Tom dials another number. He enters with Lucas, who is unwilling to follow him.

Tom Lucas . . .

Lucas Tom, I'm in a meeting . . .

Tom Just wanted to tell you Tania's gaining on the Aussie.

Lucas Yeah, that's great, Tom, catch you later. (*Lucas rings off.*)

Tom (*to himself*) She can't catch them now . . . can she?

Philippe wobbles.

Tania Careful, Philippe.

Philippe Tomorrow they can organise an airlift for me . . .

Tania Only if the wind decreases . . .

Philippe . . . or have another boat come alongside to take me off *Team Spirit*.

Tania The forecast doesn't look good enough.

Philippe If I don't go, you'll be disqualified.

Tania So what? Coming in second won't be enough, Tom and I will lose the boat, our home . . .

Philippe This is the deal you made?

Tania Come in first or our sponsor will pull out.

Philippe Sounds like a pact with the devil.

Tania The devil who is no doubt watching and listening in right now, so be careful for my sake.

Philippe They have their logos on the boat, your face on computer screens around the world, what more do they want?

Tania Blood? (*Looks at her arm.*) Seems they have that too.

Philippe You are inspiring people out there . . .

Tania To find freedom – or sell their soul for a company logo? The wind's changing, gotta get back to the helm.

Tom's mobile rings. Enter Ronny with Tom.

Ronny Tom, is it true that if *Team Spirit* doesn't come in first, it'll be the end of the dream?

Tom Why don't you ring Lucas at Pendragon Holdings and ask him that question?

Ronny So Tania's reward for her heroism could be financial ruin?

Tom Unless of course we can find a new sponsor for the round-the-world trip.

Ronny I'm sure many of our viewers who were gripped yesterday by the thrilling rescue would be willing to donate to a fund . . .

Tom We're talking hundreds of thousands of pounds, Ronny.

Ronny If this TV station had exclusive rights to cover the global trip . . .

Tom Well, put in your bid and we'll consider it.

Ronny Are you already talking to other broadcasters?

Tom I'm talking to everyone, Ronny. Gotta go.

Tom's phone rings again. Ronny leaves. Anne enters, barging past Ronny.

Anne Tom, can you give me a bit of background about Philippe?

Tom I've met him a few times on the circuit, seems nice enough.

Anne And will he and Tania get along over the next couple of days until they dock in Halifax?

Tom Of course, they're both professionals . . .

Anne And rivals?

Tom I suspect they'd both rather be alone on their own boats, that's the nature of them . . .

Anne Lone yachtsmen and women are a breed apart?

Tom You can say that again, Anne.

Anne If Tania doesn't win the race . . . I've been talking to my editor . . . maybe we'll have to scale down the feature . . . and unfortunately the fee . . .

Tom No way. You've signed a contract, remember?

Anne And you no doubt have read the small print, Tom.

Tom You're all heart, Anne. But remember, your paper currently has first refusal on the serialisation rights to Tania's biography . . .

Anne Which we greatly appreciate. Though are you sure there will still be a book, Tom?

Tom She has already started writing.

Anne I mean if she comes in second, if there is no global challenge . . . will your publishers still be interested?

Tom We'll get the money for Tania's record-breaking attempt come what may.

Anne Brave talk.

Tom Backed by the facts. I'm already talking to other major sponsors and broadcasters . . .

Anne Well best of luck, Tom. Keep us up to date with all the latest developments, won't you?

Tom You know you can count on me, Anne. (*He puts the phone down.*) Shallow bitch.

Chorus Wind is changing, Tania.

Tania Wind is changing. Need to move the sail to keep up speed.

Chorus Move the sail, move the sail.

Tania If my arm will let me. (*Tania moves the sail.*)

Chorus Come on, Tania.

Tania Put your back into it. (*She completes the task.*) There. God, I'm exhausted. Need to rest.

Philippe is checking the e-mail. Enter Joel.

Joel You don't have to get pissed at me, Philippe, man, just 'cos you crashed and burned. I've been spending

the whole evening on the enclosed plan . . . working
it out with pure mathematics. God knows why, when
I could've been . . . er, watching MTV or something.
I've calculated a way that Tania can beat the Australian.
If she changes course by twenty degrees, when she
reaches Point C on the attached diagram . . .

*Joel stops speaking abruptly as Philippe double-clicks
and the projection of a complicated diagram appears.
He studies it for a moment. Enter Stuart, giving Joel
a disapproving, 'Who is this yob?' look.*

Stuart Hi, Philippe, you've been going through a bad
patch recently but Pisces are resilient and you've never
lacked courage. Regarding you and Tania, she's an
Aquarian, a neighbour and fellow water sign. You'll
find both her chart and yours as attached files . . .

*He stops speaking as Philippe double-clicks. Onscreen
appears the front page of 'Stuart's Cosmic Star Chart'.
It looks a bit tacky and over the top.*

Chorus Wind is changing.

Tania Wind's changed. Shit. I've got to adjust the mainsail
and move the jib again.

Chorus You can do it.

Tania Why won't it move? Where's my strength gone? . . .
Come on, move!

Chorus You can do it!

Tania No . . . (*She rests against the mast.*) And what's
the point? I can't win now. Lucas will take the boat
away. I feel so tired . . . there's no point in going on . . .

Chorus Don't give up. You can do it.

She struggles with the jib.

Tania Come on. come on.

It won't move.

Chorus You can do it.
Tania No! I can't. I can't.

Cacophony of mobile phones, modems going online. Everyone shouts 'Tania, Tania', building to a climax.

No, no, no . . . I've had enough. I just want to go . . . to go home. (*She sits down, wiping her eyes with her fists.*)
Chorus (*soothingly*) Hey . . . hey . . .
Tania Please . . . back at control . . . terminate this broadcast . . . shut off the Internet connection. I just need to be . . . to be myself again. To remember who I am.

Philippe comes up on deck.

Philippe Tania? Tania.
Tania You shouldn't be up here, you need to rest . . .

He hugs her.

Philippe It's okay . . .
Tania I don't want every moment of my life watched –
Philippe You'll be in Halifax soon.
Tania – to do interviews, chat shows, public appearances . . .
Philippe It'll only be for a short while, maybe a few weeks . . .
Tania I can't . . .
Philippe It'll be okay. Ignore the cameras. They can't hurt you.

He takes her hand and squeezes it.

Tania I'm gonna have to have a long talk with Tom when I dock. I mean, it's bad enough out here bombarded by phone calls and e-mails, on camera twenty-four hours a day . . . but for the next two months, he's booked us a diary full of interviews, photo sessions, appearances on TV shows, opening

regattas, visiting schools and dockyards . . . and I feel
so . . . just so bloody tired of it all, you know?

Philippe You just want to be sailing.

Tania Just me, the boat and the sea. The way it used
to be.

Philippe You can't turn back the clock, I'm afraid.

Tania Yeah, there's nothing I can do about it, though, eh?
It's okay. I'll pull myself together . . .

Philippe You're strong, you're get through this.

Tania Thank you, Philippe. (*She kisses him.*)

Philippe Everything will be fine. (*A beat.*) Come and
look at your e-mail.

Tania No. I don't think I can deal . . .

Philippe There was a message from Joel . . .

Tania Oh God, he's one of the regulars. Mr Playstation.

Philippe He's got an interesting idea . . .

Tania If it's anything to do with his yachting simulator,
telling me I'm doing everything wrong, while my eyes
are numb with spray, shoulder aching, arm swelling,
knuckles skinned . . .

Philippe I think it's worth a look.

Tania Seriously?

Philippe Maybe. Come on.

*She follows him into the cabin. They sit together at
the computer.*
*Tom's phone rings. Sound of an airport. Enter Tom
and Ronny.*

Ronny Hi, Tom. Been watching the webcam footage?

Tom No, Ronny, actually I'm trying to get a little shut-
eye at the airport, waiting for a flight to Canada.

Ronny You haven't seen the latest from *Team Spirit*?

Tom I presume Tania would've called if anything was
wrong. (*He checks his phone.*) There's nothing wrong,
is there?

Ronny No . . . probably not. Though I don't know what interpretation the press will put on it tomorrow.

Tom What? Hang on a minute. That's my flight being called.

Tom's mobile rings.

Voicemail The person you have called is currently not available.

Anne (*off*) Tom, it's Anne. Tania and Philippe – have you seen the webcam footage? They do seem to have grown very close over the last few hours, don't they? Is he just comforting her, would you say? Have you spoken to her at all? How do you feel about it? You've got my extension, call me back.

Tania I can see what Joel's getting at. It might just give me the edge . . . Though working something out on a computer is all very well . . . but out here things change so quickly . . .

Philippe It's worth a try at least, no?

Tania nods, goes back on deck.

Tania (*to camera*) Slight change of plan – plotting a new course. As planned on Joel's computer. What that computer program can't predict, of course, is that wind speed, direction and weather conditions will change again. And it means moving that damn jib again.

Chorus Push it, Tania.

Tania Deep breaths.

Chorus One, two, three, push.

Tania It moved . . .

Chorus Again, two, three, push.

Tania Yes. There it is. (*She steers at the helm.*) Hoping this will give me the edge on the Aussie. (*to herself*) I should tell Tom.

She rings, gets voicemail.

Voicemail The person you have called . . .
Tania He's probably in flight by now. And Jayne must
be in the operating theatre. Puts all my problems in
perspective.

*She alters the sails, returns to the helm. Sound of
e-mail coming in. Lucas enters.*

Lucas Hi, Tania, I've arranged a boat to meet you in
approximately an hour to take Philippe off *Team
Spirit*.
Jake (*off*) Strewth, she's gaining.
Joel What did I tell you! I'm a genius man!
Tania I can see Jake . . . and he can see me gaining on
him. Come on, *Team Spirit*.
Chorus Come on, Tania.
Jake Come on, Queenie!
Chorus Come on, Tania.
Joel Go girl!
Chorus You can do it!
Jake Go Queenie!
Chorus Go Tania!

Enter Stuart.

Stuart Today miracles are possible for you, Tania.
(*Stuart looks towards Jake.*) Not such a positive day
for Capricorns, though.
Jake Shit, man, she's taking us!

Stuart walks serenely off. Jake glares at him.

Bloody Nora!

*Enter Anne, talking in a conspiratorial whisper to
Philippe.*

Anne Philippe, we can see you sitting in front of the
computer. Pendragon Holdings have arranged for you
to be transferred onto another boat, so Tania can

finish the race. Myself and a photographer from our paper will be there to capture the moment and talk to you about your relationship with Tania . . .

Philippe (*to himself*) Relationship?

Anne We've spoken to your agent and agreed terms for the exclusive.

Ronny enters, elbowing Anne aside. They glare at each other.

Ronny Philippe, tell us your thoughts about Tania. You feel close to her because she saved your life? That must be a special bond. Does that explain the kiss we all witnessed . . .

Philippe (*to himself*) Oh my God. I don't believe . . . (*to camera*) All of you . . . all of you watching . . . there is nothing going on between Tania and me. Okay. I'm going to cook now. No more stupid questions.

Everyone leaves the boat but Philippe and Tania.

Tania We're in the lead!

Jake Nightmare, the sheila's ahead.

Tania's mobile rings. Plane noises.

Tom (*off*) I'm over the Atlantic. On the plane's phone.

He appears onscreen in his seat.

Tania Can you see me far below?

Tom No.

Tania I've overtaken the *Canberra Queen*, Tom!

Tom You're back in front?

Chorus She's in the lead.

Tania I'm in the lead!

Tom I'm so proud of you.

Tania Thanks, Tom.

Tom I can't wait to see you.

Tania You too, babe.

Tom Tania . . . when this thing is over . . . you know, before we start preparing for the trans-global . . . maybe you and me, er . . . you and me . . .

Tania Yes, Tom?

Tom . . . maybe we ought to go away somewhere nice. Nice and quiet. For a week or so at least. Eh, babe?

Tania (*wearily*) Yeah.

Tom You okay? Sounding tired?

Tania I'm fine.

Tom Cool. Look, call you right back, gotta call Lucas.

She remains staring at his image as he redials.

Tania (*to herself*) I thought for a minute you were going to ask me to marry you. I'm married already . . . to the sea, I know, but sometimes . . . Oh, to hell with you.

Tom Hi, Lucas . . .

Lucas comes on stage, talking to Tom onscreen.

Lucas Great news, fantastic, knew she could do it. We're breaking out the champagne here at Pendragon. Shame you couldn't see it live on the web. The moment she passed them – the main sail billowing out, our logo lashing the breeze.

Tom I can't wait to be there on the quay to welcome her in.

Lucas It's gonna be some party, I can tell you. . . . And Tom . . . it'll be fantastic – the round-the-world record-breaking attempt . . . I can see it now . . .

Tom So can I, Lucas.

Lucas And Tom . . . don't believe what you read in the newspapers, right?

Tom What?

Lucas I mean it's all fabricated, a pack of lies, you know what they're like . . .

Tom Lucas, what do you mean?

Lucas It's not true that the camera never lies.

Tom What?

Lucas They've got it all out of proportion. Look, gotta go, arrange the corporate hospitality for our investors. We're flying about forty of them out to Halifax to see her come in.

Tom Yes, but what do you mean about the press?

Lucas Safe flight, Tom.

Exit Lucas. Tom onscreen looks puzzled. The screen returns to showing the calm sea. Tania comes below deck.

Philippe I cannot believe there is nothing to cook on this boat.

Tania There should be plenty of stuff left – tinned beans, pasta, freeze-dried stuff.

Philippe Tinned pasta, no real pasta, no coffee. How can anyone live like this? If I'd known you would not have any proper food on board I'd have dragged my stores into the life raft.

Tania Well, you should be in Halifax in a few hours now.

Philippe I know. I wanted to make you a goodbye lunch.

Tania You don't have to bother.

Philippe Tania, I want to bother.

She smiles. Her mobile rings.

Tania Tom?

Tom comes in. Airport sounds.

Tom I'm at the airport, just landed.

Tania Rough flight? You sound a bit stressed.

Tom We need to talk, Tania.

Tania What's the matter?

Tom Not now. Not with half the world listening in.

Tania And whose fault is it half the world is listening in?

Tom Tania, we agreed . . .

Tania You persuaded me . . .

Tom It was the only way to fund the boat. Sometimes you have to make compromises . . .

Tania Okay, so now we're compromised . . .

Tom We certainly are.

Tania What are you talking about?

Tom Come up on deck a minute.

Tania So it makes a nice picture – Lucas isn't content with his logo being on camera.

Tom I don't want us to row in front of Philippe.

Tania Just the rest of the world?

Tom Well, take the mobile in the bunk if you feel like that. No one can see or hear from in there.

Tania What've you got to say to me that can't be said in public?

Tom Look . . . it can wait, right. It can wait until you dock . . . but let me warn you, all the press are gonna be there . . .

Tania I know that, they were invited . . .

Tom I just don't want you talking to them . . .

Tania Because we've exclusives with Anne and Ronny, I know, I know.

Tom Because they're currently running a story . . . a negative story . . .

Tania A negative story?

Tom Let me talk to them. Leave it all to me.

Tania What negative story? Not about me, surely? I mean, there's nothing . . . in my past . . . or nothing they can dig up.

Tom Got a bit of a short memory haven't you, Tania?

Tania Tell me!

Tom Don't have a bloody clue about anything, do you? (*He rings off.*)

Tania Tom! (*to herself*) Tosser.

Philippe It was like this with my girlfriend also. On land we were like two lovebirds, when I was at sea she'd always be mad at me.

Tania Sometimes he treats me like I'm a naughty child, when it's me out here taking all the responsibility.

Sound of a boat horn.

Sounds like my lift to Halifax has arrived.

They go up on deck.

Philippe Only two hours from Halifax, it'll soon be in sight. 'Bye, Tania.
Tania 'Bye, Philippe. Take care of yourself.

They both hesitate, then kiss again. Flash bulbs go off, shouts of 'More' and 'Tania, over here'.

My God, the boat is full of press.
Philippe Ignore them. Get back to winning the race.

He climbs over the side. She waves to him.

Canadian News Reporter (*onscreen*) And the first thing we'll all want to know when she comes ashore is, has romance blossomed on the high seas?
English Reporter We'll have the exclusive story about how a girl from humble beginnings here in Plymouth –

Tania's home appears on screen. Tania on the Hoe.

– became a sailing celebrity, and was swept off her feet by a dashing Belgian yachtsman, after daringly risking her own life to save his . . .
Tania So now I'm alone again (*to camera*) apart from you guys out there.

Halifax appears onscreen.

Halifax . . . at last . . . No, wait, it's Plymouth . . . the citadel . . . the Hoe . . . it looks exactly the same as Plymouth. My dream . . . I've come all this way . . . to end up back where I started. I thought things would change . . . I'd be somewhere different, but the journey's end is no different than its beginning.

Sound of faint cheering.

The welcoming committee. The same people I thought I'd left behind. All my old problems, everything exactly how it was . . . The only person I want to see right now is you Jayne. Hope your mum is taping the broadcast for you – if she is, then I can tell you that my victory is dedicated to you, for keeping my spirits up during the voyage. (*She goes below deck.*) Final check of the e-mails before preparing to enter the harbour.

Sound of e-mails coming in. All the usual crowd come onstage.

Joel You're gonna win, Tania – wicked!

Ronny We'll have a limo waiting on the dockside to whisk you straight to a TV studio we've specially booked, here in Halifax . . .

Anne As you can imagine, the world wants to know more about this seeming love triangle. What are you going to say to Tom when you come ashore? Our paper has booked you a suite at a top Halifax hotel and there'll be champagne on ice for you and Tom – should you choose to patch up your difficulties. Alternatively, if you'd rather it was Philippe who joins you –

Tania What . . . ?

Anne – then we can arrange that too. Remember we have the exclusive deal for your story.

Stuart Mercury in your chart today, Tania, suggests you should no longer put off making a change in your direction . . .

Melanie Tania . . . I know we don't know each other . . . but I've read your e-mails to my daughter . . . and in a strange way that makes me feel close to you. Jayne made it through the operation safely, but she is still of course too weak to realise her dream to be on the quay to meet you.

Chorus We're coming into Halifax.

Everyone cheers.
Tania steps down from the yacht. Everyone rushes and engulfs her. She is swept away.
Jayne appears onscreen.

Jayne The moment you walked into the ward was like a dream.

Tania is offstage with her laptop, looking at Jayne onscreen.

Tania (*off*) Halifax was my dream.

Jayne I couldn't believe you were real. And just there with me – no computers, no cameras, no journalists.

Tania (*off*) That was just part of my journey, Jayne. It's over now.

Jayne I'm so glad we met, Tania.

Tania (*off*) Jayne, you showed me what matters. Your genuine warmth, the support you've given me during the race.

Jayne I was surprised by what you told me. What you are going to do. But I do understand. And no, of course I won't tell.

Onscreen, Melanie enters.

Melanie Thank you, Tania, for visiting my daughter. I just want to say that we've followed you every step of the way and we'll be tuning in tonight to see you on both chat shows, the news, and we'll be reading your interviews in tomorrow's press avidly, won't we, Jayne?

Jayne smiles.

Jayne Goodbye, Tania. *Bon voyage.*

Halifax appears onscreen. Sounds of more e-mails arriving. Cacophony of voices, off.

Lucas Tania, where are you?

Anne We have an exclusive! If you don't co-operate, we'll print Philippe's girlfriend's story, saying you seduced her man.

Ronny We are live on air in ten minutes! Break this contract and it'll cost you financially.

Joel You're supposed to be on telly, man.

Stuart Yours can be a solitary sign.

Ronny Tell us where you are. We'll send a car.

Anne You're supposed to stay in your suite. It's in the contract.

Lucas Tania, this is no time to be shy. Be reasonable. Do you want to sail *my* yacht again?

Tania creeps silently aboard Team Spirit, *looking around warily. E-mails arrive. Voices, off.*

Ronny Ah, you're on the boat. We're coming down with the cameras.

Anne There you are! Don't let any other press near. Remember our deal.

Lucas You're on *Pendragon Team Spirit* – how convenient for all of us. I'm bringing some people down you must meet. It's all quite informal.

Tania weighs anchor. E-mails arrive, cacophony of voices off.

Ronny Shit! Where are you going?

Anne What the hell are you doing?

Joel Whoa, dude!

Lucas Tania! Have you taken leave of your senses?

Stuart Today is a good one to make a new start . . .

Tania's mobile rings.

Tania (*distractedly*) Yeah?

Tom Tania! Tania, what are you doing? First I and the rest of the world see you onscreen, kissing Philippe Jeunet, then you slip out of your room, blowing a major interview in the process, to make a hospital visit to a sick girl. If you'd told me, this would've been amazing, would've been great publicity . . . but oh no, Tania thinks she knows best, goes there in secret, so that's a photo opportunity wasted . . . something positive to compensate for you kissing that . . . that . . . Belgian. Tania? (*A beat.*) And now –? Where the hell are you going? What the hell is going on? Tania! Tania! You can't just go off and shirk all your responsibilities. Turn the boat round right now. Tania . . . WHERE ARE YOU GOING?

Without even glancing at it, Tania drops the phone overboard. She climbs up the mast and unbolts the camera. She puts it overboard.

Tania Where is anyone going? *Bon voyage.*

A big splash as the camera hits the water. The screen goes black.
    Blackout.
    The End.